Symposium on Monte Carlo Methods

A WILEY PUBLICATION IN APPLIED STATISTICS

Symposium on Monte Carlo Methods

Held at the University of Florida

Conducted by the Statistical Laboratory

Sponsored by Wright Air Development Center
of the Air Research and Development Command

March 16 and 17, 1954

Edited by
HERBERT A. MEYER

New York   ·   John Wiley & Sons, Inc.
London   ·   Chapman & Hall, Limited

The word probability has not always meant exactly the same thing to those who use and to those who write about probability. It is not strange, then, that the term "Monte Carlo Methods" should likewise be subject to various interpretations.

In the foreword to the proceedings of a symposium held at Los Angeles June 27, 30 and July 1, 1949 entitled Monte Carlo Method, Dr. A. S. Householder defines the method as follows:

"The Monte Carlo method may briefly be described as the device of studying an artificial stochastic model of a physical or mathematical process. The device is certainly not new. Moreover, the theory of stochastic processes has been a subject of study for quite some time, and the novelty in the Monte Carlo method does not lie here. The novelty lies rather in the suggestion that where an equation arising in a nonprobabilistic context demands a numerical solution not easily obtainable by standard numerical methods, there may exist a stochastic process with distributions or parameters which satisfy the equation, and it may actually be more efficient to construct such a process and compute the statistics than to attempt to use those standard methods.

Simple and natural as this suggestion seems, once it is made, someone had to make it first in a voice loud enough to attract notice. The voices seem to have been chiefly those of Ulam and von Neumann, though Enrico Fermi .... also contributed.

.... The problems are: Given an equation, is there a stochastic process which yields a distribution such that it, or some set of its parameters, satisfies that equation? And if so, what is the efficient method of obtaining the statistics and assessing them? This much should be made clear, however; the method is probably never efficient for yielding an entire distribution unless the distribution is obtainable only by integrating out other variables. Basically, the method is one of numerical integration."

A somewhat parallel statement about Monte Carlo as given by Donsker and Kac in the Journal of Research, National Bureau of Standards, Vol. 44, 1950, is as follows:

"Certain problems leading to complicated partial or integro-differential equations have recently been approached and some actually solved by utilizing various probability techniques and sampling methods. Collectively these methods have become known as the "Monte Carlo" method.

The problems to which Monte Carlo techniques have been applied seem to be divided into two types. Typical of the first type is the problem of neutrons diffusing in material media in which the particles are subjected not only to certain deterministic influences but to random influences as well. In such a problem, the Monte Carlo approach consists in permitting a "particle" to play a game of chance, the rules of the game being such that the actual deterministic and random features of the physical process are step by step exactly imitated by the game. By considering very large numbers of particles, one can answer such questions as the distribution of the particles at the end of a certain period of time, the number of particles to escape through a shield of a specified thickness, etc. One important characteristic of the preceding approach is that the functional equation describing the diffusion process is bypassed completely, the probability model used being derived from the process itself.

A more sophisticated application of Monte Carlo methods is to the problem of finding a probability model or game whose solution is related to the solution of a partial differential equation, or .... to determine the least eigenvalue of a differential operator by means of a sampling process...."

Another definition and amplification due to John Curtiss and included in the Proceedings, IBM Computation Seminar, November, 1949, rather seems to broaden the coverage somewhat. Pertinent extracts are as follows.

"It has lately become fashionable to apply
a rather picturesque name, the "Monte Carlo
Method," to any procedure which involves the use
of sampling devices based on probabilities to
approximate the solution of mathematical or
physical problems. The Monte Carlo Method has,
so far, largely been used in connection with
functional equations and quadratures.

．．．．．

....The novelty which the method possesses lies
chiefly in its point of view. With few excep-
tions the authors cited .... proceed from a
problem in probabilities to a problem in functional equations, whose solution is then obtained
or at least proved to exist, by classical methods
and furnishes the answer to the probability problems. In the Monte Carlo Method, the situation
is reversed. The probability problem (whose solution can always be approximated by repeated
trials) is regarded as the tool for the numerical
analysis of a functional equation. Or alternatively, in a physical problem which, classically,
would call for an analytic model, the equivalent
probability problem is regarded as an adequate
model in itself, and derivation of an analytic
equivalent is considered to be superfluous....

．．．．．

     But it is worth noting that the Monte Carlo
Method is not at all novel to statisticians.
....For more than fifty years, when statisticians
have been confronted with a difficult problem in
distribution theory, they have resorted to what
they have sometimes called "model sampling." The
process consists of setting up some sort of urn
model or system, or drawings from a table of random numbers, whereby the statistic whose distribution is sought can be observed over and over
again and the distribution estimated empirically.
The theoretical distribution in question is usually a multiple integral over a peculiar region
in many dimensions, so, in such cases, "model sampling" is clearly a Monte Carlo Method of numerical
quadrature. In fact, the distribution of "Student's
t" was first determined in this way. Many other
examples can be found by leafing through the pages
of Biometrika and the other statistical journals."

At the Florida symposium the question, "Is this model sampling or is it Monte Carlo?" was frequently heard.

Historically, at least, model sampling before the name "Monte Carlo" was introduced will probably continue to be considered as model sampling. From about the middle of the twentieth century on, model sampling may or may not bear the label of Monte Carlo. There are those who hold that a Monte Carlo method is one for which the efficiency of the sampling process is an important consideration. By use of weighted or importance sampling, information is obtained with less sampling and consequent greater efficiency than by sampling without the weights or other modifications. In any event, the more efficient processes should be more productive of results and gradually replace, at least in interest, the less efficient.

The use of random numbers, either self-generated or stored, as well as calculators of card or tape input varieties, are the usual tools of the method. Custom seems now to decree that the models of Monte Carlo are models for which discrete answers are obtained, the answers arising from counting. Analogue computers as such do not, in general, seem to be linked with Monte Carlo methods. However, Neyman, at the Los Angeles Symposium, cited a model constructed to simulate a bombing problem, as a Monte Carlo example. This would seem not too far removed from early methods of using geometrical models such as the well-known Buffon's needle problem by which π was determined by counting the number of times a needle touched parallel lines out of a rather large number of tosses. Concerning such examples, it may be interesting to note Uspensky's reaction as given in his "Introduction to Mathematical Probability" page 257:

> "These examples may suffice to give an idea of problems in geometric probabilities. Sylvester Crofton and others have enriched this field by extremely ingenious methods of evaluating, or rather of avoiding evaluation of very complicated multiple integrals. However, from the standpoint of principles, these investigations, ingenious as they are, do not contribute much to the general theory of probability."

On behalf of using probability models to simulate physical processes, more than one user of such techniques has remarked that enough insight of the physical process was attained in a

Monte Carlo study so that a workable analytical model could be constructed. Such outcomes give rise to the observation that good Monte Carlo is self liquidating.

Some of the same difficulties of communication that existed at the time of the Los Angeles symposium of 1949 seemed to continue to exist, and the number of papers appearing give evidence of continued interest. Dr. P. R. Rider suggested the need of another symposium, and this idea was concurred in by Dr. A. S. Householder, Dr. H. H. Germond and Dr. John von Neumann, as well as others. The symposium which consequently resulted was sponsored by Wright Air Development Center of the Air Research and Development Command and conducted by the Statistical Laboratory of the University of Florida on the campus at Gainesville. An account is given on succeeding pages.

Since the time of the Los Angeles symposium, scattered papers have begun to appear, many in the form of technical or special reports. A bibliography of papers which seemed to come under the general heading of the definition as stated by Dr. Householder was prepared and is added to these proceedings as an appendix. Since the papers are not too readily accessible, abstracts are also included. These abstracts are in the words of the authors when such were obtainable, and in these cases are so noted. The appendix also contains a section on random digits, a section dealing with empirical sampling and a selection of papers making use of stochastic processes, including a bibliography prepared by Dr. David G. Kendall of Magdalen College, Oxford. While the section on random digits is fairly complete, no claim for completeness is made for the remainder.

Most of the papers which follow were rewritten after presentation and are mostly what the participants wished they had said rather than their actual words. In this way the fruit of questions, remarks and discussions which followed presentation was incorporated into the papers, and it is hoped the added erudition more than compensates for the spontaneity lost in going from a transcribed verbal to a written report.

FOREWORD

A symposium on Monte Carlo methods conducted by the Statistical Laboratory of the University of Florida and sponsored by Wright Air Development Center, Air Research and Development Command was held on the campus of the University of Florida, Gainesville, Florida, March 16 and 17, 1954. The symposium was followed on March 18 and 19 by sessions of the Institute of Mathematical Statistics and the Biometrics Society, ENAR.

Registration was begun on March 15 at 2 P.M. On Tuesday, March 16, Dr. John S. Allen, Vice President of the University of Florida, gave the welcoming address. Following this Dr. A. S. Householder presided at the morning session, at which time the following papers were presented: "Generation of Pseudo-random Numbers," by Olga Taussky and John Todd; "Phase Shifts - Middle Squares - Wave Equation," by N. Metropolis; "A General Theory of Stochastic Estimates of the Neumann Series for the Solution of Certain Fredholm Integral Equations," by G. E. Albert.

Dr. H. H. Germond presided as chairman of the afternoon session and the following papers were presented: "Neighbor Sets for Random Walks and Difference Equations," by Theodore S. Motzkin; "Monte Carlo Computations," by Mrs. Nancy M. Dismuke; "Applications of Monte Carlo Methods to Tactical Games," by S. Ulam; "Conditional Monte Carlo for Normal Samples," by John W. Tukey and H. F. Trotter; "Monte Carlo Techniques in a Complex Problem about Normal Samples," by John W. Tukey, H. J. Arnold, B. D. Bucher and H. F. Trotter.

At the request of many in attendance, a night session was held on the A-B-C's of Monte Carlo at which Herbert A. Meyer presided. Principal discussant was John W. Tukey, with additional remarks given by H. H. Germond, A. W. Marshall, F. Joachim Weyl and M. Horowitz. At the same time a session on Programming Monte Carlo Processes for High-speed Computers was held with G. E. Albert presiding.

On Wednesday morning, March 17, Dr. C. C. Hurd presided and the following papers were presented: "The Application of Random Sampling Techniques to the Calculation of Boundary Problems in Gamma-ray Diffusions," by M. J. Berger; "Gamma Ray Diffusion, Shallow Penetration," by Louis A. Beach; Gamma Ray Diffusion, Deep Penetration," by R. B. Theus; "Application of Multiple Stage Sampling Procedures to Monte Carlo Problems," by A. W. Marshall with additional remarks by J. E. Walsh. A paper written by C. W. Vickery, Fairchild Aircraft Corporation, entitled "Experimental Determination of Eigenvalues and Dynamic Influence Coefficients for Complex Structures Such as Airplanes" was read by H. E. Fettis, who had worked with Dr. Vickery on the project. Dr. Hurd told of applications of Monte Carlo to the field of language translation and also to transportation problems.

Dr. E. S. Quade presided at the afternoon session, at which time the following papers were presented: "Applications of Monte Carlo," by Herman Kahn; "Comparison of Efficiency of Monte Carlo Methods with that of Classical Methods for Linear Computation Problems," by J. H. Curtiss; "A Random Normal Sampling Distribution," by E. J. Lytle, Jr.; "Remarks on Generation of Distribution Functions," by J. W. Butler. The following were given by title: "On a New Iterative Algorithm for finding the Solution of Games and Linear Programming Problems," by R. Bellman of RAND Corporation; "Experiments and Models for the Monte Carlo Method," by Dr. Alwin Walther of Institut für Praktische Mathematik, Technische Hochschule, Darmstadt, Germany; "A Monte Carlo Technique for Obtaining Tests and Confidence Intervals for Insurance Mortality Rates," by J. E. Walsh and "A Poor Man's Monte Carlo," by J. M. Hammersley and K. W. Morton [now published in J. RSS (B)].

The following were in attendance:

G. E. Albert, ORNL, University of Tennessee, Knoxville.
Max Astrachan, USAF Institute of Technology, Dayton.
L. A. Beach, Naval Research Laboratory, Washington.
M. J. Berger, National Bureau of Standards, Washington.
R. K. Brown, Evans Signal Laboratories, Fort Monmouth.
F. J. Burkett, Union College, Schenectady.
J. W. Butler, Argonne National Laboratories, Lemont.
W. F. Callander, Statistical Laboratory, University of Florida.
E. D. Cashwell, Los Alamos Scientific Laboratory, Univ. of Cal.
J. H. Curtiss, Inst. of Math. Sciences, New York University.
A. E. Daniels, Directorate of Intelligence, Dept. of Targets.
Mrs. Nancy M. Dismuke, Oak Ridge National Laboratory.
James Duffett, White Sands Proving Ground, Las Cruces.
Miles Edwards, Wright Air Development Center.
Harry Ferguson, Wright Air Development Center.
H. F. Fettis, Wright Air Development Center.
C. George Fultz, Applied Science Div., IBM Corporation, Atlanta.
H. H. Germond, Directorate of Intelligence, Dept. of Targets.
K. G. Gudeley, Wright Air Development Center.
J. L. Hammersmith, Naval Research Laboratory, Washington.
W. D. Hanson, Statistical Laboratory, University of Florida.

J. O. Harrison, Jr., Operations Research, Johns Hopkins Univ.
S. Hellyer, Defence Research Board, Ottawa, Canada.
M. Horowitz, Goodyear Aircraft Corporation, Akron.
T. R. Horton, University of Florida.
A. S. Householder, Mathematics Panel, Oak Ridge Nat'l Laboratory.
W. W. Hoy, Chance Vought Aircraft Corporation, Dallas.
J. H. Hubbell, National Bureau of Standards, Washington.
C. C. Hurd, Applied Science Division, IBM Corporation, New York.
M. A. Hyman, Westinghouse, Washington.
T. L. Jordan, Jr., Los Alamos Scientific Laboratory, Univ. of Cal.
Herman Kahn, Nuclear Energy Division, The RAND Corporation, Calif.
Bruce Kelly, Florida Agricultural Experiment Station, Orlando.
Boyd Ladd, Operations Research, Johns Hopkins University.
R. A. Leibler, National Security Agency, Washington.
W. Leighton, OSR, ARDC, St. Louis, Missouri.
E. Leshan, Radiation Laboratory, University of California.
E. J. Lytle, Jr., Statistical Laboratory, University of Florida.
A. M. Mark, Southern Illinois University, Mathematics Department.
A. W. Marshall, University of Chicago and RAND Corporation.
N. Metropolis, Los Alamos Scientific Laboratory, Univ. of Cal.
Herbert A. Meyer, Director, Statistical Laboratory, Univ. of Florida.
T. S. Motzkin, Inst. of Numerical Analysis, U of Cal. at Los Angeles.
W. O'Regan, Statistical Laboratory, University of Florida.
I. E. Perlin, Georgia Institute of Technology.
J. F. Perkins, Convair, Fort Worth.
E. S. Quade, The RAND Corporation, California.
P. R. Rider, Wright Air Development Center.
D. D. Rippe, Strategic Air Command, Omaha.
E. K. Ritter, U. S. Naval Proving Ground.
Major O. A. Shaw, USAF, ARDC, Baltimore.
D. E. South, Mathematics Department, University of Florida.
M. G. Springer, U. S. Naval Ordnance Plant, Indianapolis.
G. Suzuki, David Taylor Model Basin, U. S. Navy.
Olga Taussky-Todd, National Bureau of Standards, Washington.
R. B. Theus, Naval Research Laboratory, Washington.
M. Tikson, Wright Air Development Center.
John Todd, National Bureau of Standards, Washington.
E. L. Treiber, Chief Liason Br., Eng. Res. and Dev. Lab., Ft. Belvoir.
T. L. Tuck, Los Alamos Scientific Laboratory, Univ. of Cal.
John W. Tukey, Princeton University.
S. Ulam, Los Alamos Scientific Laboratory, Univ. of Cal.
J. E. Walsh, U. S. Naval Ordnance Test Station, California.
George Watkins, Statistical Laboratory, University of Florida.
H. Weingarten, Bureau of Ordnance, U. S. Navy.
F. J. Weyl, U. S. Office of Naval Research.
B. R. Whiteley, Wright Air Development Center.
J. Widrewitz, Rome Air Development Center, Rome, New York.
J. F. Wilson, IBM Corporation, Jacksonville.
D. M. Young, Jr., Univ. of Maryland and Naval Proving Ground.

ACKNOWLEDGEMENTS

Grateful acknowledgement is made to Dr. Paul R. Rider who first suggested that such a symposium be held, and to Dr. A. S. Householder, Dr. H. H. Germond and Dr. John von Neumann, whose encouragement was given in the planning stages. To those who presented papers, those who served as chairmen and those who participated in the discussions, special thanks is given. The spontaneous enthusiasm of Dr. John Tukey and Dr. Herman Kahn during the symposium did much to convince even the skeptical of the possibilities of the Monte Carlo method. Dr. Andrew Marshall set the stage, so to speak, for Monte Carlo in general and this collection of papers in particular in his introduction. The staff of the Statistical Laboratory, including especially Landis Gephart, Norman Rasmussen, George Watkins, Ernest J. Lytle, Jr., Carlis Taylor and secretary Gail Gyles are thanked for their wholehearted help. The symposium and its publication was sponsored by a contract betweeen the University of Florida and the Wright Air Development Center of the Air Research and Development Command, whose generous support made the undertaking possible.

TABLE OF CONTENTS

PART I.

PAPERS IN ORDER OF PRESENTATION

AN INTRODUCTORY NOTE[+]

A. W. Marshall

INTRODUCTION

This introductory note is intended to fulfill several objectives. First, the symposium itself does not contain a paper summarizing progress and practice in the field of Monte Carlo during the period 1949 (the date of the last Monte Carlo symposium) to the present. This introduction is devoted in part to filling this gap. Second, symposia usually present a somewhat biased view of the state of any field because papers are devoted to new ideas rather than description of standard practice. This would not be an important defect if only experts in the field were the audience but there is considerable evidence of a new, wider interest in Monte Carlo. In the case of the present symposium the bias is somewhat less than is usual. Many of the papers give applications which should by now be standard practice in Monte Carlo computations, but are not yet so, rather than new ideas or advanced techniques. However, there is just enough of the flavor of experts talking to experts to suggest that some guidance for other than expert audiences would be worthwhile. This introductory note is therefore primarily addressed to that growing class of persons interested in Monte Carlo as a tool of numerical analysis rather than as an area of professional work. In other words it is addressed to those who are not now experts in the field but have problems which they believe Monte Carlo techniques may help solve.

Within the compass of so short a note it is not possible to completely review the progress of Monte Carlo or to point up the important aspects of each paper. The first section following upon this one is a commentary on the progress of Monte Carlo from the late forties to the present. The second section following is devoted to some explanatory remarks on the papers collected in this volume.

[+]The author wishes to acknowledge the large debt he owes to Mr. Herman Kahn for long discussions of material in this note, and to Mr. R. T. Nichols for many helpful suggestions.

1

Before going on, a word about the definition of Monte Carlo, a subject on which there is a good deal of disagreement. The original von Neumann-Ulam concept seems to have been that Monte Carlo specifically designated the use of random sampling procedures for treating deterministic mathematical problems. Some define Monte Carlo to be the use of random sampling to treat problems, whether of a deterministic or probabilistic sort. Others demand that the sampling be sophisticated (involves the use of some variance reducing technique or "swindle") in order to qualify as Monte Carlo; they reserve the names straightforward sampling, experimental sampling, or model sampling for the cases where purely random sampling is used. The writer's sympathies are with the latter view. However the economics of computing is changing so rapidly with the advent of faster and faster machines that sophistication sometimes has a high price. The test of whether it is Monte Carlo rather than model sampling, perhaps, might be whether the sampling design was rationally chosen; the possible application of the most useful variance reducing techniques always being considered in planning the treatment of any problem. As far as the definitional problem is concerned, however, most all discussion is beside the point. Because of its picturesque character and charm the use of the name Monte Carlo has a momentum all its own; the situation now is that in common usage Monte Carlo is synonymous with any use of random sampling in treatment of either deterministic or probabilistic problems.

II. THE PROGRESS OF MONTE CARLO, 1949-1954

The following history and commentary makes no pretense of completeness. Dates are only approximate, as is sufficient for the purpose of this section -- to describe the general progress of Monte Carlo from the late forties and its current state.

A. Early Dominance of the Analogue Idea

If one looks at the Monte Carlo literature of the late forties he finds that it is dominated by the intriguing idea discovered or promulgated by von Neumann and Ulam, that one can use random sampling methods to solve determinate mathematical problems. Others had earlier seen that such things could be done in some cases, for example, the calculation (estimation) of π by random drops of a needle. But they were certainly the first to advocate the idea of systematically inverting the usual situation and treating mathematical problems by finding a probabilistic analogue and then obtaining approximate answers to this analogue by some experimental sampling procedure. Their work and discussion of the basic idea stimulated widespread interest in the use of random sampling procedures in physics and engineering problems. They were also the first to point out the special adaptability of the high speed computing machine, soon to be available, to Monte Carlo type computations.

The statisticians had, of course, been using model sampling methods to investigate some of their problems, for example, the effect of non-normality on statistical test procedures devised for samples from normal (Gaussian) populations, since the early 1900's. Their use of sampling reached a peak in the period 1925-1935 and then died off. However their work was concerned with probabilistic problems so that they were not interested in the sort of thing which might lead to the original von Neumann-Ulam idea. Moreover, despite their injunctions to all other experimental professions that sampling design was crucial in maximizing the amount of information in a sample for a fixed expenditure of effort, their own work shows no attempt at design at all. Whatever ideas in sample survey design that might have been carried over at this time were not used until the past few years. In any case, the statisticians did not have the analogue idea and this is what got Monte Carlo in its current form started. In addition, they did not initiate the use of variance reducing techniques in the area of artificial sampling or model sampling. Their work in this area represents a separate stream that only today is merging with the much richer and larger one generated by the von Neumann-Ulam Monte Carlo ideas. It is always hard to decide questions of priority and direction of influence, but in the case of the current development of Monte Carlo the situation is relatively clear.

In spite of the fact that the von Neumann-Ulam ideas have in a way been very fruitful, it is possible to get an exaggerated notion of the practical importance of the analogue idea from what has just been written above and especially from the literature of the late forties. For some problems, for example, particle diffusion problems, the application of this idea meant a retranslation of problems back to the probabilistic basis they had in physical theory in the first place. The success of the idea was no accident

3

in these cases. Few, if any, basically deterministic
problems have really been treated by Monte Carlo methods.
Actually the dominance of the literature by the analogue
idea is probably due more to its novelty and its great
potentialities than to its historical achievements, and
to the professional interest of most of the people contri-
buting papers--theoretical numerical analysis rather than
applied problems of immediate practical importance. The
use of Monte Carlo methods of computation has been influ-
enced by the analogue idea mainly in an indirect way. The
most important practical applications thus far have had a
probabilistic basis; the influence of the original Monte
Carlo idea has been to suggest treating them directly as
probabilistic problems rather than attempting a difficult,
if not impossible, analytical solution. The translation
and later retranslation of problems from probabilistic
terms to non-probabilistic mathematical problems and back
again has been by-passed.

B. Early Applications of Monte Carlo

Because the most important applications have been on
basically probabilistic problems, there is a special interest in mentioning the important problems where the
pure analogue idea has already found some application.
Around 1947-49 Fermi, with Metropolis and Ulam, used it
for obtaining estimates of the eigenvalues associated with
the Schrödinger equation. A little later Kac also used
Monte Carlo methods when working on the same problem.
Work by Metropolis and Ulam is continuing at Los Alamos on
the application of Monte Carlo methods to the Schrödinger
equation. However, thus far no published results show any
marked improvements over results attainable by classical
techniques.

About 1950 matrix inversion and solution of partial
differential equations by Monte Carlo methods were developed. Here again, although these are areas in which the
analogue idea would find use, no results in cases with
important applications have been published.

The first practical problems treated by the Monte
Carlo method were connected with the design of atomic weap-
ons at Los Alamos during the war. In these problems nature
was directly modeled in its probabilistic aspects and many
problems in particle diffusion were solved. Since these
problems were first posed in terms of solving complicated
mathematical equations to obtain expected values the use of

nature's model of the same diffusion process as the analogue
problem might be considered as an application of the analogue idea. It is the author's understanding that Ulam
does consider it so. However, once one remembers that the
answers to the problem at hand are the expected values of
the stochastic process of central interest in the problem,
the use of that process in obtaining estimates of the answer does not seem to involve anything sufficiently removed
from the problem, as nature poses it, to be called an analogue. No matter what it is called, however, given that
the abstract formulation of problems often obscures their
true basis the use of nature's model was a great discovery
and very successful. Later the physicists extended the use
of these methods of calculation to other areas, such as
particle diffusion in shields, meson cascade problems, etc.

At an early date people working in the general area of
operations analysis also took up the use of the Monte Carlo
method in their problems. This use is now widely developed.

C. Initial Development of Sampling Technique

Given that one is to do problems by random sampling
methods, attention naturally turns to three topics: (1)
choosing or modeling the probability process to be sampled
(in some cases this means choice of the analogue; in others
a choice between alternative probability models of the same
process), (2) deciding how to generate random variables from
given probability distributions in some efficient way, and
(3) variance reducing techniques, i.e., ways of increasing
the efficiency of the estimates obtained from the sampling
process. On the first topic little will be said. With
regard to the second topic von Neumann was very ingenious
from the start but general techniques had not been worked
out in the early years. Indeed the literature contains some
incorrect statements of the sort--it is impossible to do
such and such--things which actually can be easily done.
Work is continuing in this area and good methods for many
distributions are available. Of course with the increased
speed of the computing machines the problem has shifted a
little; the emphasis is less on efficiency and more on just
having some way of generating the necessary random variables.

In the case of the third topic, variance reducing
techniques, von Neumann and Ulam invented the Russian Roulette and splitting ideas about 1945 (see Kahn's paper) but
there was no systematic attempt to investigate this problem
until T. E. Harris and Kahn began their work in 1948. Since

then a great deal of progress has been made but the results are not well known, nor widely used. One hopes that the publication of this volume will do something toward correcting this deficiency in the current practice of Monte Carlo.

D.   The Current State of Monte Carlo

Since the late 40's the main trends have been:

1.   A relative decline of interest among people purely concerned with technique and especially in the interest in the exploration of the pure analogue idea. The development of some first rate applications of the idea is probably required to stimulate further work in this now more or less dormant area.

2.   A very great absolute and relative increase in applied use of Monte Carlo, mostly, as has been remarked, to problems with a probabilistic basis. Overt interest in Monte Carlo probably passed through a minimum in 1951-52; the novelty had worn off in the area of theoretical interest and applied use was not as widespread as it now is.

3.   The statisticians, who all along have been by professional training eminently qualified to make important contributions, have now become interested in the field, both for use on their own problems and as a separate professional area of sampling technique. Harris and a few others were interested in and working in the field almost from the very beginning, but it is only lately that articles on Monte Carlo have begun to appear in statistics journals.[+]

[+] The development of Monte Carlo independently of the statisticians and particularly their poor showing in applying sampling techniques to their own problems may be surprising to some; especially to those who think Student invented Monte Carlo. Some writers in the field of Monte Carlo have been excessively polite and/or generous in indicating that many or all of the variance reducing ideas come from survey sampling theory. This is not true since most of the important ideas exploit the extra degrees of freedom available in the design of sampling procedures that result from the fact that one has complete control of the generation and selection of the random variables he uses. What is surprising is that the statisticians did not take the advice they gave to others on the use of efficient designs.

As to the invention of Monte Carlo by Student, it is a strange case. Student did something slightly different,

A few new areas for the application of Monte Carlo have been opened up in the past few years. The most important of these is statistical mechanics. Here Metropolis, Rosenbluth and Teller pointed out that one can exploit sampling processes possessing the right kind of ergodic properties.

---

but much better than most Monte Carlo calculations. In the case of his discovery of the t distribution he had derived the correct distribution analytically, but he had made some jumps in the logic. Being unsure, but not very unsure, of the derived distribution he tested it upon some samples he had drawn for exploratory purposes, computing t, and testing the sample distribution against the theoretical using a χ^2 test. He states that he first tried to get the distribution by sampling, but how he used the sampling results to suggest the right answer is not indicated. In his paper the sample results are used only as a check.

In the case of the distribution of the correlation coefficient, Student knew that for n=2 the distribution was degenerate and, in addition, he had some samples for $\rho = 0$ of size 4 and 8 and for $\rho = .66$ of size 4, 8, and 30. From the sample distributions and moments for the case $\rho = 0$ he conjectured that a Pearson distribution of the form $f(x,n) =$

$$k \left[1 - \frac{x^2}{\beta(n)} \right]^{\alpha(n)}$$ would approximate the distribution. Fitting α and β for n=4, 8 he rounded and guessed that $\alpha = \frac{n-4}{2}$ and $\beta = 1$, checking that for n=2 the distribution fitted exactly. Thus in the cases of both t and r, Student made magnificent guesses, partly suggested by prior samples, and supported by checking against actual samples and analytic results for large sample approximations of the moments of the distributions, etc. All of this may or may not be Monte Carlo; it is different from most applications, and in any case an isolated instance of first rate use of sampling for statistical purposes.

To the extent the later sampling experiments of the statisticians were multi-purposed this would, of course, inhibit the application of variance reducing techniques, since this requires one to select what it is that is of most interest and to concentrate upon the reduction of the variance of that particular characteristic often at the expense of increasing the variance of the others. Interest in generating data giving unbiased information about many aspects of a problem also makes it difficult to apply variance reducing techniques to many operations research problems as they tend to be stated. But in investigating such things as the effect of non-normality or comparisons of the power functions of tests, powerful techniques have long been available.

7

These sampling processes allow one to reproduce (converge to) the correct equilibrium distribution of various quantities such as the total energy of a cubic lattice system. At least two groups are now working to exploit these ideas.

There has also been an increased use of Monte Carlo methods in operations analysis problems especially as these have become more comprehensive and richer in detail and, therefore beyond the scope of analytic and classical numerical methods. In this case Monte Carlo is used almost by default, since the only feasibility limit to Monte Carlo is one of energy or computing power. As has been mentioned, the advent of more and faster computing machines has had its impact on Monte Carlo just as it has on other numerical analysis techniques. This technological growth has led to a tendency to do larger and larger problems, which if they have a probabilistic basis has tended to make Monte Carlo a preferred method of analysis.

The increase in the speed of the machines has also tended to make variance reducing techniques relatively less interesting, but has by no means eliminated their usefulness. The effect of increased computing speed in the newer machines is to make the cost of designing and coding a problem increase relative to the cost of machine running time. The use of variance reducing techniques shortens running time but at the expense of (1) increasing the time spent in designing the computations so as to adapt the classical techniques to the particular problem or in the invention of a new, more suitable technique, and (2) complicating the coding because of the more elaborate bookkeeping and calculations these techniques usually require. On the whole, however, if there is one thing that would generally increase the usefulness of Monte Carlo it is the discovery of new variance reducing techniques, or the application of known variance reducing techniques as a matter of course to the ordinary run of problems. Not only should these techniques be used whenever it is economical to do so but, in addition, since the variance reducing techniques are not yet well known there should be a bias toward using them even when they are not economical for the problem at hand. This is a way to learn about them for use in later and more suitable problems. The use of new techniques in marginal cases is almost always justified as a method of building intellectual capital. In the long run one would suppose that real thought on the design of Monte Carlo problems will be confined to problems of a basically new type whenever they first appear; standard variance reducing techniques will be available, and used, for other problems on the basis that sub-routines for computing common functions now are.

III. COMMENTS ON THE PAPERS IN THE VOLUME

In this section comments upon the papers contained in this volume will be given. The aim of the comments is mainly to assist those not now expert in the field of Monte Carlo to get a little more than they might otherwise out of reading this collection of papers.

The papers are grouped for discussion into three groups: (1) those dealing with the generation of random numbers and more general random variables; (2) theoretical papers; and (3) applied papers. Not all papers will be commented upon; in particular papers included only as abstracts will not be commented upon.

A. The Generation of Random Numbers and More General Random Variables

One of the first problems faced by anyone doing Monte Carlo calculations is the generation of the sequences of random variables required by the problem. This generally breaks down, if the problem is to be run on a high speed computing machine, into two problems: (1) how to generate sequences of random numbers uniformly distributed on the interval (0, 1); and (2) how to transform the random numbers into random variables having specified probability distributions. Previously prepared tables of random numbers and special random variables, e.g., random normal deviates, are also useful, especially if they are on punch cards or tapes suitable for feeding into computing machines. However, first rate methods are now available for the generation of random variables in the very large numbers needed for the types of problems run on high speed computing machines; tables are of real help only with hand computations (or computations with traditional IBM type equipment).

The papers of Butler, Lytle, Metropolis, and Taussky-Todd deal with various aspects of the problem of supplying random variables for use in Monte Carlo computations. The Taussky-Todd paper is an especially good summary of the currently available and tested methods of generating sequences of pseudo-random numbers in high speed computing machines. The bogus character of the randomness of the generated sequences does not seem to affect the Monte Carlo calculations, just as it is not detected by the various statistical tests to which these sequences have been subjected, and through which they have passed with flying colors. The congruential methods ($X_{n+1} = K X_n (\text{Mod } M)$ of generating pseudo-random numbers are so good for practical computational purposes that there no longer exists any problem of having an adequate supply of random numbers. Thus the discovery of newer methods, such as the Fibonacci sequence, is no longer practically important, although it may be of great theoretical interest.

The Metropolis paper contains a very interesting section on the mid-square method of generating random numbers. This was the first random number generating method adapted for use on high speed machines. It is not, however, as good a method of generating random numbers as the newer congruential methods: the two methods take about the same time to produce a random number (cost the same), but for the newer machines sequences of period on the order of 10^{12} are possible with the congruent methods no matter what starting value is used. On the other hand, Metropolis' best starting value gives a sequence of length (or period?) on the order of 10^6 and for most other starting values the sequences are probably much shorter, on the order of 10^4. It is a substantial practical advantage of the congruent method that one does not have to pick a special initial value in order to get long sequences of usable numbers. Nonetheless the study of the characteristics of sequences of random numbers generated by the mid-square method is of classical interest.

The Lytle paper provides an example of the second problem mentioned above--the transformation of random numbers into random variables with the appropriate probability distributions. The Butler paper deals more generally with this problem and describes in some detail a few of the more interesting methods of achieving the required transformations. This is an area in which ingenuity is often required for success. It is only gradually that there has developed a practical capacity to generate random variables from a wide class of probability distributions. The choice of any particular scheme of course depends upon the economics of the computation situation. For example, at RAND we currently generate random variables having the exponential distribution by taking the logarithm of random numbers, i.e., by the direct method. Excellent approximations of ln X are available for use on modern high speed machines that make this scheme competitive with, and probably more efficient than, rejection techniques.

B. Theoretical Papers on Monte Carlo

The papers concerned mainly with theoretical aspects of Monte Carlo methods are those of Albert, Curtiss, Kahn,

Marshall (with Walsh's comment), Motzkin, Trotter and Tukey, and Walsh. No comment will be made about the Motzkin or Walsh papers. The remaining papers, with the exception of Curtiss' paper, deal with the central problem of variance reduction.

Albert's paper is concerned with the application of Monte Carlo methods to certain integral equation problems. Several alternative methods of producing estimates are suggested and discussed from the point of view of the relative size of their variances. The extent to which these particular estimates have been used is not mentioned in the paper.

Kahn's paper reviews the techniques of variance reduction that have thus far proved to be most useful in Monte Carlo computations. Many of these techniques were first developed by Kahn, or at least perfected and used in important applied Monte Carlo problems for the first time by him.

My own paper investigates a more or less mechanical, two-stage sampling method for choosing good importance sampling schemes. The technique discussed is fairly straightforward but must be considered as wholly untried. Some technical problems arise in the paper because the ex- pected value of the variance of the estimate derived from the second stage in the sampling scheme is infinite, at least in a wide class of cases. Depending on how large the first sample is, however, the variance of the second stage estimate is smaller than that of the first stage with high probability. Walsh makes the very reasonable comment that in this case one might work with other measures of variation than the variance in order to avoid analytic problems. This is not the only way out, but is a good one if the other measures prove more tractable analytically and in applied numerical work.

The Trotter and Tukey paper, with its companion applied paper mentioned in the next section, is probably the most exciting paper in the volume. First, the authors introduce a new variance reducing technique (conditional Monte Carlo) and second, in the applied paper they show that it works very well. It is heartening to see mathematical statisticians really becoming interested in Monte Carlo techniques and using them on their own problems. This paper deserves close study (and needs it) to get the conditional Monte Carlo trick straight. It seems to be more complicated than, for

11

example, the methods discussed by Kahn. The paper also contains, besides the technical gem already mentioned, many wise words on the good practice of Monte Carlo which reflect an attitude that should be more widespread.

Curtiss' paper is primarily an examination of the relative accuracy of two classical, non-stochastic methods and the Monte Carlo method of computing one component of the solution of a linear equation system. The paper gives a first rate and fair comparison of the methods. One ends with the feeling that unless something can be done to increase the accuracy of the Monte Carlo method in this area that it will remain merely an interesting novelty, especially when as Curtiss suggests it is so seldom the case in actual applied problems that only one component of the solution is required.

C. Applied Monte Carlo Papers

The applied papers are those of Arnold, Bucher, Trotter and Tukey; Beach and Theus; Berger; and Dismuke. The paper by Arnold, et al, is one of the first papers to be published in which substantial and impressive reduction in variance is achieved. Other problems have been done as well, and indeed factors of 10^6 in variance reduction have been achieved in some cases, but unfortunately none of these results have been published in a form that is both convincing and instructive.

The paper of Beach and Theus also helps to fill the same gap in the literature. It, along with the Berger paper, is the best thing yet published in the field of the application of Monte Carlo to nuclear shielding problems. This is an area where some of the best Monte Carlo has been done. Kahn's Nucleonics paper describes the variance reducing techniques but numerical examples of their use were not presented. In some sense however the work behind the paper of Beach and Theus is better than the paper itself. It is not as educational as it could be. For example, much of the success in choosing good variance reducing techniques in applied Monte Carlo calculations has been due to a physical understanding of the problem or intuition as to the processes in the problem which largely determine the answer. Thus in the present paper it would be instructive to hear more about (1) the rationale behind the choice of the various sampling schemes that were tried, (2) why those that worked well did so, (3) why some combination of energy and scattering biasing and the exponential transformation would probably be required for the treatment of problems with gamma rays of lower energy, say 2 Mev, etc.

12

Berger uses variance reducing techniques that are somewhat different from those of Beach and Theus, i.e., correlated sampling and more sophisticated methods of extracting information from the random walks. These techniques are best classified under the heading of the method of expected values discussed in Kahn's paper. Unfortunately while the paper illustrates the use of the method of expected values it does not show any real advantage over straightforward sampling in some cases, for example, in the estimation of the transmission coefficients. This method, which often does very well, probably gives best results in Berger's type of problem in the range of 4-6 mean free paths. Below this (1-4 mean free paths) it does not do too well as this paper shows. Beyond 6 mean free paths the method continues to increase in efficiency relative to straightforward sampling; but not fast enough to handle the problem which is growing in difficulty by leaps and bounds. Both methods are swamped in this case. Data on the use of correlated sampling is not given although Berger has been using it. Correlation should be very effective in increasing the efficiency with which the effects of changing geometries can be studied and publications beyond this preliminary report will undoubtedly confirm this.

The Dismuke paper is completely straightforward. It describes the setup of an applied problem of the level of complexity where Monte Carlo really becomes interesting as a numerical technique.

IV. CONCLUSION

In conclusion, it may be noted that there is considerable evidence of the existence of a large non-expert interest in Monte Carlo. Unfortunately, the literature on Monte Carlo is not very helpful to anyone who wishes to do Monte Carlo problems of his own and who looks for guidance, if only through example, as to how he should best proceed. There are now a number of papers, including some in the present volume, which discuss the general principles of good Monte Carlo practice--the most usually applicable variance reducing techniques, what to look for in general, etc. However, the Monte Carlo literature is almost completely devoid of well done applied problems, which are essential to the widespread use of the techniques. Well done problems would probably be useful even if they merely

raised standards of aspiration without teaching much.
Technique can be learned by the study of well done problems, whether trivial or not. One of the good things
about the present volume is that it does contribute a
few more examples of applied Monte Carlo.

In most cases a little thought pays big dividends in
variance reduction and the use of straightforward sampling
is presumptive evidence of a lack of thought or ingenuity
in design of the sampling. Some thought is generally
required, however, since only a few people have built up
the necessary intellectual capital required to do problems
well without much effort. It is suggested that readers
who wish to really understand the various techniques (importance sampling, systematic sampling, stratified sampling,
and Russian Roulette and splitting) work through simple
problems on paper using them. The basic ideas are almost
trivial, but long and disappointing experience has shown
that they seem very hard to communicate in a useful way.
Contact with problems seems essential to understanding for
most people. Because one seems to be getting something
for nothing, it is necessary to keep straight the process
by which everything comes out all right in the end; the
efficiency of the methods in particular cases seems unbe-
lievable. The results quite literally have to be seen, and
seen through, to be believed.

GENERATION AND TESTING OF PSEUDO-RANDOM NUMBERS

Olga Taussky and John Todd
National Bureau of Standards

I. INTRODUCTION

We shall confine our attention to generation and testing of sequences of pseudo-random numbers by arithmetical[+] processes on automatic high speed digital computers. We shall also confine our attention mainly to a uniform distribution[++] of random numbers not random digits.[+++] The approximation of normal deviates and other random variates by polynomials in uniform variates has been discussed in detail by Teichroew (13); for other methods e.g., acceptance or rejection methods, see von Neumann (6, 36-38) and Votaw and Rafferty (16).

We also confine our attention to the results of testing, not to the design of tests. Apart from the "quality" of the number generated we are mainly concerned with the speed of production.

[+]There seems to be no published information about the testing of numbers generated by physical processes incorporated in automatic high speed computers such as the Ferranti or ERA machines.

[++]For practical purposes we have found it satisfactory to approximate a normal deviate by the addition of some 8 or 12 uniform deviates; for a report on experiments concerning this, see Cameron and Newman (3). See also Juncosa (17). For an application see Stegun and Youden (12).

[+++]The following caution is necessary. It might be supposed that the digits in particular fixed positions of pseudo-random numbers would be satisfactory pseudo-random digits. Tests carried out by Juncosa (17) show that this is not the case; sequences which were very good pseudo-random numbers gave rise to sequences of pseudo-random digits which could at best be classed as fair.

The written words about this topic seem to begin with Lehmer's paper (7) presented at Harvard 14 September 1949, shortly followed by Mauchly's paper (8) presented to the American Statistical Association on 29 December 1949. A fairly comprehensive account was included in a thesis of Teichroew (13).

Lehmer's definition of a pseudo-random sequence is worth repeating: it is "a vague notion embodying the idea of a sequence in which each term is unpredictable to the uninitiated and whose digits pass a certain number of tests, traditional with statisticians and depending somewhat on the uses to which the sequence is to be put."

II. MID-SQUARE METHODS

Lehmer mentioned the so-called mid-square method used on the ENIAC and due to von Neumann and Metropolis [see N. Metropolis (10)]. This can be described as follows, in a special case. Take a 4 digit number x_0, e.g., $x_0 = 2061$. Square it to obtain 04247721. Define $x_1 = 2477$, the middle four digits of x_0^2. Next $x_1^2 = 06135529$ and $x_2 = 1355$. Similarly $x_3 = 8360$, $x_4 = 8896$, etc.

The detailed steps necessary to obtain x_1, for instance, on SEAC, the National Bureau of Standards Eastern Automatic Computer are as follows: Take the low product of x_0 by itself to obtain 7721; then take the high product of this by 0100 to obtain 0077. Take the high product of x_0 by itself to obtain 0424; then take the low product of this by 0100 to obtain 2400. Add 0077 and 2400 to obtain $x_1 = 2477$. This process can be shortened and speeded up in the case of machines which have e.g., shift-orders.

For the results of some tests on numbers generated this way see Mauchly (8) and Votaw and Rafferty (16). For tests carried out by punched card equipment see Hammer (6, p. 33) and Forsythe (6, pp. 34-35). Satisfactory results have been obtained by these methods in certain cases.

III. CONGRUENTIAL METHODS - MULTIPLICATIVE

These also are first mentioned by Lehmer. He used the relation

$$x_{n+1} = kx_n \pmod{M}$$

with $k = 23$, $M = 10^8 + 1$ for ENIAC. This sequence produces 8-decimal digit numbers with period 5882352. The choice of 23 is best possible for this modulus in so far as that no larger multiplier produces a longer period and no smaller multiplier produces a period more than half as long.

Tests on 5000 numbers generated this way were carried out, using punched card equipment by L. E. Cunningham, and they were found satisfactory.

In using ENIAC it was possible to sample these pseudo-random numbers at random; this additional precautionary measure is not convenient on other machines.

In 1950, when the National Bureau of Standards Eastern Automatic Computer came into operation it was decided to carry out a series of experiments in the Monte Carlo method: solution of partial differential equations (15), inverting of matrices (14), etc. For these experiments we have used random numbers generated as follows:

$$(1) \qquad x_0 = 1, \; x_{n+1} = \rho x_n \pmod{2^{42}}$$

where ρ is any odd power of 5. In practice $\rho = 5^{17}$, (the largest power of 5 acceptable by the machine) and x_0 could be any integer satisfying $x_0 = 1 \pmod 5$. This sequence has period $2^{40} \sim 10^{12}$. It is generated by a single order: low multiplication.

We shall now illustrate the behavior of a similar sequence in a simple case. We take the residues mod 2^6 of powers of 5; these have period 16. They are, in decimal notation,

1, 5, 25, 61, 49, 53, 9, 45, 33, 37, 57, 29, 17, 21, 41, 13, 1, ... or in binary

000001, 000101, 011001, 111101, 110001, 110101, 001001, 101101, 100001, 100101, 111001, 011101, 010001, 010101, 101001, 001101 ...

17

We note that the period of the digits in a particular position in numbers increases as we move to the left; the last binary digit is always 1, the next is always zero, the next is alternatively 0 and 1, the next has period 4, and so on. In the case of the numbers (1) it is only the digit in the 42nd place which has the full period 2^{40}. This phenomenon was noted by R. Kersh and J. B. Rosser. In practice this behavior is not troublesome, for we usually only require random numbers with a few binary digits. For instance, in the case of random walks on a plane lattice (15) we have to decide in which of the intervals

$$(0, \frac{1}{4}), \quad (\frac{1}{4}, \frac{1}{2}), \quad (\frac{1}{2}, \frac{3}{4}), \quad (\frac{3}{4}, 1),$$

the random number lies, and we therefore only use the first two binary digits.

A set of 16,384 of these numbers (not individual digits) were subjected to a series of tests (1), (2). The results obtained indicate that this sequence is satisfactory; they are described in paragraph 4 below.

Later, similar processes were used for other machines. Teichroew used on SWAC the numbers produced by

$$x_0 = 1, \ x_{n+1} = \rho \, x_n (\text{mod } 2^{36}), \ \rho = 5^{13}$$

which have period $2^{34} \doteq 2 \times 10^{10}$. The sequence

$$x_0 = 1, \ x_{n+1} = \rho \, x_n (\text{mod } 10^{10})$$

has period

$$2^7 \cdot 5^8 = 5 \times 10^7$$

for $\rho = 7$. This sequence is suitable for use in the OARAC.

The sequence

(3.2) $\qquad x_0$ any odd number, $x_{n+1} = 5^{13} \, x_n (\text{mod } 2^{39})$

has been used on ORDVAC (17); the sequence

$$x_0 \text{ any odd number, } x_{n+1} = 5^{17} x_n \pmod{2^{43}}$$

has been used on EDVAC (17).

The sequence

$$x_0 = 1, \; x_{n+1} = 7^{4k+1} x_n \pmod{10^{11}}$$

is suitable for UNIVAC. The period for this is

$$5 \times 10^8.$$

These have been tested by J. Moshman (9). Moshman examined (the first six digits of) 10,000 numbers as a whole, and in groups of 2,000. Reasonable results were obtained, apart from the sixth digit, which appeared "too random." An account of processes for obtaining pseudo-random numbers on ENIAC, for which the convenient moduli are 10^5 and 10^{10}, are given by Juncosa (17).

A systematic account of the periods of sequences obtained by congruence methods has been given by Duparc, Lekkerkerker and Peremans (1953). We shall not attempt to summarize this paper.

IV. RESULTS OF TESTS

A series of tests on the numbers generated on SEAC by the relation (3.1) were carried out in collaboration with J. M. Cameron and B. F. Handy, Jr., (1). A summary of the results obtained is given below; all these results are satisfactory.

A. Frequency Test

    a) of all 16,384 numbers (32 intervals). Test of goodness of fit to rectangular distribution:

$$\chi^2 = 22.18, \; \text{d.f.} = 31, \; \Pr\left\{\chi^2 > 22.18\right\} = .9;$$

    b) of 128 sets of 128 numbers (32 intervals). Test of goodness of fit of 128 values of χ^2 to the χ^2 distribution:

$$\chi^2 = 8.07, \; \text{d.f.} = 7, \; \Pr\left\{\chi^2 > 8.07\right\} = .3.$$

B. Conformance of distribution of certain statistics to expectation

Statistic	Observed average[+]	Expected average	Observed variance[+]	Expected variance
$\Sigma x_i/128$	.49829	.50000	.000 6792	.000 6510
$\Sigma x_i^2/128$	.33163	.33333	.000 7344	.000 6944
$\dfrac{\Sigma(x_i - x_{i+1})^2}{128}$	.16508	.16536	.000 3272	.000 3869

[+]Based on 128 values.

Distribution of mean ($\Sigma x_i/128$) should be approximately normal. Goodness-of-fit test of means to normal distribution gave:

$$\chi^2 = 5.87, \text{ d.f.} = 9, \text{ Pr}\left\{ \chi^2 > 5.87 \right\} = .75.$$

C. Runs up and down

Length of run	1	2	3	4	≥ 5	Any length
Observed average number of runs[+]	425.3	187.9	55.4	10.4	2.7	681.8
Expected average number of runs	426.8	187.5	53.9	11.7	2.4	682.3
Observed variance of number of runs[+]	400.9	97.3	24.1	15.2	2.1	181.7
Expected variance of number of runs	433.3	115.2	42.8	10.9	2.4	181.0

[+]Based on 16 sets of 1024.

D. Runs above and below the mean

Length of run	1	2	3	4	5	6	7	8	9	10	Any length
Observed avge. No. of runs[+]	251.2	122.4	65.5	32.7	17.7	8.4	3.9	1.9	1.1	.62	505.5
Expected avge. No. of runs	256	128	64	32	16	8	4	2	1	.1	513

+Based on 16 sets of 1024.

A further series of tests were carried out on numbers generated on ORDVAC by the relation (3.2) by M. L. Juncosa (17). Among these was a test for serial correlation with lag 3. All results were satisfactory.

V. CONGRUENTIAL METHODS - ADDITIVE

The only practical reason to search further for processes to generate random numbers is to gain speed. The obvious suggestion is to try using addition instead of multiplication. This has been discussed by Duparc, Lekkerkerker and Peremans (4). For instance, consider the (reduced) Fibonacci sequence:

$$F_0 = 0, \ F_1 = 1, \ F_{n+2} = F_{n+1} + F_n \ (\text{mod } M) \quad n = 0,1,\ldots \ .$$

If we take $M = 2^{44}$, as is appropriate for SEAC, we find that the Fibonacci sequence has period

$$3 \times 2^{43} \sim 2.5 \times 10^{13}$$

The speed of generation, and the period of these numbers seem satisfactory. However, the numbers are obviously not independent

The reduction mod 2^{44} is accomplished merely by disregarding overflow in the addition

$$F_{n+2} = F_{n+1} + F_n;$$

21

SEAC operates with numbers of 44 binary digits. To illustrate the behavior of this type of sequence consider the simple case $M = 2^3$: the resulting sequence has period 12 and is obtained by repetition of

$$0,1,1,2,3,5,0,5,5,2,7,1.$$

The following heuristic arguments indicate that the sequence may, nevertheless, give satisfactory pseudo-random numbers. It is well known that if $f_o = 0$, $f_1 = 1$; then

$$f_n = (\lambda^n - \mu^n)/\sqrt{5}$$

where

$$\lambda = 1/2 \, (\sqrt{5} + 1), \ \mu = 1/2 \, (-\sqrt{5} + 1)$$

Now, clearly,

$$F_n \equiv f_n \ (\mathrm{mod} \ 2^{44})$$

but, since $\mu < 1$, we have

$$F_n \doteq (\lambda^n/\sqrt{5})(\mathrm{mod} \ 2^{44})$$

and we are again dealing with residues of powers.

We therefore began an investigation of this system. Some of the results obtained to date are reported in detail in the next section; here we summarize our results. The sequence $\{F_n\}$ gave satisfactory results as far as the frequency and moment test were concerned; however, the results for runs were unsatisfactory, there being a preponderance of runs of length 2. This suggested that instead we use the sequence $\{F_{2n}\}$ of alternate members of the sequence $\{F_n\}$. The results of the frequency, moments and run test appear satisfactory, but not as good as the power residues.

VI. RESULTS OF SOME TESTS ON THE REDUCED FIBONACCI SEQUENCE

At present we have not completed a comprehensive series of tests. We report some of the results obtained; a full report will appear in (2).

A. <u>Frequency test</u>. The distribution of three sets of 16384 numbers $\{F_{2n}\}$ in 32 intervals were the following:

516, 462, 525, 507, 506, 516, 512, 517, 487, 488, 466, 506,
512, 482, 538, 539, 558, 487, 523, 503, 519, 524, 512, 519,
509, 522, 551, 522, 501, 508, 524, 523.

513, 499, 508, 497, 507, 563, 525, 511, 534, 487, 500, 542,
497, 506, 545, 491, 521, 505, 503, 515, 480, 487, 491, 510,
501, 548, 525, 540, 522, 494, 480, 537.

561, 533, 488, 520, 514, 551, 493, 504, 492, 509, 513, 482,
549, 516, 546, 531, 503, 522, 536, 511, 540, 483, 530, 473,
504, 515, 504, 479, 469, 526, 503, 484.

The corresponding values of χ^2 are

$$26.88, \quad 27.16, \quad 35.17, \quad d.f. = 31.$$

B. <u>Moments</u>. Here are ten sets of values of the moments[+] of 128 numbers of the sequence F_n.

.5073	.5169	.5518	.5104	.4819	.5051	.4912	.4562	.5028	.4907	$\Sigma x_i/128$
.3414	.3474	.3896	.3409	.3087	.3356	.3265	.2840	.3321	.3316	$\Sigma x_i^2/128$
.2594	.2620	.3032	.2549	.2222	.2492	.2439	.2013	.2469	.2533	$\Sigma x_i^3/128$
.2103	.2100	.2486	.2028	.1712	.1968	.1937	.1532	.1964	.2062	$\Sigma x_i^4/128$
.1922	.1495	.1581	.1596	.1559	.1705	.1656	.1512	.1421	.1920	$\Sigma(x_i-x_{i+1})^2/128$
.1664	.1813	.1776	.1538	.1332	.1687	.1813	.1469	.1733	.1608	$\Sigma(x_i-x_{i+2})^2/128$
.1641	.1762	.1940	.1674	.1676	.1698	.1763	.1721	.1601	.1850	$\Sigma(x_i-x_{i+3})^2/128$
.1752	.1465	.2191	.1574	.1518	.1417	.1636	.1628	.1737	.1696	$\Sigma(x_i-x_{i+4})^2/128$

[+]The theoretical expected values are: .5000, .3333, .2500, .2000, .1654, .1641, .1628, .1615.

C. _Runs up and down_. In the table below the first three columns record the numbers of runs up and down in a series of three sets of 1024 numbers of the sequence $\{F_n\}$; the next three columns give similar results for the sequence $\{F_{2n}\}$; the last column gives the theoretical expected results.

		F_n			F_{2n}			
UP	1	87	83	80	206	211	204	213.4
	2	112	118	112	77	96	107	93.8
	3	35	36	30	44	24	23	27.0
	4	11	9	17	8	5	3	5.9
	5	5	6	5	0	2	0	
	6	1	0	3	0	0	0	1.2
	7	1	1	0	0	0	0	
	8	1	1	1	0	0	0	
DOWN	1	79	84	76	213	199	200	213.4
	2	116	119	119	89	101	99	93.8
	3	40	32	29	24	31	31	27.0
	4	12	10	17	9	6	7	5.9
	5	6	6	7	0	0	1	
	6	1	2	1	0	0	0	1.2
	7	0	1	0	0	0	0	
	8	0	1	0	0	0	0	

D. _Runs above and below the means_. In the table below we record the number of runs above and below the mean in a series of six sets of 1024 numbers of the sequence $\{F_{2n}\}$; the last column gives the theoretical expected results.

ABOVE	1	134	140	133	125	128	132	128
	2	52	48	54	64	52	44	64
	3	45	32	45	38	30	48	32
	4	16	28	16	27	35	23	16
	5	10	10	11	9	10	11	8
	6	0	3	4	3	2	2	4
	7	0	0	1	1	0	0	2
	8	1	0	0	0	0	0	2
BELOW	1	119	141	154	150	137	134	128
	2	55	44	36	53	47	56	64
	3	49	45	42	38	39	44	32
	4	22	14	19	18	26	16	16
	5	10	13	10	6	7	9	8
	6	1	2	3	1	2	2	4
	7	1	2	0	0	0	0	2
	8	0	0	0	0	0	0	2

The numbers of the observed averages, in a series of 16 sets of 1024 numbers from $\{F_{2n}\}$, with runs above and below the mean of the same length added, were

Length:	1	2	3	4	5	6	7	8
Observed count:	261.9	103.4	82	43.1	18.9	4.6	0.9	0.1
Theoretical count:	256.0	128.0	64	32.0	16.0	8.0	4.0	4.0

The observed averages, in a series of 16 sets of 1024 numbers from $\{F_{2n}\}$, with the runs up and down of the same length added together were:

Length:	1	2	3	4	5
Observed count:	425.6	187.1	58.9	10.6	1.32
Theoretical count:	426.8	187.5	53.9	11.7	2.4

VII. MISCELLANEOUS METHODS

Forsythe (5) discusses a scheme suggested by Rosser for the generation of random digits. We describe a simple example. Take four "random" numbers with say 3,4,5,7 binary digits and repeat these numbers, as indicated below:

```
1 0 1 1 0 1 1 0 1 1 0 1 1 0 1 1 0 1 1 0 1 1 0 ...
1 0 0 1 1 0 0 1 1 0 0 1 1 0 0 1 1 0 0 1 1 0 0 1 ...
0 1 1 0 0 0 1 1 0 0 0 1 1 0 0 0 1 1 0 0 0 1 1 0 0 ...
1 0 1 1 0 0 1 1 0 1 1 0 0 1 1 0 1 1 0 0 1 1 0 1 1 0 0 ...
```

The first line contains repetitions of the number 101, the second repetitions of 1001, and so on. Consider the sequence obtained by adding (modulo 2) successive columns of this array. This is

```
1 1 1 1 1 1 1 0 0 1 1 1 1 0 0 1 1 1 1 ...
```

25

This sequence has period not greater than 3 x 4 x 5 x 7 = 420. Forsythe examined on SWAC, the National Bureau of Standards Western Automatic Computer, a series of 1217370 digits obtained in this way from four random numbers with 31, 33, 34 and 35 binary digits. Among the tests which he applied was the following: let s_j be the sum of 100 consecutive digits, then he examined twelve groups each of 1000 sums s_j. Of these, eleven were in reasonable fit with the theoretical binomial distribution; the twelfth was a bad fit.

The sequence of digits in certain algebraic and transcendental numbers have been tested. For a summary and references see Teichroew (13). Some pass and some do not pass the standard test; e.g., e is apparently bad. Apart from the difficulty in generating these, this seems sufficient reason to discard this method.

We note here that Richtmyer (11) has used algebraic numbers in connection with a quasi-Monte Carlo problem on SEAC. Roughly speaking, an integral is evaluated by "systematic" sampling at points depending on certain quadratic surds; satisfactory deterministic error bounds can be obtained from the theory of algebraic numbers.

In certain recent investigations, e.g., in connection with the assignment problem, the generating of random permutations has become of interest. It is possible to use any of the pseudo-random sequences described above to generate pseudo-random permutations.[+] More direct constructions have been suggested by T. S. Motzkin and D. H. Lehmer.

VIII. BIBLIOGRAPHY

1. J. M. Cameron, Results on some tests of randomness on pseudo-random numbers. Abstract in Annals Math. Stat, 23 (1952), p. 138.

2. J. M. Cameron, M. Newman, O. Taussky, J. Todd. The generation and testing of pseudo-random numbers on SEAC, to appear.

[+]Cf. f.n. [+++]on p. 1.

3. J. M. Cameron and M. Newman. The generation of normal deviates on SEAC, to appear.

4. H. J. A. Duparc, C. G. Lekkerkerker and W. Peremans. Reduced sequences of integers and pseudo-random numbers, Math. Centrum, Amsterdam, Report ZW 1953-002 (also Report ZW 1952-013).

5. G. E. Forsythe, Generation and testing of 1,217,370 random binary digits on SWAC. Bull. American Math. Soc. 57, (1951), p. 304.

6. G. E. Forsythe, H. H. Germond and A. S. Householder, editors, Monte Carlo Method, NBS Applied Mathematics Series 12, U. S. Government Printing Office (1951).

7. D. H. Lehmer, Mathematical methods on large-scale computing units, Harvard University Computation Laboratory, Annals 26 (1951), pp. 141-6.

8. J. W. Mauchly, Pseudo-random numbers, presented to American Statistical Assoc., 29 Dec. 1949.

9. J. Moshman, The generation of pseudo-random numbers on a decimal calculator, Journal Association for Computing Machinery 1 (1954), pp. 88-91.

10. N. Metropolis, this volume.

11. R. D. Richtmyer, The evaluation of definite integrals, and a quasi-Monte Carlo method based on the properties of algebraic numbers, Los Alamos report 13, October 1951.

12. I. A. Stegun and W. J. Youden, The location of the mean in random samples from a normal population, to appear.

13. D. Teichroew, Distribution sampling with high speed computers, Ph.D. thesis, U. of N.C., 1953.

14. J. Todd, Experiments on the inversion of a 16x16 matrix in simultaneous linear equations and the determination of eigenvalues, National Bureau of Standards Appl. Math. Series 29 (U. S. Government Printing Office, 1953), pp. 113-15.

15. J. Todd, Experiments in the solution of a differential equation by Monte Carlo methods, J. Washington Acad. of Sciences 44, (1954), pp. 377-81.

16. D. F. Votaw, Jr., and J. A. Rafferty, High speed sampling, MTAC 5 (1951), pp. 1-8.

17. M. L. Juncosa, Random number generation, on the BRL high-speed computing machines, Ballistic Research Lab. report 855, 1954, Aberdeen Proving Ground, Maryland.

18. H. A. Meyer, L. S. Gephart, N. L. Rasmussen, On the generation and testing of random digits, Wright Air Development Center Tech. Report 54-55, 1954.

PHASE SHIFTS - MIDDLE SQUARES - WAVE EQUATION

N. Metropolis

Los Alamos Scientific Laboratory

University of California

INTRODUCTION

I should like to describe very briefly three separate
and quite independent topics that are somewhat related to
Monte Carlo methods. The first is a problem suggested by,
and worked with, Professor E. Fermi, of the University of
Chicago, and concerns a phase shift analysis of nuclear
scattering experiments. The second is a start into a study
of the "middle square" process of producing uniformly distributed random digits for use in Monte Carlo problems.
This part is being investigated with Cook-Leurgans, of our
computing staff. The third is a Monte Carlo approach to
solutions of the Schrödinger equation. This is an approach
suggested by E. Fermi and the study is being made in collaboration with S. Ulam, J. Pasta, and M. Tsingou.

PHASE SHIFT ANALYSIS

Since the work upon which this portion was based has
been reported in detail in The Physical Review[+], it is
herewith abstracted:

Experimental results on the scattering of pions by
hydrogen have been analyzed in terms of phase shifts. Experimentally, a pion beam of each of the three known types
was scattered by a hydrogen target, and the intensity of
the scattered particles measured as a function of the scattering angle. The problem was reduced to that of finding
relative minima on a six-dimensional toroidal surface.
Starting points were selected at random in the six-
dimensional space and two different plans of action were

[+]Fermi, Metropolis, Alei, Phys. Rev., 95, 6: 1581-1585,
September, 1954.

de Hoffman, Metropolis, Alei and Bethe, Phys. Rev.,
95, 6: 1586-1605, September, 1954.

described. One involved determining minima by changing one variable at a time, in cycles, until a relative minimum was obtained. The other approach proceeded from a random start along the gradient of deepest descent.

GENERATION OF RANDOM NUMBERS

In general, Monte Carlo problems make use of long sequences of uniformly distributed random digits. In the present economy of electronic computation, it is desirable to have some scheme of generating sufficiently uniformly distributed random digits rather than having access to known tables of such digits. One scheme, proposed by von Neumann, is the so-called "middle square." Beginning with some n (usually even) digit number, X_o, one obtains the first iterate, X_1, by forming X_o^2, and extracting the middle n digits from it. X_2 is obtained by squaring X_1, etc. The iterative scheme is simple and requires the storage in the computer of a single number. The sequence of iterates is the set of random digits.

We have tried to study some of the characteristics of such an iterative process. Inasmuch as the sequence of distinct iterates is finite, a cycle is eventually reached. Some questions that naturally arise are:

(i)   starting with a number of n digits, how many distinct iterates are produced; i.e., what sort of chain lengths are found in practice,

(ii)   how many iterates are contained in the part that repeats itself; i.e., how large are the "loops,"

(iii)   how many different loops are associated with a given n,

(iv)   how do these various characteristics depend on the base system that is used.

We have made some preliminary experiments with binary middle squares inasmuch as our computer, the Maniac, has a binary arithmetic structure. The results were somewhat surprising. Figure 1 shows the various developments for

30

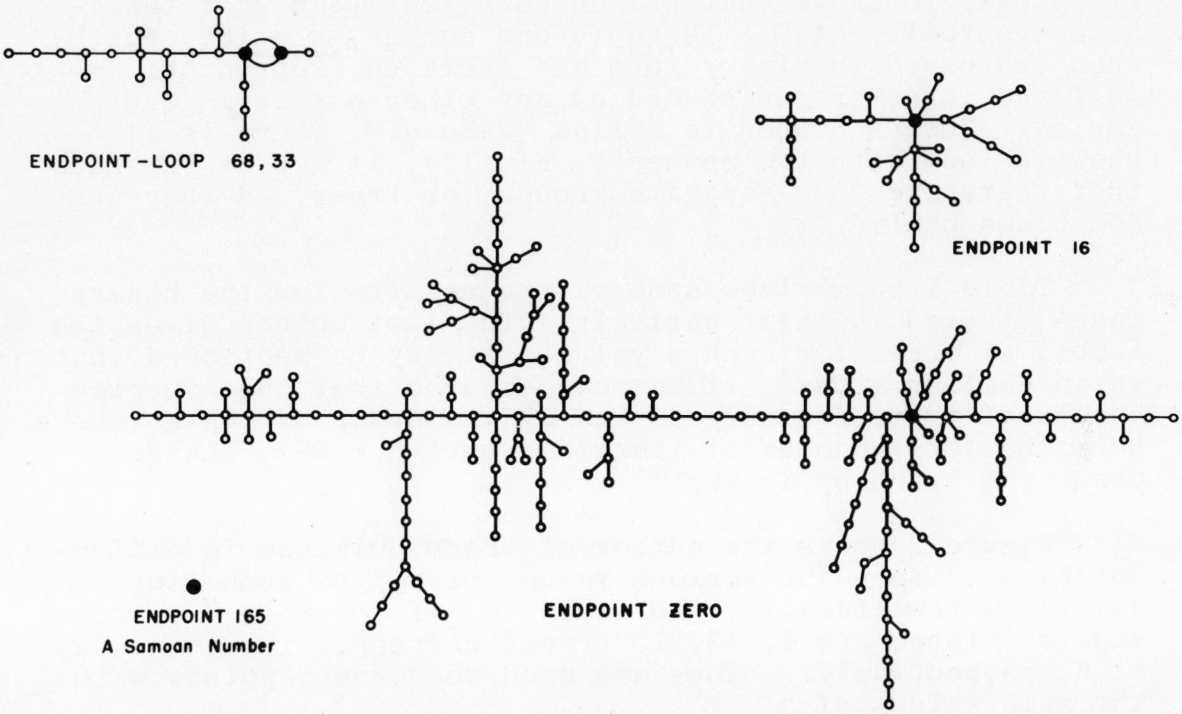

ENDPOINT-LOOP 68,33

ENDPOINT 16

ENDPOINT 165

A Samoan Number

ENDPOINT ZERO

Fig. 1. Genealogy of "middle square" iterates for the
binary case n = 8. Solid circles are the
endpoints for each group.

31

the case of n = 8. The open circles correspond to distinct eight binary digit numbers. The somewhat larger, solid circles are "repeating" numbers. The loops are quite small; in fact, three of them contain only one member; i.e., are self-reproducing. These latter may be called terminal, or end points.

One observes that most numbers terminate at 0 or $2^{n/2}$.

It is easy to prove that all numbers less than $2^{n/2}$ terminate eventually at 0. There is one number, x = 165, which, when expressed in binary form and iterated, reproduces itself and is never reproduced by any other number in the series. Such a number is called "samoan." There is also shown a loop with two members. Finally, it may be remarked that there are four separate groups, or trees, as they are sometimes called.

Table I summarizes some of the results for the binary cases studied in their entirety. The last column gives the number of trees for each n value. It may be mentioned that in an earlier study[+], it was conjectured that the expected number of trees for large N was of the order of log N (where N is the total number of iterates; here N = 2^n). Later a proof was given by Kruskal[++].

Figure 2 shows the number of trees obtained in different base systems for various values of n, the number of digits in the iterates. For example, if the base 7 is considered, there are 4, 13, 15 treest corresponding to n = 2, 4, 6, respectively. Lines are used to connect points with the same values of n.

For practical purposes n is, of course, larger than the cases discussed above. For our various Monte Carlo problems, n = 38 is convenient (the standard size of numbers in our computer is 39 binary digits and a sign). Guided by these very preliminary studies, we have found some very long chains. In one chain, there are some 500,000 iterates, and in another approximately 750,000. Both terminate at 0.

We have made an unsophisticated statistical analysis of this longest chain by considering it as one sequence of 750,000 x 38 binary digits broken up into groups of ten, and analyzing the distribution of these decades in terms of a running Chi-square test. Results were satisfactory.

[+]N. Metropolis and S. Ulam, Amer. Math. Monthly, LX, 252 (1953).

[++]M. Kruskal, Amer. Math. Monthly, LXI, 392 (1954).

Number of Binary Digits	Number of Iterates	Longest Loop	Trees
6	64	1	3
8	256	2	4
10	1024	5	5
12	4096	10	7
14	16,384	56	10
16	65,536	111	13
18	262,144	197	12
20	1,048,576	142	13

BINARY BASE

Table 1. Summary of the various binary bases.

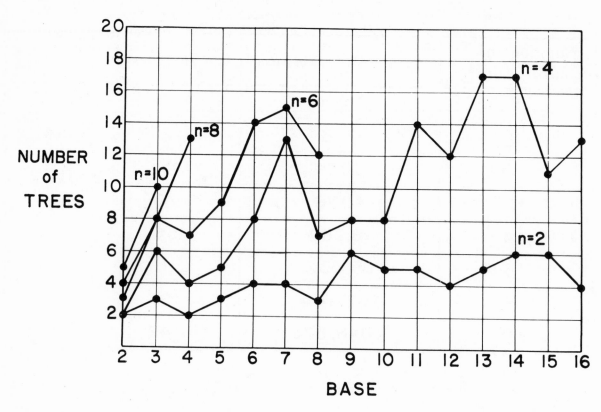

NUMBER of TREES for VARIOUS BASES

Fig. 2. Summary of the various cases. n is the number
of digits in each iterate for the particular
base system.

34

MONTE CARLO SOLUTIONS OF THE SCHRÖDINGER EQUATION

Analytical solutions of the time-independent Schrödinger equations are known for very simple forms of the potential energy function; e.g., $V = 1/r$ for the Coulomb case and $V = kr^2$ for the harmonic oscillator. Potential energy functions with odd shapes and discontinuous derivatives are less tractable, and cases with several particles are not practical even with standard numerical procedures. Consequently, it seemed interesting to pursue a suggestion by Fermi and attempt a Monte Carlo approach. The particular formulation used here is due to S. Ulam.

The Schrödinger equation may be written symbolically as

$$H \psi = E \psi \qquad (5)$$

where H is the Hamiltonian of the system, E is the total energy parameter and ψ is the eigenfunction. One may write Equation (5) in the following finite difference form:

$$\frac{1}{6} \left[\psi_{x+k,y,z} + \psi_{x-k,y,z} + \psi_{x,y-1,z} + \psi_{x,y,z+k} + \psi_{x,y,z-k} \right] + F(V) \psi_{x,y,z} = \alpha \psi_{x,y,z} \qquad (6)$$

where k is the grid spacing, $F(V)$ is an appropriate function of the potential energy and α a constant. Equation (6) is to be iterated in the following manner: the next approximation to ψ_{xyz} (apart from a constant) is obtained by taking the average value of its six nearest neighbors plus a "multiplication" of its own value by a factor determined by the particular potential energy function.

It is easily seen that the appropriate Monte Carlo "game" is the following:

Assume that you have a collection of particles distributed somehow by the game thus far. A cycle consists of the following:

A six-way game of chance is first played to determine whether the particle is to be moved or "diffused" along +x-, +y- or +z-direction by an amount small k. The "multiplication term" is evaluated, and with it another game of chance played to determine how many times the particle at x,y,z is to be reproduced. This process is repeated for all particles; this is one cycle, and of course many cycles are done. The system is super-critical, or can conveniently be made so; i.e., the population is increasing.

In the computer, there was room to store the coordinates of four hundred particles. When an adequate number of cycles had been processed, the positions of the particles were analyzed according to their radial values. From that distribution a new set of initial particles was selected and the whole game repeated, statistics being accumulated along the way.

The nice thing about such a set-up from the computational point of view is that the number of required multiplication and division operations, the relatively time-consuming parts, are very few; and in less than an hour, one can accumulate statistics for 25,000 particles.

We have very recently tried a few experiments with various potentials in order to get a feeling for a few of the parameters and the statistics.

We tried first the Coulomb potential, by way of practice, and then a square well with two steps. Such practical questions as the size of the diffusion step, the treatment of particles escaping from the system, the background multiplication (i.e., the constant term in the potential), the number of cycles, have still to be optimized, but the preliminary results are quite encouraging that this is a feasible approach.

A GENERAL THEORY OF STOCHASTIC ESTIMATES OF THE NEUMANN SERIES FOR THE SOLUTIONS OF CERTAIN FREDHOLM INTEGRAL EQUATIONS AND RELATED SERIES

G. E. Albert

ORNL and University of Tennessee
Knoxville

This talk is extracted from a report issued by the
Oak Ridge National Laboratory under the same title. It is
available to interested parties upon request. The reference is to ORNL-1508 Physics. I claim no credit for the
basic ideas used in that report. Brief papers by Herman
Kahn, R. E. Cutkowski and G. Goertzel excited my interest
in the subject and provided the basic methods. The report
contains a good deal of generalization (too much for practical use) and some discussion of the practicability or
impracticability of certain specializations. Above all,
it provides a fairly rigorous and complete treatment of
the theory of certain general classes of stochastic processes that might be conceived as applying to the problem
of estimating the solutions of integral equations.

It has been emphasized by mathematical statisticians
that the first step in any statistical study should be a
careful description of the sampling space and probability
measures to be used. This point has been somewhat slighted
in the literature on Monte Carlo methods and I have tried
to fill the gap. This question is not purely academic.
Little or no attention has been given in the published literature to the design of Monte Carlo solutions of integral
equations for use on high speed electronic equipment. To
attack such a problem it seems to me that we should proceed in two phases. First, define a very general class of
estimating processes using the most rigorous methods available; second, give attention to various ways of specializ-
ing for practicability and efficiency. In particular, it
seems that the variance reducing tricks such as stratified
sampling should be given due consideration. I do not see
how any consideration can be given to stratified sampling
unless the sampling space and probability measure are
fully understood.

The full extent of the theory discussed in my report
is too complicated for this talk. I will try to approach

the subject in a more or less intuitive manner. We are interested in estimating the solution of the integral equation

$$(1) \qquad \phi(x) = g(x) + \int_R K(x, y)\phi(y)dy.$$

I assume that the Neumann series

$$(2) \qquad \phi(x) = g(x) + \sum_{k=1}^{\infty} I_k(x),$$

with terms

$$(3) \quad I_1(x) = \int_R K(x, y)g(y)dy, \quad I_{k+1}(x) = \int_R K(x, y)I_k(y)dy,$$

is convergent. There are two basic reasons for contemplating stochastic estimates of values of this series. First, in many practical problems the series is exceedingly slowly convergent; second, the integrals (3) are often completely intractable by ordinary methods of integration.

The relations (3) are immediately suggestive of transition probabilities. This suggestion has been exploited to a certain extent in actual Monte Carlo experiments in which an analogue of a physical diffusion process is set up within the computing laboratory. One obtains a histogram type of solution for the equation (1). For example, the paper given by Mrs. N. M. Dismuke at this symposium presented such a process. I have been more interested in a more sophisticated (perhaps I should say more artificial) method that depends upon estimation via average values of a certain random variable. That is, we define a sampling space Ω of elements ω, a probability measure $P(\Lambda)$ on a Borel field of subsets Λ of Ω and a P-measurable function $g(\omega)$ with, say, the property

$$Eg(\omega) = \phi(x).$$

The statistician's problem, as I see it, is to choose the process (Ω, P) and the random variable $g(\omega)$ in such a way that the latter is an efficient estimate of the solution

of the integral equation. Efficiency here may mean different things to different computers. To the man who works
with tables of random numbers and of functions and who is
limited to nomograms and a desk calculator, efficiency may
mean that the average of a small number of independent
values of $g(\omega)$ should be close to $\phi(x)$ with large probability. Let's call this statistical efficiency. On the
other hand, to a man who works with a large electronic
calculator, efficiency must mean something quite different.
Here, all kinds of tables are essentially useless. The
machine computes everything that it uses by simple operations. Millions of these operations are the rule. The
statistician's problem is to make efficient use of these
millions of operations. Of course, the ideal might be a
balance between these two kinds of efficiency. To my knowledge, that ideal is not yet in sight for the present type
of problem.

To proceed with some general definitions, let us consider some sampling distributions. I want to define a
procedure for obtaining sample chains

$$x_0, \; x_1, \; x_2, \; \ldots, \; x_n \; .$$

The initial point x_0 will be chosen either arbitrarily or
at random using a probability density function $f_0(x_0)$.
Which alternative is used depends upon the problem and
will be made clear later. Successive points of the chain
are to be drawn from the conditional distributions

$$f_k(x_k | x_0, \; \ldots, \; x_{k-1})$$

obtained in the standard manner from a consistent family
of joint distributions as indicated in the definitions:

$$
(4) \quad
\begin{cases}
f_k(x_1, \; x_2, \; \ldots, \; x_k | x_0), \quad k = 1, 2, 3, \ldots, \text{ a con-} \\
\qquad\qquad \text{sistent family of probability (density)} \\
\qquad\qquad \text{functions;} \\[2mm]
p_k(x_0, \; x_1, \; \ldots, \; x_k), \quad k = 1, 2, 3, \ldots, \quad 0 \leqslant p_k \leqslant 1, \\[2mm]
\qquad q_k = 1 - p_k, \\[2mm]
p_0(x_0) = 0, \qquad q_0(x_0) = 1.
\end{cases}
$$

After drawing each x of the chain a decision is to be made
to end the chain there with probability p_k or to continue
the drawing with probability q_k. The chain points and its
length n are random. The probability P_k that the chain be of
length n = k is given by the formula:

$$P_k \equiv \Pr\left[n = k \mid x_0\right]$$

$$(5) \qquad = \int_R \cdots \int_R f_k(x_1, x_2, \ldots, x_k \mid x_0) p_k(x_0, \ldots, x_k)$$

$$\left[\prod_{i=1}^{k-1} q_i(x_0, \ldots, x_i)\right] dx_1 \ldots dx_k .$$

I see little point in chains that stop at x_0. Thus, I
choose $p_0(x_0) = 0$. One may define the conditional distribution of $x_1, \ldots, x_n$ under the condition n = k by the
formula

$$g_k(x_1, \ldots, x_k \mid n = k, x_0)$$

$$(6) \qquad \equiv \frac{f_k(x_1, \ldots, x_k \mid x_0) p_k(x_0, \ldots, x_k) \left[\prod_{i=1}^{k-1} q_i(x_0, \ldots, x_i)\right]}{P_k} .$$

Having these distributions, the sampling could be conceived
in a different way. One might first draw an integer n from
the distribution (5) of chain lengths and then draw the
chain points using the distribution (6). This conception
is helpful in understanding certain random variables that
I shall use and may even be practical in some designs.

I know of two random variables defined on such chains
that will estimate the value of $\phi(x_0)$ at an arbitrarily
chosen point x_0 in R. They are given in equations (7) and
(8).

$$(7) \quad \hat{\phi}_k(x_0) \equiv g(x_0) + \frac{g(x_k) \prod_{i=1}^{k} K(x_{i-1}, x_i)}{P_k \cdot g_k(x_1, \ldots, x_k \mid n = k, x_0)}$$

$$\text{if } n = k,$$

(8) $\displaystyle \hat{\hat{\phi}}_k(x_0) \equiv g(x_0) + \sum_{j=1}^{k} \left[\hat{\phi}_j(x_0) - g(x_0) \right] p_j(x_0, \ldots, x_j).$

Note that the number P_k cancels in the denominator of (7). The quantity (8) is defined in terms of (7). Both of these variables are unbiased estimates of $\phi(x_0)$. Consider, for example, (7). We have

$$E\hat{\phi}_n(x_0) = g(x_0) + \sum_{k=1}^{\infty} \int \ldots \int \hat{\phi}_k(x_0) P_k \cdot g_k(x_1, \ldots, x_k | n =$$

$$= k, \, x_0) dx_1 \ldots dx_k$$

$$= \phi(x_0)$$

from the Neumann series. To show that (8) is unbiased is harder and will not be done here.

If you are wondering where my definition of the space Ω and the measure P are, the omission is purposeful. If I have time, I will say something about these definitions at the end of the paper.

Special cases of the estimator (7) have been treated by the authors mentioned at the beginning. What (7) amounts to is the following. Draw a chain length n from its distribution then the chain from (6). Estimate the integral $I_n(x_0)$ by the quantity

$$P_n \left[\hat{\phi}_n(x_0) - g(x_0) \right]$$

and then adjust this as indicated in (7) to form an estimate of the entire Neumann series. Intuitively it appears that such a procedure for estimating the series (2) must be pretty wild. This is not necessarily so, as will appear later.

To within my knowledge, not much attention has been given to the estimator (8). It is too hard to handle. It generalizes the collision counting type of physical analogue process that I just barely mentioned earlier. Some parties have argued that (8) should be a better estimator than (7) but this is not necessarily so. I shall say little more about (8).

41

Averages of many independent values of (7) should give estimates for which the precision can be estimated by standard statistical methods.

The random variable

$$(9) \qquad \hat{J}(x) \equiv \frac{w(x, x_0)\hat{\phi}(x_0)}{f_0(x_0)}$$

serves to estimate the integral

$$J(x) = \int_R w(x, u)\phi(u)du.$$

Here we make x_0 random and use either (7) or (8) to estimate $\phi(x_0)$. $\hat{J}(x)$ is an unbiased estimate of the function $J(x)$ for all x in R. To see this

$$E\hat{J}(x) = E\left[E\left\{\frac{w(x, x_0)\hat{\phi}_n(x_0)}{f_0(x_0)} \mid x_0\right\}\right] = E\left[\frac{w(x, x_0)}{f_0(x_0)}E\left\{\hat{\phi}_n(x_0) \mid x_0\right\}\right]$$

$$= \int_R \frac{w(x,x_0)\phi_n(x_0)}{f_0(x_0)}f_0(x_0)dx_0 = J(x).$$

If the weight function $w(x, u)$ is chosen to be the kernel $K(x, u)$ of the integral equation (1), then $J(x) = \phi(x) - g(x)$ and we have a way of estimating the entire function $\phi(x)$ instead of its value at a chosen point.

Let's consider the random variable (7) in more detail. It has excited considerable attention in the literature in view of the fact that a choice of the distribution functions (4) exists which will make (7) a perfect estimator for $\phi(x)$. It is supposed that an approximate solution $\alpha(x)$ is known and that its iterate $\beta(x) \equiv g(x) + \int_R K(x, y) \alpha(y)dy$ can be computed. The distribution functions (4) are then specialized to

42

$$f_k \equiv \prod_{i=0}^{k-1} \frac{K(x_i, x_{i+1}) \, \alpha(x_{i+1})}{\beta(x_i) - g(x_i)}, \qquad p_k \equiv \frac{g(x_k)}{\beta(x_k)} .$$

The random variable (7) takes the form

$$\hat{\phi}_k(x_0) = g(x_0) + \left[\beta(x_0) - g(x_0)\right] \prod_{i=1}^{k} \frac{\beta(x_i)}{\alpha(x_i)} .$$

Note that, if $\alpha \cong \beta$ and as a consequence, both are equal to ϕ, this estimator gives the exact value of $\phi(x_0)$. Certain writers have argued that the designer's efforts should be directed toward attempts to approximate this situation. I think that there are difficulties. Not the least of these is the likelihood that the sampling functions may be very hard to use on an electronic machine. Also, since the idea of the process is based upon knowledge of an approximation to the solution, the Monte Carlo must satisfy the requirement that it give a better approximation than the initial one; that is, the variance of the average of independent values of $\hat{\phi}$ should be small relative to $(\beta - \phi)^2$--and this, presumably with a small sample size, since the idea of the construction is to achieve statistical efficiency. I think there are difficulties here too. I refer the interested listener to pages 20-21 of my report for more details.

There is an alternative estimator, also based upon an initial approximation and its iterate, that I believe deserves some attention. $\alpha(x)$ and $\beta(x)$ being at hand, we have an integral equation with the same kernel as (1) but whose solution is known:

$$\alpha(x) = \left[g(x) + \alpha(x) - \beta(x)\right] + \int_R K(x, y) \, \alpha(y) dy .$$

Choose simple distributions (4) that are easy to handle on a machine and estimate $\alpha(x_0)$ and $\phi(x_0)$ simultaneously with each chain. If the ratio

$$\frac{g(x) + \alpha(x) - \beta(x)}{g(x)}$$

43

is fairly constant over R, these two estimates will be highly correlated. The known error $\hat{\alpha}(x_0) - \alpha(x_0)$ may then be used to correct the estimate $\hat{\phi}(x_0)$. How best to use such a correlation correction, whether via the usual linear correlation equation or something fancier, needs consideration and I suspect that such consideration will depend upon the actual integral equation under study. This procedure eliminates the sampling difficulties of the previous case and, I suspect, will satisfy the requirement of giving better accuracy than the initial approximation.

I have spent a good deal of effort in my report, ORNL-1508, on the construction of processes that use the statistician's device called representative sampling from a stratified process. How practicable this device may be in a Monte Carlo is questionable. To describe such a process we must have the concepts for which I argued at the beginning, namely, the sample space Ω and the probability measure P. Partition Ω into non-overlapping subsets Ω_j, $j = 1, 2, \ldots, S$, with $P(\Omega_j) > 0$ and define the conditional probability measures

$$P^{(j)}(\Lambda) \equiv \frac{P(\Lambda \Omega_j)}{P(\Omega_j)}$$

If $\phi_j(x_0)$ is defined as the conditional expectation of (7),

$$\phi_j(x_0) \equiv E\left[\hat{\phi}_k(x_0) \,|\, \omega \varepsilon \, \Omega_j\right], \qquad j = 1, \ldots, S,$$

then the solution value $\phi(x_0)$ is expressible in terms of these new parameters,

$$\phi(x_0) = \sum_{j=1}^{S} \phi_j(x_0) P(\Omega_j),$$

and we can estimate this solution value by means of representative sampling. It is well known that this sampling method reduces the variance of estimate. The difficulty here is in the computation of the sampling distributions for the conditional probability measures. I know of one

44

simple case. If the original measure P is described in simple enough terms for the computation of the probabilities (5), then stratification relative to chain lengths can be effected. This may yield an important reduction in the variance of the estimate especially if the convergence of the Neumann series (2) is very slow. Other possible stratifications that I have considered are much too complex for any mention here and are perhaps impracticable.

Let me close with a few remarks about the general structure of the process (Ω, P). The sampling procedures suggested above bear a striking resemblance to the procedures familiar to statisticians in the theory of sequential tests of hypotheses and it is my firm conviction that the stochastic processes (Ω, P) should be envisaged in the light of that resemblance. Specifically, the space Ω should be made up of elements ω that are infinite sequences $\omega = \{\alpha_i\}$ where the α_i are number pairs $\alpha_i = (x_i, y_i)$, x_i in R and $y_i = 0$ or 1, $i = 1, 2, 3, \ldots$. In the intuitive language of particle collisions, x_i is the position of a collision and $y_i = 0$ if the particle is not absorbed at x_i or $y_i = 1$ if the particle is absorbed at x_i. Define an integral valued function $n(\omega)$ over Ω by $n(\omega)$ equals the least integer k such that $y_k = 1$ in ω. The value of $n(\omega)$ on any particular element ω of Ω is the length n of the finite chain used in the estimation procedures above. The x_i of α_i for $i \leqslant n(\omega)$ are the chain points.

An appropriate probability measure $P(\Lambda)$ on Borel subsets Λ of Ω may be defined in a variety of ways. The essential trick in the definition is to set up P in such a way that the α_i for $i > n(\omega)$ are unrecognized. One simple way to proceed is the following. Let A_k denote the set of all ω on which $n(\omega) = k$ and let $B = \Omega - \sum_{k=1}^{\infty} A_k$.
Assign $P(B) = 0$. For any Borel subset Λ of Ω, define the sets $\Lambda_k = \Lambda A_k$ and assign $P(\Lambda) = \sum_{k=1}^{\infty} P(\Lambda_k)$ where

$$P(\Lambda_k) \equiv \int_{\Lambda_k} \ldots \int P_k \cdot g_k(x_1, \ldots, x_k | n = k, x_0)$$

$$dx_1 \ldots dx_k .$$

For this function $P(\Lambda)$ to constitute a probability measure on Ω it is essential that $P(\Omega) = 1$. This can be effected by placing requirements on the sampling functions (4) such that

$$\lim_{N \rightarrow \infty} \sum_{k=N}^{\infty} P(A_k) = 0.$$

Note that the definition of P will depend in general upon the choice of x_0 although that has not been indicated in the notation. Other more complex definitions for (Ω, P) are given in the reference report. Also, some technique for handling such general definitions is given there.

NEIGHBOR SETS FOR RANDOM WALKS AND DIFFERENCE EQUATIONS

Theodore S. Motzkin

University of California at Los Angeles

U. S. Department of Commerce
National Bureau of Standards

A random walk on the points of an n-dimensional lattice (grid) L consisting of all $P = \Sigma \lambda_i e_i$, where $\lambda_1, \ldots, \lambda_n$ are integers and $e_1, \ldots, e_n$ given independent vectors, is frequently restricted by one or more of the following eight requirements.

1. Definiteness of successor set: For every point P the successor belongs to a given set S(P), irrespective of the past part of the walk.

2. Finiteness of successor set: S(P) has a finite number s_p of elements.

3. Fixed valence: $s_p = s$ is independent of P.

4. Reversibility: $Q \in S(P)$ entails $P \in S(Q)$. The graph (set of pairs) of neighbors (P, Q) will be denoted by G.

5. Adherence: For $Q \in S(P)$, Q-P equals some e_i or $-e_i$.

6. Exhaustion of L: Starting from a given P, any other point of L is accessible after a finite succession of steps.

7. Invariance: The definition of S(P) is invariant under an n-dimensional discrete group of translations. The translation vectors form a sublattice L' of L.

8. Complete invariance: L' = L.

Such sets S(P) of neighbors, fulfilling 1-3, 7, 8, and partly also 4, 5 or 6, occur for instance in [1] and [2], in the setting up of partial difference equations.

In the following we show

(I)   Presupposing 1 - 4, 6, n > 1 <u>and</u> s = 2, <u>no trans-
       lation can leave the definition of</u> S(P) <u>invariant</u>;

(II)   <u>For every</u> n > 1 <u>and</u> 3 ≤ s ≤ 2n, 1 - 7 <u>can be ful-
       filled simultaneously</u>.

Denoting by v the quotient of the volume of the fundamental domain of L' by that of L (the number of equivalence
classes of L-points under the group L') there exists thus a
positive integer v(s, n) equal to the minimal v for which
1 - 7 can be fulfilled. Concerning v(s, n) we obtain

(III) v(s, n) > 1 <u>for</u> s < 2n; v(s, n) ≤ 2n - s + 1 <u>for
       odd and</u> ≤ n - s/2 + 1 <u>for even</u> s; <u>hence in parti-
       cular</u>, v(2n - 2, n) = v(2n - 1, n) = 2, v(2n, n) =
       1.

To prove (I) we note that for 1 - 4, 6 and s = 2 the
points of L can be arranged in a sequence (P_i), i = ...,
-1, 0, 1, ... with $S(P_i) = \left[P_{i-1}, P_{i+1} \right]$. For a translation
τ leaving the definition of S(P) invariant we have either
$\tau P_i = P_{i+t}$ for a fixed t, or $\tau P_i = P_{t-i}$. The latter implies $\tau^2 P_i = P_i$ which is impossible for a proper translation. In the case $\tau P_i = P_{i+t}$ every P_i is congruent,
modulo τ, to one of P_1, ..., P_t. This can happen (in fact,
in many ways) only for n = 1.

The case s = 2n of (II) is obvious by letting S(P) =
$\left[P + e_1, P - e_1, ..., P + e_n, P - e_n \right]$. Here L' = L; conversely if L' = L, that is, if all points of L are equivalent under L' then s = 2n, since omission of, say, $P + e_1$
from S(P) implies, by 4, omission of $P - e_1$, so that by 5
all points accessible from each other have equal λ_1, in
contradiction to 6. Hence v(s, n) > 1 for s < 2n.

With s = 3, n = 2, define S(P) for every $P = \lambda_1 e_1 +
\lambda_2 e_2$ as $\left[P + e_1, P - e_1, P + (-1)^{\lambda_1 + \lambda_2} e_2 \right]$. This brick-
like graph $G_{3,2}$ fulfills evidently 1 - 7. Points P and P'
are equivalent if $\lambda_1 + \lambda_2 = \lambda_1' + \lambda_2'$ (mod 2) whence v = 2.

Similarly, with s = n + 1, let $S(P) = \left[P + e_1, \ P - e_1, \right.$
$P + (-1)^{\lambda_1+\lambda_2} e_2, \ P + (-1)^{\lambda_1+\lambda_2+\lambda_3} e_3, \ \ldots, \ \left. P + (-1)^{\Sigma \lambda_i} e_n \right]$,

for $P = \Sigma \lambda_i e_i$. The fulfillment of 1 - 7 for this graph $G_{n+1,n}$ is again easily verified. Points P and P' are equivalent if $\lambda_1 + \lambda_2 \equiv \lambda_1' + \lambda_2'$ and $\lambda_i' \equiv \lambda_i$ (mod 2) for i = 3, ..., n. Hence the number of equivalence classes $v = 2^{n-1}$.

A related graph where s = n + 1 and S(P) is a regular simplex with center P enables the solution of the corresponding difference equation to approximate that of certain differential equations to a higher order than otherwise with equally many or fewer neighbors [3]. The graph connects the points of two parallel lattices and is defined by induction as follows. Let $\alpha_n = $ arc cos 1/n be the angle between a face of a regular simplex in n-space and a line through its center and a vertex. Suppose the graph is known in (n -1)-space Σ and that its points can be divided into A-points and B-points so that every segment connects an A-point and a B-point. Now move the B-points in n-space orthogonally to Σ until the segments form an angle α_n with Σ. Do the same with parallel copies of Σ, but alternatingly in opposite directions, so that the B'-points (B-points of next copy) are at the same distance from the corresponding B-points as these from their A-neighbors, and similarly for the latter. Connect corresponding points and obtain the desired graph, with its obvious divisibility into two classes of points. The graph is most simply described as the set of all integral points in (n + 1)-space with coordinate sum zero (A-points) and of the same points + (n, -1, -1, ..., -1)/(n + 1) (B-points), connected by segments of length $\left[n/(n + 1) \right]^{1/2}$. This representation or its projection on n-space is convenient in the above-mentioned numerical application.

A graph as needed for the case s = n = 3 of (II) is constructed from $G_{3,2}$ by first deleting infinitely many disjoint segments $(P^+, \ Q^+)$, retaining connectedness (6) and invariance for some two-dimensional translation group, copying the remaining graph in parallel planes of a three-dimensional lattice, and then connecting P^+ and Q^+ with the corresponding point in the preceding and succeeding plane respectively. By repetition of the procedure we obtain the cases $s = 3$, $n > 3$. Likewise, using $G_{s, s-1}$, we can get all cases with $s \leq n + 1$. For the remaining cases, $n + 1 < s < 2n$, consider a graph obtained from $G_{n+1, n}$ by adding all segments in one or more directions.

Among devices to form at once a (P, Q)-graph with $s = 3$ and arbitrarily given $n > 1$ we mention the following construction. Just as in $G_{3,2}$ we will connect every P with $P + e_1$ and $P - e_1$, while the third neighbor of P, $P + e_1$, $P + 2e_1$, ... lies successively in all other L-directions. To achieve this, write the e_1-coordinate of P in the form $\lambda_1' = \lambda_1(n - 1) + k$, λ_1 integral, $2 \leq k \leq n$, set

$P = \lambda_1' e_1 + \lambda_2 e_2 + \ldots + \lambda_n e_n$, and let

$$S(P) = \left[P + e_1, \; P - e_1, \; P + (-1)^{\Sigma \lambda_i} e_k \right].$$ 1 - 7 are readily verified and v is only $2(n - 1)$.

Likewise the definitions $S(P) = \left[P \pm e_1, \; \ldots \; P \pm \right.$

$\left. e_{(s-1)/2}, \; P + (-1)^{\Sigma \lambda_i} e_k \right]$ for odd s, $3 \leq s \leq 2n - 1$, and

$$S(P) = \left[P \pm e_1, \; \ldots, \; P \pm e_{s/2-1}, \; P \pm e_k \right]$$ for even s, $4 \leq s \leq 2n - 2$, with $P = (\lambda_1(n - [(s - 1)/2]) + k)e_1 + \lambda_2 e_2 + \ldots \lambda_n e_n$, $k = [(s + 1)/2]$, ..., n, give admissible neighbor sets with $v = 2n - s + 1$ and $v = n - s/2 + 1$. Thus (III) is proved.

BIBLIOGRAPHY

[1] J. H. Curtiss, "Sampling Methods Applied to Differential and Difference Equations," Proceedings of Seminar on Scientific Computation (November 1949), 23 pages, IBM Corporation.

[2] T. S. Motzkin and W. Wasow, "On the Approximation of Linear Elliptic Differential Equations by Difference Equations with Positive Coefficients," Journal of Mathematics and Physics 31 (1953), pp. 253-259.

[3] M. E. Muller, "Some Monte Carlo Methods for the Dirichlet Problem," Thesis, U.C.L.A. (1954), 113 pages, in particular pp. 80, 92, 93.

Note: This paper was sponsored (in part) by the Office of Scientific Research, USAF.

MONTE CARLO COMPUTATIONS

Nancy M. Dismuke

Oak Ridge National Laboratory, Tennessee

In recent years neutrons have played an increasingly important role in the physical sciences. While neutron sources become more and more common and readily available as tools for research and development, the effect upon tissue of neutron irradiation becomes a vital question.

The Health Physics Division of Oak Ridge National Laboratory has been engaged for some years in a study of the effects on tissue of neutron irradiation. The theoretical phase of this study has been largely the concern of W. S. Snyder and J. Neufeld. I would like to describe some Monte Carlo calculations which have been programmed in connection with this study for solution on the ORACLE, Oak Ridge National Laboratory's high speed computing machine.

The type of problem I am concerned with is a natural Monte Carlo problem in the sense that the physical model suffices as the model for proceeding with the calculation. An experiment is carried out (on a computing machine) which at every stage resembles closely the true physical situation. Whenever a random selection must be made in our experiment, the corresponding physical situation seems to be a matter of random choice.

I wish to consider in some detail the following problem. A broad beam of monoenergetic neutrons of energy E_0 irradiates a slab of human tissue. E_0 is a problem parameter which may have any value between 100 ev and 0.3 mev. The interaction types to be considered are elastic scattering in H, C, N and O and the absorption reactions $H(n, \gamma)$ and $N(n, p)$. Neutrons above thermal energies are scattered isotropically in the center of mass system. Thermal neutrons are scattered isotropically in the laboratory system.

With this model a sample of 10,000 neutrons is used to estimate several functions from which the damage may be determined. The functions of interest are denoted by $\mathcal{E}^T(x)$, $C(x)$, $S_1(x)$ and $S_{th}(x)$. In each case (x) indicates dependence on slab penetration, x. $\mathcal{E}^T(x)$ is the average energy imparted to tissue atoms by interaction type T (one of six possible types). C(x) is the collision density of thermal neutrons. $S_1(x)$ and $S_{th}(x)$ are the sources created by neutrons slowing past the 1 ev and 1/40 ev levels.

We consider that tissue is composed of a homogeneous mixture of H, C, N and O in the following proportions

	H	C	N	O
10^{22} atoms/cm^3	6.02	0.602	0.171	2.74
Per cent by weight	10.1	12.1	4.0	73.6

Hence we are concerned with the interaction of neutrons with the elements H, C, N, O. It is customary to represent the probability of a particular process (e.g., scattering, absorption) which occurs when neutrons pass through matter by giving the effective target area of the bombarded nucleus for that particular process. This quantity is known as the cross-section of the nucleus for that process and is usually denoted by the symbol σ. The units of σ are 10^{-24}cm^2. The cross sections of the elements for neutrons vary with energy.

Suppose that neutrons of energy E are travelling through the tissue specified above. Then the probability that a neutron is scattered by a hydrogen nucleus is proportional to $\sigma_S^H(E)$ (6.02 x 10^{22}). This product is usually denoted by Σ and its units are (cm)$^{-1}$.

The cross sections for the elements we are considering are sketched in Figure 1.

At neutron energies above a few mev inelastic scatterings may occur and increases with increasing neutron energy. For the elements we are considering, anistropy in scattering is negligible below 0.3 mev where the peaks in the O cross section begin. These effects are probably negligible in the interaction of tissue with neutrons up to 10 mev since most of the collisions in tissue are with H which scatters elastically and isotropically in the center of mass system. From the composition of tissue and the cross section data it is seen that for fast neutrons the most important process by which neutrons impart energy to tissue atoms is through elastic scattering. For slow neutrons, however, energy is given to the tissue atoms primarily by the γ-rays and protons produced in the nuclear reactions $H(n, \gamma)$ and $N(n, p)$. The contribution made by the $N(n, \alpha)$ reaction is so small that we shall not consider it here.

It is generally assumed that the biological damage to tissue irradiated by fast neutrons is due primarily to the energy dissipation of the recoil ions produced. For thermal neutron irradiation, the damage is due to the energy dissipation of the γ-rays and protons emitted in the absorption reactions $H(n, \gamma)$ and $N(n, p)$. The damage inflicted by neutrons of energies intermediate to these extremes is through a combination of these processes. The recoil atoms and protons lose their energy within a small fraction of a cm of the point of collision. However, the gamma rays may be absorbed at large distances from the point of their origin.

In order that irradiations by a fairly wide range of neutron energies may be considered, we shall assume that the average damage to tissue inflicted over each type of interaction is proportional to the average energy imparted to the tissue atoms in the interaction. The proportionality factors, known as RBE factors, relate the biological effectiveness to the energy loss by a specific process.

The configuration of the Monte Carlo experiment to be performed is pictured in Figure 2. The slab of tissue is given by $0 \leqslant x \leqslant t = 30$ cm. A neutron history begins at the origin in the direction of the positive x-axis with initial energy E_0. The distance ρ_1 traveled before the first collision occurs is selected at random from the distribution of free paths of a neutron of energy E_0 passing through tissue. The coordinates of the first collision are then determined. If the collision is within the slab the interaction type is picked at random from its distribution for E_0. For collisions which result in scattering, the new energy must be determined. The new direction in the center of mass system is then chosen from a spherically symmetrical distribution. With this new direction, the mass number of the scattering atom, and the neutron direction and energy before collision, the new energy and the direction in the laboratory system may be determined. For each collision in the tissue above thermal energy, the contribution of that collision is added to $\mathcal{E}^T(x)$. For thermal energies the collision contribution to $C(x)$ is added. If one of the energy levels of interest has been crossed, this fact is recorded along with the corresponding x. The neutron history continues until the neutron is absorbed by a tissue atom or leaks out of the slab.

For each collision from one to three random selections must be made. With 10,000 neutrons making on the average from 50 to 100 collisions each, a fairly large supply of random numbers is required. The congruence method for generating random numbers was used. Adapted for the ORACLE the algorithm is

$$\mathcal{H}_n = \mathcal{H} \cdot \mathcal{H}_{n-1} \pmod{2^{39}}$$

where $\mathcal{H} = 5^{2p+1} = 5^{15}$ and $\mathcal{H}_0 = 1$. We extract from the 39 binary digits of $\mathcal{H}_n$ the middle 20 digits. The binary point precedes 19 or 20 digits according to whether our random number k is to be selected from the interval $(-1,1)$ or from the interval $(0,1)$.

To select a free path, ρ, from the distribution $\Sigma(E) \, e^{-\Sigma(E)\rho}$, a random number k_1 from the interval $(0,1)$ is obtained by the scheme just described. The free path then is

$$\rho = - \frac{1}{\Sigma(E)} \ln(1 - k_1) \, .$$

A second random number k_2 is required for determining the interaction type. The interval $(0,1)$ is split into six subintervals with lengths equal to the probabilities of interaction of the six possible types. The subinterval into which k_2 falls denotes the interaction type.

At least three random numbers k_3, k_4, and k_5 from the interval $(-1,1)$ are required to choose a direction from a spherically symmetric distribution. If the sum of the squares of these three numbers lies between 2^{-39} and 1 they are taken as the direction numbers in the center of mass system of the required direction.

A better picture of the computation procedure can be seen by referring to the flow chart given in Figure 4.

About 1000 neutron histories can be run per hour. The output for the problem is a tabulation of 540 numbers.

x in cm	$\varepsilon^{H,S}$	$\varepsilon^{C,S}$	$\varepsilon^{N,S}$	$\varepsilon^{O,S}$	$\varepsilon^{H(n,\gamma)}$	$\varepsilon^{N(n,p)}$	C	S_l	S_{th}
0 - 0.5									
0.5 - 1.0									
.									
.			(Condensed plan of table 1)						
.									
29 - 29.5									
29.5 - 30									

The problem required altogether about 1000 words of the ORACLE's internal memory. The mean, m, and the standard deviation of the mean, $\sigma(m)$, computed from ten sets of 1000 neutron histories, are shown in Table 1 for the case E_0 = .005 mev.

Some preliminary work has been done on a slightly more complicated problem. A cylindrical tissue phantom is irradiated by an isotropic source of monoenergetic neutrons, at a distance d from one of the faces of the cylinder. For this problem the average energy loss as a function of the space coordinates was tabulated for neutrons slowing down to thermal energy in the phantom. For thermal neutrons the collision density was tabulated. A study will be made of the dependence of damage upon the neutron source energy and distance from the body. Memory requirements are higher for this problem. The preliminary computations made use of the ORACLE's 2000 word memory.

I expect that most members of the Mathematics Panel have contributed to this problem in some way, especially C. P. Hubbard, Jack Moshman and Phyllis Brown Sweeton.

TABLE 1

Upper limit of x	$\mathcal{E}_S^H$ in mev			$\mathcal{E}_S^C$ in mev			$\mathcal{E}_S^N$ in mev		
	m	σ(m)		m	σ(m)		m	σ(m)	
0.5	.1411	.001985	(-2)	.9417	.01339	(-5)	.3351	.005631	(-5)
1.0	.1091	.001148		.7337	.007818		.2954	.003767	
1.5	.7731	.01623	(-3)	.5222	.01105		.2258	.004965	
2.0	.5188	.01123		.3514	.007612		.1588	.003423	
2.5	.3249	.007867		.2204	.004863		.1032	.002376	
3.0	.2201	.006103		.1495	.004153		.7124	.02023	(-6)
3.5	.1370	.007652		.9304	.05174	(-6)	.4487	.02273	
4.0	.9307	.05171	(-4)	.6325	.03500		.3106	.01598	
4.5	.5369	.03696		.3647	.02546		.1807	.01119	
5.0	.3793	.02586		.2574	.01771		.1258	.008407	
5.5	.2284	.01590		.1548	.01088		.7710	.05569	(-7)
6.0	.1578	.01346		.1070	.009203		.5440	.04583	
6.5	.7739	.04251	(-5)	.5240	.09252	(-7)	.2660	.01694	
7.0	.4821	.08281		.3260	.05632		.1660	.02782	
7.5	.2989	.04833		.2000	.03360		.1040	.01655	
8.0	.1518	.02590		.1030	.01764		.5300	.09196	(-8)
8.5	.8936	.2930	(-6)	.6000	.2017	(-8)	.3100	.03281	
9.0	.7421	.3110		.4900	.2105		.2600	.03406	
9.5	.6750	.3088		.4600	.2083		.2400	.03307	
10.0	.4858	.2055		.3400	.1447		.1600	.07630	
10.5	.1051	.05308		.7000	.1252	(-9)	.3000	.06750	(-9)
11.0	.475	.233	(-7)	.2000	.04217		.2000	.04217	
11.5	.669	.258		.5000	.1667		.2000	.04217	
12.0	.83	.52	(-8)	0	0				
12.5	1.96	1.27		.1000	.1000				
13.0	1.04	.952							
13.5	.39	.26							
14.0	11.34	11.34							
14.5	.02	.02							
15.0	.02	.013							
15.5	7.88	7.88							
16.0	3.43	1.08							
16.5	0	0							
17.0	.24	.24							
17.5									
18.0									
18.5									
19.0									
19.5									
20.0									
20.5									
21.0									
21.5									
22.0									
22.5									

Note: The figures in parentheses indicate the power of ten by which the tabulated entries [both m and σ(m)] alongside and below in the same columns are to be multiplied.

57

TABLE 1 (Continued)

Upper limit of x	$\mathcal{E}_S^O$ in mev			$\mathcal{E}_a^H$ in mev			$\mathcal{E}_a^N$ in mev		
	m	σ(m)		m	σ(m)		m	σ(m)	
0.5	.2686	.003820	(-4)	.2219	.006525	(-2)	.8619	.02534	(-4)
1.0	.2090	.002222		.2772	.006065		.1076	.002356	(-3)
1.5	.1486	.003144		.3105	.01108		.1206	.004302	
2.0	.9997	.02171	(-5)	.3181	.009740		.1235	.003783	
2.5	.6270	.01386		.3279	.009968		.1274	.003870	
3.0	.4251	.01179		.3061	.005725		.1189	.002223	
3.5	.2646	.01471		.2758	.006703		.1071	.002602	
4.0	.1799	.009988		.2510	.004647		.9750	.01805	(-4)
4.5	.1037	.007127		.2181	.005948		.8469	.02310	
5.0	.7326	.05032	(-6)	.1811	.003811		.7033	.01480	
5.5	.4408	.03088		.1528	.005337		.5935	.02072	
6.0	.3049	.02652		.1298	.004979		.5040	.01934	
6.5	.1491	.008337		.9104	.04795	(-3)	.3536	.01862	
7.0	.9280	.1596	(-7)	.7701	.05045		.2991	.01963	
7.5	.5740	.09385		.6109	.06093		.2372	.02366	
3.0	.2910	.05010		.4670	.05371		.1814	.02086	
8.5	.1730	.05714		.3734	.02836		.1450	.01102	
9.0	.1430	.06092		.2717	.02846		.1055	.01105	
9.5	.1300	.01889		.1794	.05185		.6085	.C9052	(-5)
10.0	.9200	.3938	(-8)	.1288	.01885		.5001	.07321	
10.5	.2000	.1075		.9303	.1192	(-4)	.3613	.04629	
11.0	.0900	.04583		.7016	.1347		.2725	.05232	
11.5	.1300	.05175		.5312	.08617		.2063	.03348	
12.0	.1000	.1000	(-9)	.5204	.1145		.2021	.04449	
12.5	.4000	.2211		.2440	.06888		.9478	.2675	(-6)
13.0				.1888	.05418		.7331	.2105	
13.5				.2178	.07683		.8460	.2984	
14.0				.4591	.2291	(-5)	.1784	.08898	
14.5				.7810	.4181		.3034	.1624	
15.0				.7964	.3503		.3093	.1361	
15.5				.1075	.1061		.4180	.1304	
16.0				.1244	.1120		.4830	.1377	(-7)
16.5				0	0		0		
17.0				.5016	.5016	(-5)	.1984	.1984	(-6)
17.5									
18.0									
18.5									
19.0									
19.5									
20.0									
20.5									
21.0									
21.5									
22.0									
22.5									
23.0									
23.5									
24.0									
24.5									

TABLE 1 (Continued)

Upper limit of x	C(x)		S_1		S_{th}	
	m	σ (m)	m	σ (m)	m	σ (m)
0.5	824.1	36.28	51.2	1.67	37.1	1.45
1.0	1519.	46.67	66.2	2.99	46.5	2.13
1.5	2001.	56.43	73.1	2.72	51.1	3.26
2.0	2419.	75.90	70.5	2.15	55.8	1.95
2.5	2724.	91.84	71.2	2.93	57.9	2.33
3.0	2856.	86.50	66.6	3.30	54.7	1.58
3.5	2925.	91.04	60.1	1.32	52.4	2.40
4.0	2823.	97.08	52.9	2.15	50.7	1.46
4.5	2771.	75.66	44.2	1.94	40.1	1.45
5.0	2564.	58.33	36.6	1.22	34.5	1.99
5.5	2370.	69.46	26.5	1.67	29.9	2.26
6.0	2143.	67.59	20.9	1.44	24.3	1.58
6.5	1965.	48.50	14.7	1.70	17.9	.994
7.0	1738.	37.08	13.9	1.18	16.8	1.24
7.5	1509.	34.54	9.8	1.28	12.1	1.74
8.0	1342.	35.61	8.4	.872	11.0	1.54
8.5	1109.	37.93	5.4	.499	8.4	.76
9.0	948.5	40.89	4.8	.512	5.7	1.00
9.5	810.4	26.10	2.8	.359	4.3	.52
10.0	703.2	23.36	.9	.35	2.1	.41
10.5	583.6	21.04	.6	.27	1.9	.38
11.0	485.2	21.87	1.1	.35	1.8	.49
11.5	426.4	33.62	.9	.31	1.4	.37
12.0	341.4	19.28	.6	.16	1.4	.31
12.5	284.3	30.61	.3	.21	.4	.22
13.0	272.8	33.44	.2	.13	.2	.13
13.5	242.6	35.78	.2	.13	.6	.22
14.0	201.2	21.27	0	0	.1	.1
14.5	158.4	20.76	.1	.1	.1	.1
15.0	141.1	24.63	.1	.1	.2	.13
15.5	127.3	24.55	0	0	0	0
16.0	103.3	21.69	0	0	.1	.1
16.5	100.3	25.34	0	0	0	0
17.0	84.6	21.28	.1	.1	.1	.1
17.5	55.0	17.48				
18.0	52.8	18.21				
18.5	38.4	10.94				
19.0	31.4	9.75				
19.5	29.7	7.20				
20.0	24.5	6.22				
20.5	16.1	4.99				
21.0	11.2	4.20				
21.5	8.4	3.12				
22.0	8.2	4.38				
22.5	5.7	3.04				
23.0	3.8	2.31				
23.5	1.8	1.00				
24.0	.3	.21				
24.5	.6	.6				

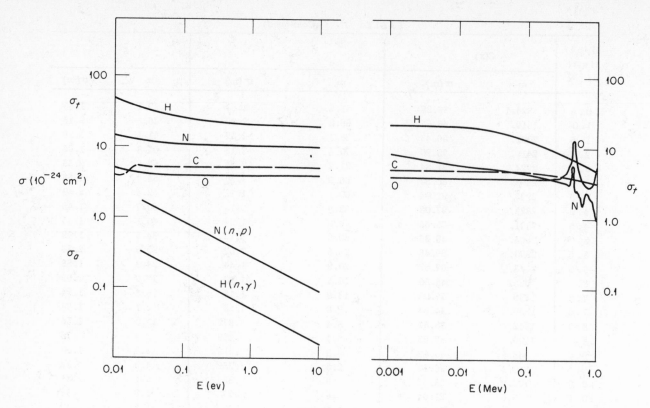

Figure 1

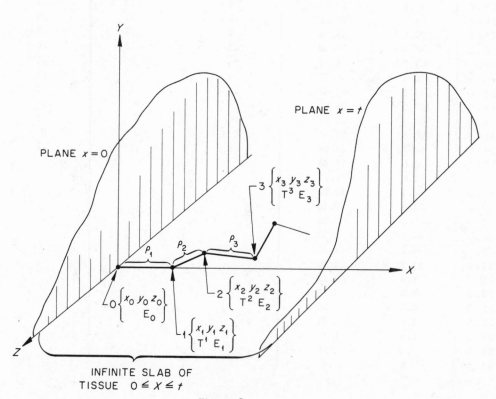

Figure 2

60

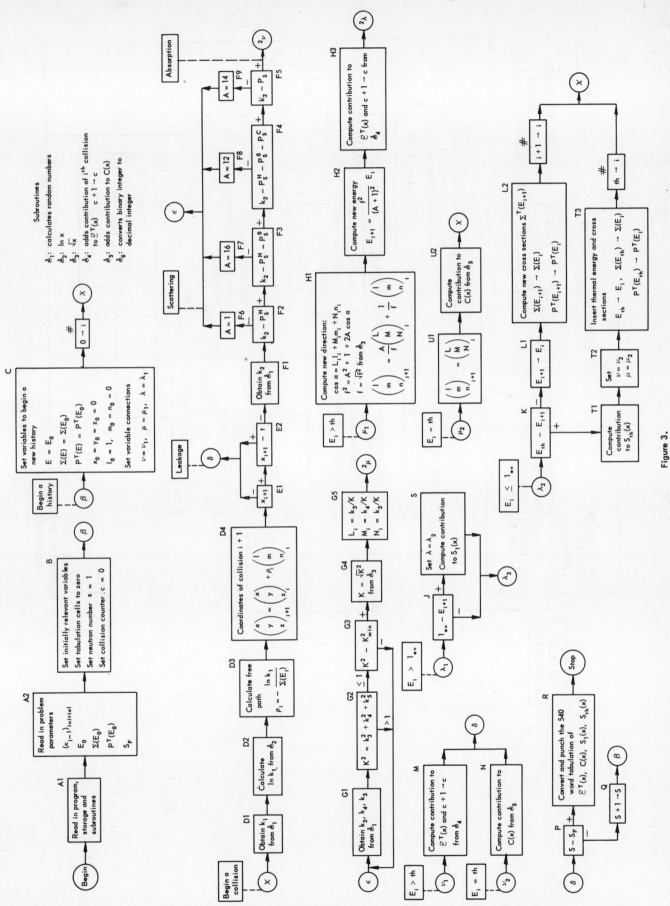

Figure 3.

61

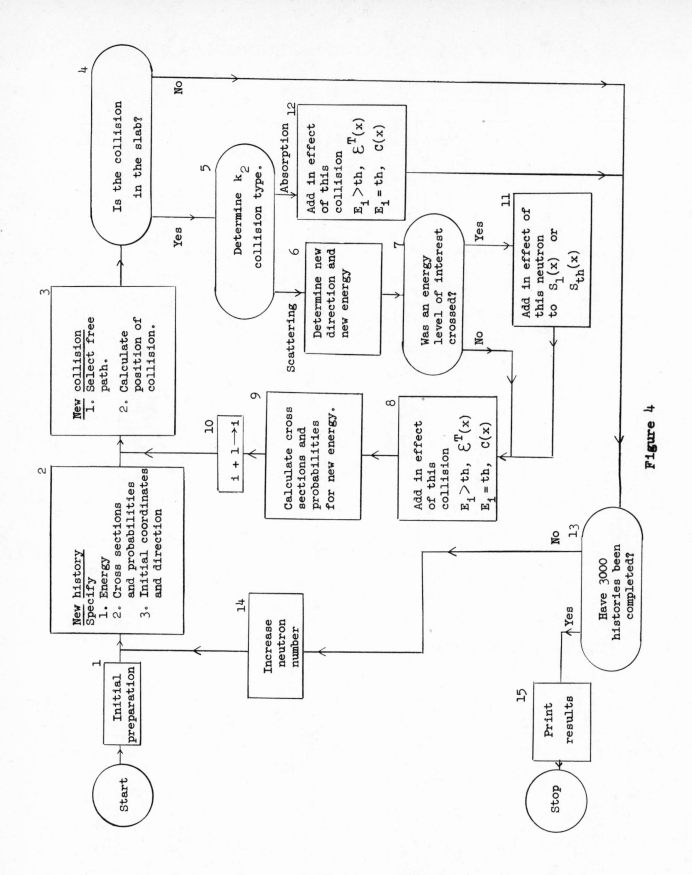

Figure 4

APPLICATIONS OF MONTE CARLO
METHODS TO TACTICAL GAMES

S. Ulam

University of California
Los Alamos Scientific Laboratory

ABSTRACT

The paper deals with applications of the so-called
Monte Carlo method to strategy in games. A rather general
scheme for a game played between two persons, A, B, may be
the following: Let E be the set of integers (a finite set
or the set of all integers). These integers denote all
possible positions in the game. W is a given subset of it
consisting of integers which describe the "winning positions." To each integer i is ascribed a set of integers
denoted by $F(i) = (n_1, n_2, \ldots, n_{k_i})$, the game being

played as follows: A selects an integer i_1, then B
selects any integer he wants, i_2 from the set $F(i_1)$, then
A selects an integer from $F(i_2)$, and so on. The first
player who manages to select an element of the set W, wins.
One can define analogously a game between $k > 2$.

An algebraical classification of such games is under-
taken--one can define equivalence, homomorphism, the
relation of containing, a sum, product and iteration of
such games.

The role of chance can be now introduced on top of
such a scheme but assuming the probability distribution
which affects (but does not determine) the choice of an
element in F(i) (this can be interpreted as, for example,
the probability of errors in judgment or insufficient
knowledge of the possibilities in the game). A successful
strategy will be one which maximizes the probability of
winning against the "best plays of the opponent." Various
schemes are discussed of approximating such a strategy by
statistical experiments, that is to say, methods of "learning the game" in a most economical way.

In the case when the set E is truly infinite, a win
would, of course, necessitate a proof of the existence of
a method of play. Such a game, with a given probability
distribution would generalize a game first introduced by
S. Mazur in 1928 and recently rediscovered by Stewart and
Gale.

CONDITIONAL MONTE CARLO FOR NORMAL SAMPLES[+]

Hale F. Trotter and John W. Tukey

Princeton University

The techniques presented here represent what sometimes happens to lazy people who start doing a computation before they quite know what they are going to do. Contrary to experience and high moral principles, this time it worked out all right. We solved our problem (cp. "Monte Carlo techniques in a complex problem about normal samples" pp. 80 ff., below) and we were able to extract some relatively general techniques from what we were driven to do in attempting to solve a particular problem.

2. We have not tried to express our results in the greatest possible generality, suspecting that there may be enough difficulty in coming to grips with them in a relatively special case -- however, we shall say a word or two about greater generality at the end of the account. In very rough terms we seek to use a family of transformations to convert given samples into samples conditioned on a given characteristic. We find that we can do this legitimately, and can even reuse the same samples when conditioning to another value. This seems unlikely and of doubtful legitimacy, but adequate arguments can be given for its validity and wisdom.

MONTE CARLO IN GENERAL

3. We shall begin by talking about Monte Carlo in general. One of our neighbors in the audience was asking us about the previous paper -- asking whether it was an example of Monte Carlo, or of synthetic (experimental) sampling, or whether Monte Carlo had taken synthetic sampling over. Our answer was that we thought that the last paper was experimental sampling -- that we should not like to call it Monte Carlo unless the sampling was a bit trickier. Leaving aside the important ways of using ratio and regression estimates (and covariance in general), the way in which sampling is made trickier is by the use of weights. (In the simplest situations, the weights are, of course, inversely proportional to the factor by which the probability of occurrence has been distorted.)

[+]Prepared in connection with research sponsored by the Office of Naval Research.

4. As long as we stick to the simpler situations of Monte Carlo -- and we will talk (both here and in the later paper) only about sampling from a very simple distribution -- the one essential point is that any sample can come from any distribution. The particular distribution with which we are concerned is reflected, sometimes dimly, in the weights to be attached to the samples. A table of random samples from the unit normal distribution can be used as a table of random samples from any distribution (over real numbers) whatever -- if we use the correct weights. The whole trick is to generate samples and weights which match them in such a way as to get efficient results in a manageable manner. We must, therefore, study processes which provide us pairs, say (y, w) where y is the number, sample, neutron path, or what not in whose properties we are interested, and w is the corresponding weight.

5. A process generating pairs (y, w), w real, is said to produce weighted samples from a given distribution if two conditions are satisfied:

(a) the pairs (y, w) are samples from some joint distribution, and

(b) for all reasonable real-valued functions ϕ (y) we have the equality:

$$\text{ave} \left[w \, \phi(y) \mid \text{process} \right] = \text{ave} \left[\phi(z) \mid \text{distribution} \right]$$

6. Almost all Monte Carlo techniques are devoted to finding suitable processes yielding weighted samples, and then using the results of the process to estimate the average of one (or more) interesting function(s) of z, where z has a prescribed distribution. As noted above, the values of z (and y) may be numbers, vectors, samples of numbers, samples of vectors, neutron paths or what have you. The two conditions above are of very different nature and importance. Condition (b) states that we get the right answer on the average. Condition (a) says something about the convergence of means toward this average -- saying that means behave like (exactly like!) means of random samples. We are interested in learning ways to make new processes out of old ones, retaining condition (b) as we do this. In some of our heuristic proofs, we shall go through certain intermediate processes which satisfy (b) but not (a). This failure of (a) will be unimportant, since the necessary

convergence can be established by arguments which we shall omit. Notice that condition (a) is always fulfilled in two limiting situations

(1) the x are a sample, and $w = w(x)$ depends on x alone

(2) the x are a sample, w is independent of x, the w are a sample (in particular, are constant).

7. If we have N weighted samples (y_1, w_1), (y_2, w_2), ..., (y_N, w_N) from some distribution and are interested in ave $\left[\phi(z) \mid \text{distribution}\right]$ we can estimate the average either by

$$\frac{\Sigma w_i \phi(y_i)}{N} \qquad \text{or by} \qquad \frac{\Sigma w_i \phi(y_i)}{\Sigma w_i}$$

Experience shows that the former is almost always better than the latter (as well as being unbiased).

8. The equivalence for large samples of these two estimates follows from 5(b) by taking $\phi(z) \equiv 1$, whence

$$\text{ave} \left[w \mid \text{process}\right] = 1.$$

Initially we didn't realize how important it was to distinguish these two estimates -- but experience showed the advantage of dividing by N, the average total weight, rather than by the realized total weight, Σw_i. Indeed, it is possible to use

$$\frac{\Sigma w_i \phi(y_i)}{\lambda N + (1 - \lambda) \Sigma w_i}$$

for any real λ, and there is some ground for anticipating that λ's somewhat larger than unity will often be best. (We don't know of any practical experience with such more general estimates.)

MONTE CARLO FOR STATISTICIANS

9. Today we are interested in Monte Carlo to solve
problems which come up in statistics. There are many
places where the statistician can properly say "I think I
know how to analyze the data in principle, but how can I
find the critical numbers?" For this reason, statisticians
are going to use more and more Monte Carlo as time goes on.
Because their main interest is in critical numbers (critical values), their Monte Carlo problems tend to be simpler
than those of some others. As statisticians we are likely
to need the solution of some such relation as

$$\text{Prob (something} \geq h) = 5\%$$

or

$$\text{Prob (something} \geq h) = 1\%$$

for h, where "something" is likely to be a rather complex
function of a number, sample of numbers, etc. which has a
given distribution. It is not quite obvious that such problems are asymptotically of the form

$$\text{find} \quad \text{ave} \left[\phi(z) \mid \text{distribution}\right]$$

but if we give a couple of wisely chosen values to h, and
for each put

$$\phi(z) = \begin{cases} 0, & \text{something} < h, \\ 1, & \text{something} \geq h, \end{cases}$$

we can show the asymptotic equivalence.

10. In dealing with such functions $\phi(z)$, where $\phi^2 \equiv \phi$,
we find it relatively easy to specify what are good Monte
Carlo processes. The statistician often works with the
variance, defined by

$$\text{var}(u) = \text{ave}(u^2) - \left[\text{ave}(u)\right]^2$$

as his measure of nonconstancy. We have

$$\text{var}\left[\frac{\Sigma w_i \phi(y_i)}{N}\right] = \frac{1}{N} \text{var}\left[w \phi(y)\right]$$

$$= \frac{1}{N}\left[\text{ave}\left[w^2 \phi(y)\right] - \left[\text{ave}\left[w \phi(y)\right]\right]^2\right]$$

67

where we have made use of 5(a) and have written $w^2 \phi(y)$
for $w^2 \phi^2(y)$ as we may since $\phi^2 = \phi$ If now we observe
that ave $\left[w \phi(y) \right]$ = ave $\left[\phi(z) \mid \text{distribution} \right]$ is exactly
what we are trying to find and is therefore constant, we
see that minimizing the variance of estimate is merely
minimizing ave $\left[w^2 \phi(y) \right]$. If we call those y's for which
$\phi(y) = 1$ the exceptional set, then we are to try to make
w^2 small for exceptional y's. In most cases we do very
well with the rule of thumb that the largest w for an exceptional y should be kept as small as possible. (The w's
for non-exceptional y's are multiplied by $\phi(y) = 0$ and are
of no account.) This helps to simplify Monte Carlo for
statisticians. (Indeed, we give an important part of the
picture if we say that small weights in the exceptional
sets must be reflected in many samples in the exceptional
set, while having many samples actually involved in the
computation tends to reduce the effect of sampling fluctuations. All this is true, but it is only part of the story.)

CONDITIONAL MONTE CARLO

11. All of the group here today should be quite clear
that the only good Monte Carlos are dead Monte Carlos -- the
Monte Carlos we don't have to do. In other words, good
Monte Carlo ducks chance processes as much as possible. In
particular, if the last step of the process we are studying
is a probability of reaction, it is wasteful, often very
wasteful, to force a "yes" or "no" with a random number instead of accepting the numerical value of the probability
of reaction and averaging this numerical value. The use of
conditional Monte Carlo is, in a certain sense, the con-
verse of this process, since it leads to integration over
the first coordinate instead of over the last. As a way of
reducing the sway of chance processes, it is almost always
useful and sometimes exceedingly useful.

12. We are concerned with Monte Carlo for the statistical problems associated with samples from a normal distribution. Such problems involving "plus," "minus," "times,"
and "divided by" have a reasonably good chance of being
solved by analytic means and avoiding Monte Carlo. It is
the problems which involve "max," "min," "or" and "and"
which have given rise to difficulty. These are the connectives which will drive the statistician to Monte Carlo. And
for these connectives, conditional distributions are particularly advantageous. For example, if "or" means "either or
both," we have:

$$\text{Prob}\left[A(z) \geq a \ \underline{\text{or}} \ B(z) \geq b\right] = \int_{-\infty}^{a} \text{Prob}\left[B(z) \geq b \mid A(z) = (t)\right] dF_A(t) + \text{Prob}\left[A(z) \geq a\right].$$

where $\text{Prob}\left[B(z) \geq b \mid A(z) = t\right]$ signifies the probability that $B(z) \geq b$ under the condition that $A(z) = t$, and $F_A(t) = \text{Prob}\left[A(z) \leq t\right]$ is the cumulative distribution of $A(z)$.

This example is not unrelated to our general class of problems and the form of the answer is particularly helpful. Often we can calculate the last term analytically, and if it is larger than the integrated term we have notably reduced the size of the probability to be evaluated by Monte Carlo. This automatically improves the sampling situation.

13. We remark that, in many problems, the natural conditions are conditions of scale, so that we may choose $A(z)$ to be homogeneous of the first degree in the elements of the sample. Indeed the two most prominent choices are the range (highest minus lowest) of the sample and alternatively, the square root of the sum of deviations. Both of these are invariant under translation, a property that we shall also find convenient.

NORMAL SAMPLES

14. We shall need some notation, and shall begin by writing $x = (x_1, x_2, \ldots, x_m)$ for the sample and its elements. Multiplication by a real number proceeds coordinate-wise, so that $\alpha x = (\alpha x_1, \alpha x_2, \ldots, \alpha x_m)$.

15. Some abbreviations for hypotheses are useful. We shall use:

NID $(0, 1)$ = randomly normally and independently distributed with mean zero and unit variance,

NID' $(0, 1)$ = same modulo translations,

ONID $(0, 1)$ = like NID $(0, 1)$ except that entries in each sample are rearranged to run from - to +,

ONID' $(0, 1)$ = ordered NID' $(0, 1)$.

Here by "modulo translations" we mean that $(x_1, x_2, \ldots, x_m)$ and $(x_1 + h, x_2 + h, \ldots, x_m + h)$ are identified (treated as equivalent) for all values of h. (This may, if we wish, be described for special purposes as going from $(x_1, x_2, \ldots, x_m)$ to $(x_1 - \bar{x}, x_2 - \bar{x}, \ldots, x_m - \bar{x})$, where $m\bar{x} = \Sigma x_j$, or in terms of any other special representation.) Many problems have the corresponding invariance under translation.

16. If we really accepted the idea that a sample from one distribution is a sample from any distribution (if appropriately weighted) then we should not be surprised at the next two results stated below. It requires only a look at the probability densities to determine the factor by which the weights are altered. The case $w(x) \equiv 1$ will account for most of the uses of these results, but there is no difficulty in including the general case.

17. If x is NID (0, 1) with weight $w(x)$, and if α is either fixed, or distributed independently of x, then $y = \alpha x$ is NID (0, 1) with weight

$$w(\alpha, x) = w(x)\ \alpha^m\ e^{-\frac{1}{2}(\alpha^2 - 1)\Sigma x_i^2}$$

18. If x is NID' (0, 1) with weight $w(x)$, and if α is either fixed, or distributed independently of x, then $y = \alpha x$ is NID' (0, 1) with weight

$$w(\alpha, x) = w(x)\ \alpha^{m-1}\ e^{-\frac{1}{2}(\alpha^2 - 1)\ S(x)}$$

where $S(x) = \Sigma(x_i - \bar{x})^2 = \Sigma x_i^2 - \frac{1}{m}(\Sigma x_i)^2$.

19. In both of the last statements, the dependence of $w(x)$ on x need not be definite, the real condition is as in 5(a) that (x, w) be a sample from a joint distribution with the cases w = a sure function of x and w = 1 as special cases. Exactly similar results apply when NID or NID' is replaced by ONID or ONID'.

20. We come now to the central results -- results
which at first glance will seem unintuitive, improper and
obviously wrong. All these discomforts are associated
with the appearance of a new, additional weight function
which has <u>nothing</u> at all to do with the way in which our
samples were drawn. It is clear that there should be no
place for such an additional weight function, yet it has
a place, and in the next section we shall try to explain
what this is.

21. We now introduce an <u>arbitrary</u> additional weight
function $\mu(\alpha)$ with

(a) $\mu(\alpha) \geq 0$ and

(b) $\int \mu(\alpha)\, d\alpha/\alpha = 1$,

where the integration is over nonnegative α, and a homogeneous real-valued function $A(x)$ which is

(a) almost never zero and

(b) positively homogeneous of the first degree
in the components of the sample, so that
$A(\alpha x) = \alpha A(x)$.

We shall be interested in obtaining, from arbitrary samples,
weighted normal samples conditioned on $A(y)$ = a given constant. In view of our build-up it should be clear that we
are going to do this by placing $y = \alpha x$ and choosing α
separately for each x so that $A(y) = A(\alpha x) = \alpha A(x)$ has
the correct value. Choosing α is easy, but do there exist
any weights that will serve and what are they?

22. If $y = \alpha x$ is, for <u>each</u> fixed α, a sample from
the given distribution with weight $w(\alpha, x)$, then $y = \alpha x$,
with $\alpha = \alpha(x, R)$ <u>varying</u> from one x to another so that
$A(\alpha x) = R$, R fixed, in a sample from the same distribution
<u>conditioned</u> on $A(y) = R$ with weight

$$\frac{1}{K}\mu(\alpha)\, w(\alpha, x) = \frac{1}{K(R)}\, \mu[R/A(x)]\, w[R/A(x), x]$$

where

$$K = R \frac{d \; \text{Prob} \left[A(x) < R \right]}{dR}$$

23. We shall try to explain the possibility of this result before we apply it.

PARTIAL EXPLANATION

24. Our explanation will take the form of an analogy. We discuss the case where we are dealing with (u, v), v real, which is a sample from a given distribution with weight w = w(u, v), and with its translations (u, v + γ) which, for γ fixed, are samples from the same given distribution with weight w(γ, u, v). We shall be concerned with this given distribution conditioned on v = 0. This version has two advantages. On the one hand, if we take u to be a scalar we can draw illuminating pictures (and we urge the reader to draw them). On the other, if we take u to be a vector, we can derive the result of 21. So this form is unusually convenient.

25. In principle, and heuristically, we are quite clear about how to find the distribution of (u, v) conditioned on v = 0. (Our language will now refer to the case where u is a scalar, although the arguments will be of general applicability.) We have only to draw the lines v = $\pm \epsilon$, to take a very large sample of pairs (u, v), and to record the set of u's among them for which $- \epsilon < v < \epsilon$. Then we repeat this with a smaller value for ϵ and an even larger sample. In the limit, the sets of u's we obtain converge to the conditional distribution of u with v = 0. (The appearance of weights makes no essential change in this procedure.) We shall follow this process with some inversions of limiting processes. In particular, we shall fix ϵ until further notice.

26. For each fixed γ, (u, v + γ) is a sample from the desired distribution with weight w(γ, u, v). If we give γ not 1 single fixed value for each and every (u, v), but instead 2 fixed values, 3 fixed values, ... for each and every (u, v) what we obtain will be a weighted sample for the desired distribution in a sense which is an inessential generalization of 5. The generalization lies in the fact that 5(a) fails through the (u + v + γ)'s appearing in 2's, 3's, ... with fixed spacings along the v-axis, all else being as in a sample. This generalization does not affect

anything material. As far as 5(b) is concerned, if the
values of γ are γ_p, p = 1, 2, ..., P we have

$$\frac{\Sigma_i\ \Sigma_p\ w(\gamma_p,\ u_i,\ v_i)\ \phi(u_i,\ v_i + \gamma_p)}{NP} =$$

$$\frac{1}{P}\ \Sigma_p\ \frac{\Sigma_i\ w(\gamma_p,\ u_i,\ v_i)\ \phi(u_i,\ v_i + \gamma_p)}{N}$$

and hence the average of the left hand side is the mean of
the averages of the P terms on the right. But each of these
P averages is known to have the desired value, so the average of the left hand side also has the same value, and 5(b)
holds.

27.   If we can give γ 1 value, or 2 values, or 137
values or 5,937,263 values, there is nothing heuristic
which prevents us from giving γ a distribution, say $\nu(\gamma)d\gamma$.
Now every pair (u, v) has many translates (u, v + γ) which
fall in the magic strip - $\epsilon \leq v \leq +\epsilon$. Neglecting terms
of higher order there will be a number proportional to

$$\int_{-v-\epsilon}^{-v+\epsilon} \nu(\gamma)\ d\gamma \sim 2\epsilon\ \nu(-v)$$

each with weight

$$w(\gamma,\ u,\ v) \sim w(-v,\ u,\ v)$$

and the total weight corresponding to $(u_i,\ v_i)$ is proportional to the product

$$2\epsilon\ \nu(-v_i)\ w(-v_i,\ u_i,\ v_i).$$

Going now to the limit with ϵ , we find that $(u_i,\ 0)$ with
weight

$$\frac{1}{K}\ \nu(-v_i)\ w(-v_i,\ u_i,\ v_i)$$

is behaving as a weighted sample from the desired distribution conditioned on v = 0.

73

28. In this analog, we can see how the arbitrary distribution $\nu(\gamma)d\gamma$ enters. It is the result of a perfectly legitimate choice, and arises quite naturally. Indeed, we see that it need not be constant, for if we replace $\nu(\gamma)$ by $\nu(\gamma, u) \geq 0$ with $\int \nu(\gamma, u) d\gamma = 1$ for every u, we shall be able to carry through the same argument.

29. To obtain the form given in 22, we have only (a) to determine K and (b) to place

$$v = \log A(x) - \log R,$$

$$u = (A(x))^{-1} x.$$

Thus there is reason to 22 after all.

FIRST APPLICATIONS

30. We can now go back and combine 22 with 17 and 18. The results are interesting and powerful.

31. If x is NID (0, 1) with weight w(x), then $y = \alpha x$, with $A(y) = A(\alpha x) = R$ determining $\alpha = \alpha(x, R)$, is NID (0, 1) <u>conditional</u> on A(y) = R with weight

$$\frac{1}{K} \mu(\alpha) \, w(x) \, \alpha^m \, e^{-\frac{1}{2}(\alpha^2 - 1)\, \Sigma x_i^2}$$

32. If x is NID' (0, 1) with weight w(x) and A(z) is invariant under translation, then $y = \alpha x$ with A(y) = R is NID' (0, 1) <u>conditional</u> on A(y) = R with weight

$$\frac{1}{K} \mu(\alpha) \, w(x) \, \alpha^{m-1} \, e^{-\frac{1}{2}(\alpha^2 - 1)\, S(x)}$$

33. Similar statements also apply with ONID replacing NID and with ONID' replacing NID'.

34. These results mean, in particular, that if we start out with 1,000 samples of m from a normal distribution, we can rescale each sample so that its range is $\pi = 3.14159...,$

74

and provided we use the right weights, we can use the 1,000 rescaled samples as samples from a unit normal distribution conditioned by "range $= \pi$". And so on.

35. In particular, the following choice for μ is admissable for any $k > 0$:

$$\mu(\alpha) = \frac{2\left[kR/\sqrt{2}\right]^{m-1} e^{-\frac{1}{2}k^2 R^2} \alpha^{1-m} e^{\frac{1}{2}k^2(\alpha^2 - 1) A^2(x)}}{\Gamma\left[\frac{m-1}{2}\right]}$$

$$= \frac{2\left[kR/\sqrt{2}\right]^{m-1} e^{-\frac{1}{2}k^2 R^2} \alpha^{1-m} e^{\frac{1}{2}k^2(\alpha^2 - 1) R^2/\alpha^2}}{\Gamma\left[\frac{m-1}{2}\right]}$$

Notice that although the first form looks unusable since $A(x)$ depends on x, the substitution $A(x) = R/\alpha$ eliminates this dependence, as we see in the second form.

36. The use of 35 in 32 gives for the weight function

$$\frac{2w(x)}{K \Gamma\left[\frac{m-1}{2}\right]} \left[kR/\sqrt{2}\right]^{m-1} e^{-\frac{1}{2}k^2 R^2} e^{-\frac{1}{2}(\alpha^2 - 1)\left[S(x) - k^2 A^2(x)\right]}$$

Here we begin to reach a specifically applicable formula -- one we shall need in the later paper.

REUSE OF SAMPLES

37. We have a method for starting with an unconditioned set of samples and converting all of them to meet the condition $A(y) = R$. We could convert the very same set of samples to meet $A(y) = R_1$, where $R_1 \neq R$. And to meet $A(y) = R_2$. And so on. For each of these values of R taken separately we

obtain a weighted sample from the corresponding conditional distribution. Each by itself is obviously all right. But when we use conditional distributions we usually need to use them for a number of values of the condition, summing or integrating over these values. If this is what we are up to, is it proper to reuse the original set of samples without change? The answer turns out to be that it is proper, but the result may not be as precise as if we drew a new sample for each condition. In terms of precision for a given amount of effort, however, we may be very much better off to reuse the single set.

38. If we return to our example (in 12) of a possible use for conditional distributions, we have

$$\text{Prob}\left[A(z) \geq a \ \underline{\text{or}} \ B(z) \geq b\right] = \int_{-\infty}^{a} \text{Prob}\left[B(z) \geq b \mid A(z) = t\right] dF_A(t) + \text{Prob}\left[A(z) \geq a\right]$$

and if we know the distribution of A(z) then we have only (a) to find, or at least to estimate, the conditional probability that $B(z) \geq b$ conditional on A(z) equalling suitable values, and (b) to evaluate the integral. One natural approach is to choose a moderate number of values for the condition, obtain a single set of samples, adjust each and every one of them to meet each and every condition, thereby obtaining estimates of each of the corresponding conditional probabilities, and then use some reasonable quadrature formula of numerical integration to approximately estimate the value of the integral. (As we shall see in the later paper, this works quite well.)

39. Another approach is to use each sample not just for a few conditioning values, but rather to use it for every possible conditioning value and integrate out the result. The estimate for the integral will be the integral of our conditional estimates. Each conditional estimate can be written as the mean over the finite set of samples of certain expressions. If we invert the operations of integration and finite summation, as we always may, we obtain an estimate for the integral as the mean over the finite set of samples of certain integrals. If $\phi(z)$ is always either 0 or 1, these integrals need be extended only over values of α with $\phi(\alpha x) = 1$. Assuming that this condition describes manageable sets of α's, we obtain the results which follow.

40. If $y = \alpha x$, for each fixed α, is a sample from a given distribution with weight $w(\alpha, x)$, and if we wish to estimate

$$\text{ave } [\phi(z)] = \text{prob } [g(z) = 1]$$

then we may use

$$\frac{1}{N} \Sigma \int_{\phi(\alpha x)=1} \mu(\alpha)\, w(\alpha, x)\, \frac{d\alpha}{\alpha}$$

where the summation is over the N samples x and the integration is over the α for which $\phi(\alpha x) = 1$ (over the α for which αx is exceptional).

41. If x is NID $(0, 1)$ with weight $w(x)$, and we wish to estimate

$$\text{ave } [\phi(z)] = \text{prob } [g(z) = 1]$$

we may use

$$\frac{1}{N} \Sigma\, w(x) \int_{g(\alpha x)=1} \frac{\mu(\alpha)}{\alpha}\, \alpha^m\, e^{-\frac{1}{2}(\alpha^2 - 1)\Sigma x_i^2}\, d\alpha$$

as the estimate, where $\mu(\alpha)$ is as in 21.

42. If x is NID' $(0, 1)$ with weight $w(x)$, and $\phi(x)$ is invariant under translation, then we may estimate

$$\text{ave } [\phi(z)] = \text{prob } [g(z) = 1]$$

by means of

$$\frac{1}{N} \Sigma\, w(x) \int_{g(\alpha x)=1} \frac{\mu(\alpha)}{\alpha}\, \alpha^{m-1}\, e^{-\frac{1}{2}(\alpha^2 - 1)\, S(x)}\, d\alpha$$

where $S(x) = \Sigma(x_i - \bar{x})^2$ and $\mu(\alpha)$ is as in 21.

43. Under the hypotheses of 42 we may use

77

$$\frac{1}{N} \sum \frac{2w(x)}{\Gamma\left[\frac{m-1}{2}\right]} \left[kA(x)/\sqrt{2}\right]^{m-1} e^{\frac{1}{2}\left[S(x) - k^2A^2(x)\right]} \int_{g(\alpha x)=1} \alpha^{m-2} e^{-\frac{1}{2}\alpha^2 S(x)} d\alpha$$

as an estimate.

44. Clearly 41, 42, and 43 derive from 40 by using 31, 32, and 36. Entirely similar statements hold when NID or NID' is replaced by ONID or ONID'. The form of these estimates -- as the means of suitable functions of the separate samples -- implies a variance of estimate proportional to $\frac{1}{N}$. Thus either the variance is infinite (which does not occur for reasonable cases) or it converges to zero. This provides a proof that this technique of infinite reuse really works. (We have not made any empirical tests to see how well it works -- however, tables of incomplete normal moment functions are all that is needed to make 43 operate.)

TROTTER'S TECHNIQUE

45. The particular problem which led to the development of these techniques involved the special case where $A(x) =$ range $[x_i]$. A special technique applicable to this case was developed and proved unusually useful. For convenience we shall say that $(x_1, x_2, \ldots, x_k)$ are UID $[0, 1]$ if they are uniformly and independently distributed on the interval $[0, 1]$ -- that is to say if they are independent random numbers (not random digits) in the usual sense of these words. We write OUID $[0, 1]$ for the ordered case. With these definitions we have the following results.

46. If a, b, ..., j are m - 2 quantities OUID $[0, 1]$, then y = Rx = (0, Ra, Rb, ..., Rj, R) is a sample from ONID' (0, 1) conditioned by range $[y_i]$ = R with weight

$$(2\pi)^{-(m-1)/2} R^{m-2} \frac{e^{-\frac{1}{2}SR^2}}{f(R)} .$$

where f(R) is the density function of the distribution of the unit normal range of m, and S = $(a^2 + b^2 + \ldots + j^2 + 1) - \frac{1}{m}(a + b + \ldots + j + 1)^2$.

78

47. Under the hypotheses of 42 and 46, we may take as an estimate

$$\frac{1}{N} \Sigma \ (2\pi \ S)^{-(m-1)/2} \int_{g(ux/\sqrt{S})=1} u^{m-2} \ e^{-\frac{1}{2}u^2} \ du \ .$$

MORALS AND EXTENSIONS

48. If there are any morals to this development, we feel that these are the two most important ones:

(a) there are many ways to introduce good "swindles" into Monte Carlo, and only a few have been discovered -- when in trouble look for a new one,

(b) so long as we deal with linear problems and have choices, it is likely to be worthwhile to take our choices several different ways at once.

To (a) this account offers the example of the whole method. To (b) it offers two examples which may be less clear to the reader. On the one hand, the use of many values of α (and the selection of only the relevant one) lies back of the procedure of getting a conditional sample. On the other hand, the use of the same original sample as a contributor to estimates for several or many values of the condition is the other novel feature. Both of these may properly be thought of as examples of taking several choices simultaneously where the naive approach would be to take only one choice. Linearity is a great thing.

49. As for extensions, there are likely to be many. We have discussed only the case where the family of transformations are one-dimensional, but extensions to several dimensions undoubtedly exist. We have covered simple additive and multiplicative transformations, but the transformation

$$(x_1, \ x_2, \ x_3, \ x_4, \ x_5, \ x_6) \rightarrow (\alpha x_1, \ \alpha x_2, \ x_3, \ x_4, \ x_5, \ x_6)$$

might be useful in obtaining critical values of

$$\frac{|x_1 - x_2|}{|x_3 - x_4| + |x_5 - x_6|}$$

We leave this, and other possibilities, to the reader.

79

MONTE CARLO TECHNIQUES IN A COMPLEX
PROBLEM ABOUT NORMAL SAMPLES[+]

Harvey J. Arnold, Bradley D. Bucher, Hale F. Trotter
and John W. Tukey

Princeton University

In this paper we discuss a specific practical
application of the techniques presented in the earlier
paper. It will turn out that 1,000 samples properly
treated will give us the same accuracy as simple experimental sampling would have given with 500,000 samples in
one case and 5,000,000 samples in another. This means
that 10 or 20 samples properly treated would have given us
the minimum accuracy we needed, although 1,000 samples in
simple experimental sampling would not have been enough.

THE PROBLEM

2. This is a preliminary report on a first step in
the calculation of some statistically interesting critical
values. This first step is the approximate calculation of
J_0, defined as follows:

(a) x_1, x_2, x_3, x_4 are ordered values, normally
and independently distributed with mean
zero and unit variance

(b) $G = \max \left[x_2 - x_1, x_3 - x_2, x_4 - x_3 \right] =$
largest gap

$H = \max \left[x_3 - x_1, x_4 - x_2 \right] =$ largest 3-stretch

$J = x_4 - x_1 =$ range = largest 4-stretch

(c) the desired J_0 is defined by

$\text{Prob} \left[G \geq 3.17 \ \underline{\text{or}} \ H \geq 3.31 \ \underline{\text{or}} \ J \geq J_0 \right] = 5\%$, exactly.

[+]Prepared in connection with research sponsored by the
Office of Naval Research.

Here "or" means "either or both." Less formally, we wish to find a number J_0 to add to the sequence 3.17, 3.31 and plan to regard a gap as exceptional when it exceeds 3.17, a 3-stretch as exceptional when it exceeds 3.31, and a 4-stretch as exceptional when it exceeds J_0. We wish to choose J_0 so that, if four normal deviates of unit variance all have the same mean, we shall find one or more exceptional characteristics in 5% of all cases. (If the normal deviates have different means, we expect to find exceptional characteristics more frequently.) This special case with m = 4 x's of known variance is only the beginning. We will want, eventually, to let m increase to 10 or 20 and to deal with the case where the variances are estimated rather than known.

3. It would be nice to do the problem analytically. Because the definitions of G, H and J are independent of translation, we can reduce it to a problem about a three-dimensional normal distribution. The problem is just to integrate the unit normal outside a certain polyhedron. However, the polyhedron is not simple, and not convex. Even if we had good tables (instead of none) for the three-dimensional normal, the computations would be quite messy. In principle, this first step (m = 4, variance known) could just barely be done analytically, although we did not care to contemplate doing it this way. The later steps seem analytically entirely out of the question.

4. If we were to attack this problem by straightforward experimental sampling, our inefficient procedure would go about as follows:

> (a) draw, say, 1,000 random samples of 4 from the unit normal
>
> (b) calculate G, H and J for each sample
>
> (c) isolate samples with G $\geq$ 3.17 <u>or</u> H $\geq$ 3.31,
>
> (d) list J, in decreasing order, for the remaining samples.

We are looking for a value J_0 so that 5% of all samples will be exceptional. The best we can do with only 1,000 samples is to pick J_0 so that 5% of our particular 1,000 are exceptional. All the samples isolated at step (c) are exceptional -- let us suppose for purposes of illustration there are 14 of them. We then count down 50 - 14 = 36 samples in the listing of J made in (d) and estimate that J_0 lies be-tween the 36th and 37th value from the top. Anyone who has tried to estimate a 5% point in such a way is aware of its inaccuracy. We have counted down 50, and hoped to reach 5%. Out of 1,000, the piece cut off by the true 5% point is moderately sure to contain between 37 and 64. In prac-tice, the 37th and 64th from the top are not very similar in value. In simple experimental sampling for a 5% point, 1,000 samples are unlikely to be enough, and 10,000 may not be enough for comfort.

CONDITIONAL APPROACH

5. What we actually did was to use the conditional approach of the earlier paper. If we replace:

$$B(z) \geq b \text{ by } (G \geq 3.17 \text{ or } H \geq 3.31)$$

and

$$A(z) \geq a \text{ by } J = \text{range} \geq J_0$$

in C-12 (paragraph 12 of previous paper, "Conditional Monte Carlo for Normal Samples") we obtain

$$\text{Prob} \left[G \geq 3.17 \text{ or } H \geq 3.31 \text{ or } J \geq J_0 \right]$$

$$= \int_{-\infty}^{J_0} \text{Prob} \left[G \geq 3.17 \text{ or } H \geq 3.31 \mid \text{range} = J \right] dF(J)$$

$$+ \text{Prob} \left[\text{range} \geq J_0 \right]$$

where $F(J)$ is the cumulative distribution of ranges of 4 from the unit normal, a tabulated function. If we can use conditional Monte Carlo to estimate the conditional proba-bilities in the integrand, and then use a quadrature formula to approximate the integral, we shall have our answer. Since $G \leq H \leq J = \text{range}$, the conditional probability vanishes for $J \leq 3.17$, so that we have only to evaluate

$$\int_{3.17}^{J_0} \text{Prob} \left[G \geq 3.17 \text{ or } H \geq 3.31 \mid \text{range} = J \right] df(J) + \text{Prob} \left[\text{range} \geq J_0 \right]$$

82

and since Prob (range $\geq$ 3.63) = 5% we know that $J_0 \geq$ 3.63 but we expect that J_0 is near 3.63. Thus we need conditional probabilities over only a narrow range of values for J. We actually worked with J = 3.2, 3.4, 3.6, and 3.8, expecting $J_0 \leq$ 3.8 with moderate confidence.

6. If we were to do the samples one at a time by hand, we would proceed about as follows: We should first (in principle) determine the additional weighting function $\left[\mu(\alpha)\right.$ in C-21, C-22, C-35 ff$\left.\right]$ which we plan to use. Then we should draw a random sample of 4 and order its elements, say $x_1 \leq x_2 \leq x_3 \leq x_4$, then we should choose α so that $\alpha x_4 - \alpha x_1 = 3.6$, say, and form $\alpha x_1, \alpha x_2, \alpha x_3, \alpha x_4$ as a sample conditioned on J = 3.6. For this new sample we would then calculate G and H and look to see if

$$G \geq 3.17 \quad \underline{or} \quad H \geq 3.31 .$$

If yes, we reckon this sample as one for which $\phi(z) = 1$ and record the corresponding weight. Then we repeat this procedure for many samples and for J = 3.2, 3.4, 3.6, and 3.8.

7. Clearly we can simplify the arithmetic considerably. The ratios G/J and H/J are the same for (x_1, x_2, x_3, x_4) as for $(\alpha x_1, \alpha x_2, \alpha x_3, \alpha x_4)$. Thus we have only to test

$$\frac{G}{J} \geq \frac{3.31}{3.6} \quad \underline{or} \quad \frac{H}{J} > \frac{3.31}{3.6}$$

where G, H and J may as well be calculated for the original sample. Secondly, the weight will depend on only one (or a few) characteristic(s) of the sample, so we can group samples by these characteristic(s) and calculate one weight for each group with good approximation.

ACTUAL COMPUTATION

8. We chose, for lack of better judgement, to use the special additional weighting function of C-35, which with w(x) = 1 leads (cp. C-36) to the combined weight function

$$\frac{2}{K\ \Gamma\left[\dfrac{m-1}{2}\right]}\ (kR/\sqrt{2})^{m-1} e^{-\frac{1}{2}k^2R^2}\ e^{-\frac{1}{2}(\alpha^2-1)(S-k^2J^2)}$$

where K is a constant derivable from the distribution of the normal range, k is a parameter not yet chosen, $R = 3.2, 3.4, 3.6$ or 3.8 and $S = \Sigma (x_i - \bar{x})^2$. The only characteristic of the sample on which this weight depends is

$$(\alpha^2 - 1)(S - k^2J^2) = (\frac{R^2}{J^2} - 1)(S - k^2J^2)$$

and it is relevant to notice that, for samples of 4,

$$0.5 \le \frac{S}{J^2} \le 1.0$$

Since this characteristic occurs in an exponential, and since we wish to avoid large weights for exceptional samples we probably wish to select k^2 between 0.5 and 1.0. One natural choice is 0.75. In addition, we considered the implications for the arrangement of the x's of various ratios S/J^2 and convinced ourselves that a smaller value of k^2 might be worth-while. We actually tried $k^2 = 0.60$ and $k^2 = 0.75$. Of these $k^2 = 0.60$ turned out better. (There was a hint that $k^2 = 0.65$ would be still better.)

9.   1,000 samples of 4, NID (0, 1) were punched to three decimals, one sample per card. These cards were processed on an IBM 605 to obtain and punch G, H, J, G/J, H/J and S for each. (This should have taken about an hour's machine time, and actually may have taken two hours.) After some examination of the results $S - k^2J^2$ was obtained and punched for $k^2 = 0.60$ and $k^2 = 0.75$. For any given value of R it was now easy to select the exceptional samples with

$$\frac{G}{J} \ge \frac{3.17}{R} \quad \text{or} \quad \frac{H}{J} \ge \frac{3.31}{R}$$

and arrange them in groups for the calculation of weights. This was a sorter, tabulator list, and desk calculator operation and took only a few hours.

RESULTS

10. The results of calculating conditional probabilities, applying quadrature formulas, and interpolating to a total exceptional probability of 5% came out as follows for the choice $k^2 = 0.60$:

(a) The full 1,000 samples gave $J_0 = 3.684$ with a contribution of $0.00447 = 0.447\%$ from the integral

(b) Blocks of 200 samples each gave, as the contribution from the integral:

First 200 samples	0.40%
Second 200 samples	0.56%
Third 200 samples	0.47%
Fourth 200 samples	0.38%
Fifth 200 samples	0.43%

which was rewarding agreement

(c) Based on the differences in result among these five subsamples, the estimated standard deviation of the integral contribution for all 1,000 samples was $\pm 0.032\%$.

Thus neglecting quadrature formula errors and errors in tabling the distribution of the range, we may rather confidently expect that $J_0 = 3.684$ corresponds to a total exceptional probability between 4.91% and 5.09%. This is high accuracy.

11. If we equate this estimated standard error with what we would have obtained by simple experimental sampling with enough samples, we obtain interesting and illuminating results. For simple experimental sampling (as in 4 above) we have

$$0.00032 = \sqrt{\frac{(.05)(.95)}{N}}$$

which leads to $N \sim 470,000$. Thus our techniques have gained us a factor of about 500 over simple experimental sampling. This gain did not all come from the conditional Monte Carlo, since the use of the split into integrated and tabular part and use of experimental sampling for the integrated part only corresponds to

$$0.00032 = \sqrt{\frac{(.00447)(.99553)}{N}}$$

which leads to N~45,000. Thus we gained a factor of a little more than 10 from the split and a further factor of about 45 from the conditional calculation. All this at a price of, say, a factor of 3 to 5 in computational labor.

SECOND COMPUTATION

12. We also made a computation according to the special technique of C-46. To this end we required samples $x =$ (0, a, b, 1) with (a, b) uniformly and independently distributed on [0, 1] with weight w(x) or a reasonable facsimile thereof. It was convenient and useful to play some minor tricks in this connection.

13. The basic problem deals with ordered samples and depends on G, H and J, which are invariant under $x_i \rightarrow -x_i$, so that we may as well require $0 \leq a \leq b \leq 1 - a$. Samples which are uniformly and independently distributed on [0, 1] except for the effects of this special condition will be described as SUID [0, 1].

14. The basic problem is to find the conditional probabilities

$$\text{Prob} \left[\frac{G}{J} \geq \frac{3.17}{R} \quad \text{or} \quad \frac{H}{J} \geq \frac{3.31}{R} \mid J = R \right]$$

and we note that if $J \leq 3.8$, as we expect, there will be no exceptional x for which

$$\frac{G}{J} \leq \frac{H}{J} \leq \frac{3.17}{3.8} = 0.834.$$

Hence, among our x = (0, a, b, 1) with $a \leq 1 - b$ there will be no exceptional x with $a \geq 0.166$. Therefore, we may accept infinite weights for x's with $a \geq 0.166$.

15. 1,000 samples of 4 with range 1 were prepared as follows:

(a) x_1 and x_2 were uniformly and independently distributed on [0, 1]

(b) that one of (0, $.17x_2$, x_1, 1), (0, x_1, $.17x_2$, 1), (0, 1 - $.17x_2$, 1 - x_1, 1) or (0, 1 - x_1, 1 - $.17x_2$, 1) was taken as (0, a, b, 1) for which $a \leq b$, 1 - b.

The resulting samples have (a, b) SUID [0, 1] with a rather peculiar system of weights namely:

for $a \geq 0.17$ the weight is infinite

for $a \leq 0.17 \leq b \leq 0.83$ the weight is .17

for $a \leq b \leq 0.17$ or $a \leq 0.17 \leq 0.83 \leq b \leq 1 - a$ the

weight is $\frac{1}{2}(.17)$.

As noted in 14, the infinite weights for nonexistent samples give no difficulty, since they correspond to a zero contribution.

16.   The formulas specified in C-46 were applied in a manner entirely analogous to the first computation.

SECOND RESULTS

17.   The results ran as follows:

(a)   The full 1,000 samples gave $J_0 = 3.684$ with a contribution of $0.00450 = 0.450\%$ from the integral.

(b)   Blocks of 200 samples each gave, as the contribution from the integral,

First 200	0.43%
Second 200	0.43%
Third 200	0.44%
Fourth 200	0.48%
Fifth 200	0.47%

which was even better agreement than in the first computation.

(c)   The differences among these 5 results lead to an estimated standard deviation for the integral contribution estimated from all 1,000 samples of $\pm 0.010\%$.

Thus, neglecting quadrature formula errors, and errors in tabling the distribution of the range, we may rather confidently expect that $J_0 = 3.684$ corresponds to a total exceptional probability between 4.97% and 5.03%.   This is unnecessarily high accuracy.

18.   If we equate this accuracy to that of simple experimental sampling, we have

$$0.00010 = \sqrt{\frac{(.05)(.95)}{N}}$$

which yields N~4,700,000, or a gain by a factor of about 5,000.

19.   Again a factor of about 10 comes from splitting of the tabulated part, but a factor of about 500 still remains. This must be credited to the conditional approach and the wise choice of weights.

DISCUSSION

20.   The two computations came out as follows:

Estimated J_0	Estimated integral contr.
3.684	0.447 ± 0.032 %
3.684	0.450 ± 0.010 %

Note that although the estimated integral contributions differ by 3 times the standard error of the second computation, the J_0 values are the same to three decimals. Thus sampling fluctuations are very unlikely to affect J_0 by more than 0.001. This represents unnecessary accuracy from the practicing statistician's point of view.

21.   If we had used 10 samples according to the second computation, we would probably have tied J_0 down to ± 0.01, which is closer than really necessary. Look again at the problem, and think about the fact that a satisfactory answer could have been had with only 10 samples.

22.   As mentioned in the earlier paper (close of C-10), one aim of weighting is to bring more samples into the exceptional set. In the problem, if we had not made it conditional, we would have expected about 4 or 5 samples per 1,000, on the average, to contribute to the integrated portion (0.45%). In one of the evaluations of a conditional probability actually made, some 800 of the 1,000 contributed. This illustrates one of the sources of gain.

AN APPLICATION OF THE MONTE CARLO METHOD TO A
PROBLEM IN GAMMA RAY DIFFUSION

Martin J. Berger
National Bureau of Standards
Washington, D. C.

I. INTRODUCTION

A. The Problem. This report presents preliminary
results of an investigation of the following problem in
gamma ray diffusion. A beam of monoenergetic gamma rays
is incident at a given angle on a plane parallel barrier
that has a finite thickness in one dimension but is infinite in the other two dimensions. When the gamma rays
enter the barrier they may interact with it in two ways:
(1) they may be scattered (Compton effect) whereby their
energy is lowered and their direction of motion changed;
(2) they may be absorbed (photoelectric effect, pair production). These are stochastic processes in the sense
that the distance travelled by the gamma rays between
successive events (scatterings or absorption) as well as
the energy and directional changes resulting from a scattering are random variables with probability distributions
specified by the relevant physical laws. As the result of
these processes, some gamma rays of the original beam will
be transmitted through the barrier, others will be reflected, and the remaining ones will be absorbed in the
barrier. The problem is to determine the magnitude as
well as the energetic and angular composition of the reflected and transmitted beams.

B. Method of Solution. An analytical attack on this
problem by a solution of the relevant transport equation
leads to very great mathematical difficulties. In order
to by-pass these difficulties, explore the problem and
obtain at least an approximate solution, this investigation employs the Monte Carlo (random sampling) method.
All numerical work was carried out on the automatic computer of the National Bureau of Standards (SEAC).

The calculation is divided, both in regard to method
and in practice, into two rather distinct parts: (1) a

stochastic calculation, using random sampling, of gamma ray
random walks in an infinite Compton scatterer (a medium in
which only scattering but no absorption is assumed to be
possible); (2) an analytical calculation, using these random walks as input data, in which gamma ray absorption is
taken into account, and the appropriate boundary conditions
are imposed. There were a number of reasons for this division. For one thing, it reduced the required computer
memory size. More importantly, the random walks have a
"universal" character, i.e. they can be used for the calculation of different boundary problems involving different
geometries as well as different scattering and absorbing
media. Not only will the repeated use of the same set of
random walks often lead to computing economy, but it may
also increase the accuracy of a calculation. Suppose, for
example, that we wish to determine the difference in transmission for two beams incident on a barrier at different
angles but otherwise identical. It will then be to our
advantage to base the comparison on the same set of random
walks since irrelevant differences resulting from statistical fluctuations will thereby be largely eliminated.

II. GAMMA RAY RANDOM WALKS IN AN INFINITE
COMPTON SCATTERER

A. <u>Definitions</u>. The state S of a gamma ray can be
specified by a set of six quantities:

$$S = (E, \Theta, \phi, x, y, z)$$

where E is the gamma ray energy, Θ and ϕ are angular coordinates describing the direction of motion (in a spherical
coordinate system with the z-axis as polar axis), and x, y
and z are Cartesian coordinates of position. Let the state
of the gamma ray immediately after the n-th scattering
event occurring in a given random walk be denoted by S_n
(n = 1,2,...) and let S_o denote the state in which it was
introduced into the scattering medium. A random walk is
then described by a sequence

$$\left\{ S_o, S_1, S_2, \ldots S_L \right\}$$

each term (except S_o) depending stochastically on its immediate predecessor only (Markov process). The length L of

such a sequence would be infinite, but in the present work the random walks are terminated when the energy E drops below 30 kev. This arbitrary cut-off[+] results in an average value $\langle L \rangle_{Av} \sim 18$ for an initial energy $E_O = 660$ kev.

It will be observed that for the problem of transmission and reflection by plane parallel barriers only the variables E, Θ and one space variable, say z, are required. Nevertheless it is worthwhile to calculate the other three variables also. The random walks are thus made applicable to other boundary problems with different geometrical conditions. Moreover, we can use the same set of random walks for barrier problems with different angles of incidence. One can always set $\Theta_O = 0$ and rotate the boundaries as required by using, instead of cos Θ and z,

$$\cos \Theta' = \cos \Theta \cos \alpha + \sin \Theta \sin \alpha \cos \phi$$

$$z' = x \sin \alpha + z \cos \alpha \qquad (1)$$

where $\alpha = \Theta_O'$ is the angle of incidence.

B. _Random Sampling_. Next we describe the sampling scheme whereby successive states S_n are selected, the initial state being specified as $S_O = \{E_O, 0, 0, 0, 0, 0\}$. Calculations of a set of random walks with this initial condition will serve for the solution of problems involving monoenergetic beams of energy E_O, and arbitrary direction of incidence α. Because of the linearity of the gamma ray diffusion equation it is possible to obtain solutions for incident beams of specified energetic and angular composition by superposition of the results obtained with different E_O's and α's.

Prior to the discussion of the detailed steps in the sampling process, some comment is in order concerning the required random numbers. With a high-speed computer the use of tables of random numbers is clearly impractical. Instead,

---

[+]The cut-off is actually justified on physical grounds because radiation at energies below 30 kev is always so heavily absorbed that it makes only a negligible contribution to the emergent radiation flux.

so-called pseudo-random numbers r_m ($0 < r_m < 1$) were used which were generated as required in the course of the computation by a method developed by O. Taussky-Todd[+]. They are defined by the relations

$$r_m = 2^{-42} R_m$$

$$R_{m+1} = 5^{17} R_m \text{ modulo } 2^{42}, \quad R_0 = 1 \tag{2}$$

It may be shown that the period r_m is 2^{40}, i.e. that a sequence of 2^{40} different numbers will be obtained before repetition occurs. Extensive testing carried out at the National Bureau of Standards has shown that these pseudo-random numbers satisfy the various accepted statistical criteria of randomness. It is an advantageous feature of this method that identical random walks may be recreated repeatedly for checking purposes, provided the initial random number used for the walk is recorded.

The various steps in the calculation of S_{n+1}, given S_n are listed below:

1. Energy change:

$$\left\{ \int_{E_{n+1}}^{E_n} k(E_n,E)dE \Bigg/ \int_o^{E_n} k(E_n,E)dE \right\} = r \tag{3}$$

where r is a random number and $k(E_n,E)$ is the Klein-Nishina differential coefficient (per unit path length) for Compton scattering with energy change from E_n to E.

2. Change of direction:

$$\cos \omega_n = 1 - \frac{511}{E_{n+1}} + \frac{511}{E_n} \tag{4}$$

where ω_n is the angle between the directions of motion immediately before and after the n + 1-st scattering. (The numerical coefficient 511 is to be used if the energy is expressed in kev).

[+]Cf. H.A. Meyer, L.S. Gephart and N.L. Rasmussen, "On the Generation and Testing of Random Digits," WADC Technical Report 54-55 (1954).

The azimuthal deflection χ_n is a random quantity distributed uniformly between 0 and 2π. But we need the sine and cosine of χ_n rather than χ_n itself. Hence we took advantage of the following convenient computational scheme suggested by von Neumann[+]. Choose random numbers a and b satisfying the condition $a^2 + b^2 < 1$, and let c be a random number that is equal to ± 1, with probability 1/2. Then

$$\cos \chi_n = \frac{2abc}{a^2 + b^2} \quad \text{and} \quad \sin \chi_n = \frac{a^2 - b^2}{a^2 + b^2} \ . \quad (5)$$

From the actual deflections ω_n and χ_n, the new angular coordinates are then determined by the following trigonometric relationships.

$$\cos \Theta_{n+1} = \cos \Theta_n \cos \omega_n + \sin \Theta_n \sin \omega_n \cos \chi_n$$

$$\sin (\phi_{n+1} - \phi_n) = \frac{\sin \chi_n \sin \omega_n}{\sin \Theta_{n+1}}$$

$$\cos (\phi_{n+1} - \phi_n) = \frac{\cos \omega_n - \cos \Theta_n \cos \Theta_{n+1}}{\sin \Theta_n \sin \Theta_{n+1}}$$

$$(6)$$

3. Displacement:

$$x_{n+1} = x_n - \frac{\sin \Theta_n \cos \phi_n}{\mu_s(E_n)} \log r$$

$$y_{n+1} = y_n - \frac{\sin \Theta_n \sin \phi_n}{\mu_s(E_n)} \log r \quad (7)$$

$$z_{n+1} = z_n - \frac{\cos \Theta_n}{\mu_s(E_n)} \log r$$

where r is a random number, and $\mu_s(E_n) = \int_0^{E_n} k(E_n, E) dE$.

[+]"Monte Carlo Method," NBS Appl. Math. Series, 12 (1951).

93

III. THE TRANSMISSION-REFLECTION BOUNDARY PROBLEM

A. The Scoring Scheme. We now consider a plane parallel barrier of given composition, located between the planes z = 0 and z = B. In order to obtain greater accuracy with the use of a fixed number of random walks than could be obtained by a direct stochastic analog treatment of absorption and boundary effects, we have instead used the following somewhat more elaborate scoring method to determine the characteristics of reflected and transmitted radiation.[+]

Radiation emerging from the barrier is classified according to energy E and direction cos θ; in the computer program, provision is made for 32 energy intervals and 10 angular intervals. Two different tallies are set up, one for transmitted, the other for reflected radiation.

Each score recorded in the appropriate energy angle interval is the product of two factors: a survival probability and an emergence probability.

The survival probability is a measure of the likelihood that the gamma ray is not absorbed prior to undergoing n'th scattering. It is given by

$$P_n = \prod_{m=0}^{n-1} \exp \left\{ - \frac{z_{m+1} - z_m}{\mu_A(E_m)} \frac{1}{\cos \Theta_n} \right\} \tag{8}$$

where $\mu_A(E)$ is the probability of absorption per unit path length.

The probability of emergence is a measure of the likelihood that a gamma ray that has undergone n scatterings in the barrier will emerge from it without any further scatterings or absorption. We distinguish two such probabilities:

1. Transmission probability

$$T_n = \exp \left\{ - \frac{B-Z_n}{\mu(E_n)} \frac{1}{\cos \Theta_n} \right\} \quad \begin{array}{l} 0 < \cos \Theta \leqslant 1 \\ 0 \leqslant Z_n \leqslant B \end{array} \tag{9}$$

= 0 otherwise.

[+]The procedure is closely related to suggestions by H. Kahn, (Ref. 2).

2. Reflection probability

$$R_n = \exp\left\{\frac{Z_n}{\mu(E_n)\cos\Theta_n}\right\} \qquad \begin{array}{l} -1 \leqslant \cos\Theta < 0 \\[4pt] 0 \leqslant Z_n \leqslant B \end{array} \qquad (10)$$

$$= 0 \text{ otherwise}$$

In Equations (9) and (10), $\mu(E) = \mu_s(E) + \mu_A(E)$ is the probability scattering or absorption per unit path length.

B. Flow Diagram. The successive steps in the scoring procedure are illustrated by the flow-chart in Fig. 1. It is assumed that the input data for the calculation consists of J random walks, labeled $j = 1, 2, \ldots J$. It can be seen that a score is obtained (either for reflection or for transmission) for each scattering event inside the barrier that has been reached by a trajectory lying entirely within the barrier. With the direct analog method, only those random walks contribute scores which actually cross the specified boundaries, but the scoring procedure used here results in many partial scores for each random walk, and in particular gives proper credit to "near misses," i.e. scattering events taking place close to a boundary. For each random walk, the scoring is started not with state S_0 but with state S_1 since the score $T_0 P_0$ (referring to unscattered radiation) is the same for all random walks and can be added after all random walks are processed.

In addition to the "finite barrier" problem, we have also considered the corresponding "infinite medium" problem, i.e. the radiation flux through the planes $z = 0$ and $z = B$ (from both directions) to be expected when a plane source at $z = 0$ is embedded in an infinite homogeneous scattering medium. By comparing the solutions of the two problems, the effects of the barrier boundaries can be established, the comparison being most effective when based on the use of the same set of random walks for both problems. For the "infinite medium" problem, the scoring method is altered by allowing additional scores, both in the transmission and reflection tallies, whenever $Z_n < 0$ and $\cos\Theta_n > 0$ or when $Z_n > B$ and $\cos\Theta_n < 0$. The reflection tally now refers to the internal flux through the plane $z = B$.

95

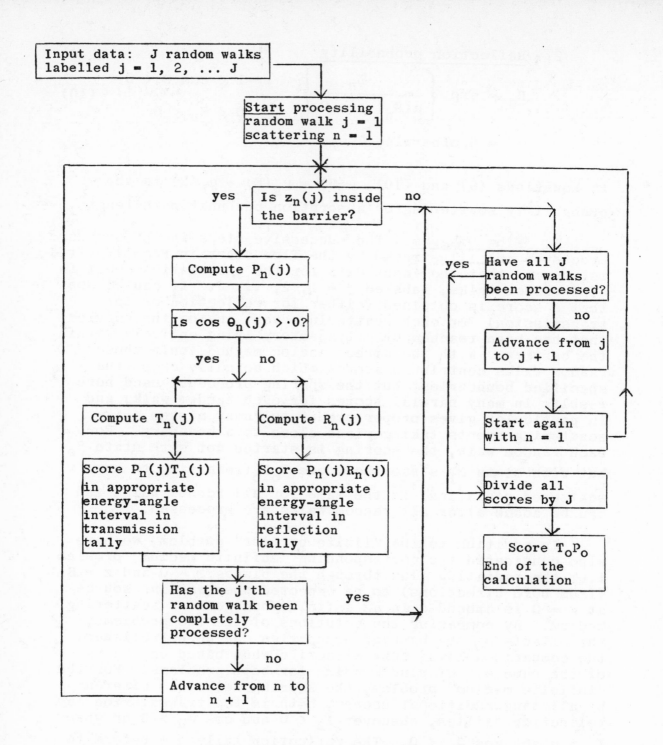

Fig. 1.   Flow-chart of Scoring Procedure.

IV. SAMPLE CALCULATIONS

Illustrative results are present for incident radiation with an energy E_O = 660 kev, and a scattering medium of water. They are also applicable--in good approximation--to other media of low atomic number, such as air, concrete, etc., provided allowance is made for the electron density. The slab thickness B is expressed in units of mean free paths (mfp) of the incident radiation (1 mfp = $1/\mu(E_O)$).

These thicknesses can readily be converted to distances in cm for a given medium with the use of tables of gamma ray absorption coefficients;[+] e.g. for incident radiation with E_O = 660 kev, 1 mfp = 11.7 cm of water.

A. _Spectra_. In Fig. 2, the curve labeled "Finite Slab" shows the transmitted (scattered) gamma ray number flux T(E) as a function of energy, for a barrier two mfp thick, upon which the original beam is incident perpendicularly. The companion curve shows the "Infinite Medium" internal flux through the plane z = 2 mfp, and the shaded area between the two curves is a measure of the boundary effect. It can be seen that only low energy radiation is affected by the boundary.

In Fig. 3, the reflected number flux R(E) is shown as a function of energy for similar conditions ('Finite Slab"). The curve "Semi-infinite Medium" refers to reflection from a semi-infinite medium bounded by the plane z = 0 and extending to infinite in the positive z-direction, while the third curve again shows the "Infinite Medium" flux. It is noteworthy that a layer of water 23 cm thick has very nearly the same reflecting power as an ocean.

The results of Figs. 2 and 3 are based on the analysis of 200 random walks. Fig. 4 shows an analysis of another set of 200 random walks in the form of the angular spectrum of the flux transmitted through barriers of various thicknesses, for two angles of incidence (α = 0° and α = 60°). (The angles of incidence (α) and emergence (θ) are both measured with respect to the normal to the barrier). It is interesting to note that for a thin barrier (1 mfp) the angular spectrum of transmitted radiation depends strongly on the direction of incidence, but that this difference disappears for thicker barriers (4 mfp). This means that the gamma rays have "forgotten" their original direction after travelling a sufficient distance.

[+]G. White, X-ray Attenuation Coefficients, NBS Report 1003 (1952).

B. <u>Transmission and Reflection Coefficients</u>. For quantitative purposes it is convenient to summarize the properties of barriers by appropriate coefficients which are ratios of the emergent number (energy) flux divided by the incident number (energy) flux.

Number Transmission Coefficient: $t_n = \int_0^{E_o} T(E)\,dE + e^{-B/\cos\alpha}$

Energy Transmission Coefficient: $t_E = \int_0^{E_o} \left[\dfrac{E}{E_o}\right] T(E)\,dE + e^{-B/\cos\alpha}$

Number Reflection Coefficient (Number Albedo): $\qquad r_n = \int_0^{E_o} R(E)\,dE$ $\qquad$ (11)

Energy Reflection Coefficient (Energy Albedo) $\qquad r_E = \int_0^{E_o} \left[\dfrac{E}{E_o}\right] R(E)\,dE$

The term $e^{-B/\cos\alpha}$ in the transmission coefficients takes into account unscattered radiation. In Table 1 a set of such coefficients is listed, which is based on the analysis of 200 random walks. Standard deviations of the coefficients are also shown. The reflection coefficients for a semi-infinite barrier are in good agreement with those calculated by Hayward and Hubbell[+] for 1 Mev radiation reflected from water.

TABLE 1

TRANSMISSION AND REFLECTION COEFFICIENTS FOR 660 KEV GAMMA
RADIATION INCIDENT ON A WATER BARRIER

B (mfp)	α	t_n	r_n	t_E	r_E
1	0°	0.769 ± 0.060	0.185 ± 0.028	0.594 ± 0.021	0.057 ± 0.021
2	0°	0.533 ± 0.062	0.287 ± 0.028	0.338 ± 0.034	0.068 ± 0.010
4	0°	0.150 ± 0.043	0.310 ± 0.045	0.067 ± 0.007	0.072 ± 0.012
semi-∞	0°		0.314 ± 0.046		0.073 ± 0.016
1	60°	0.738 ± 0.076	0.286 ± 0.052	0.578 ± 0.031	0.096 ± 0.030
2	60°	0.556 ± 0.094	0.407 ± 0.057	0.337 ± 0.030	0.128 ± 0.027
4	60°	0.282 ± 0.051	0.475 ± 0.057	0.109 ± 0.021	0.142 ± 0.021
semi-∞	60°		0.483 ± 0.056		0.145 ± 0.025

[+]E. Hayward and J. Hubbell, Phys. Rev. <u>93</u>, 955 (1954).

V. REMARKS

It should be emphasized that the results presented above have only a preliminary character. Larger random walk samples must be analyzed and the statistical analysis must be refined. Moreover, the scoring method used here will not be very successful for penetrations greater than 4-6 mfp, since it would require excessively large sample sizes. An effort is now in progress to re-calculate the barrier transmission-reflection problem and extend the method to deep penetrations by a more powerful technique in which random sampling is confined to the energy and angular variables, while the space variable is treated analytically. These efforts have shown promise of success.

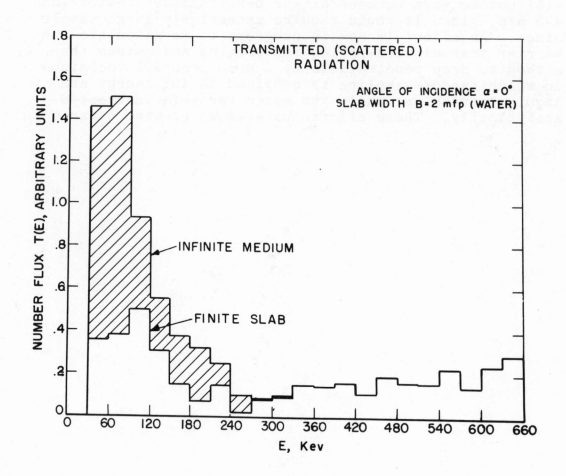

Figure 2.

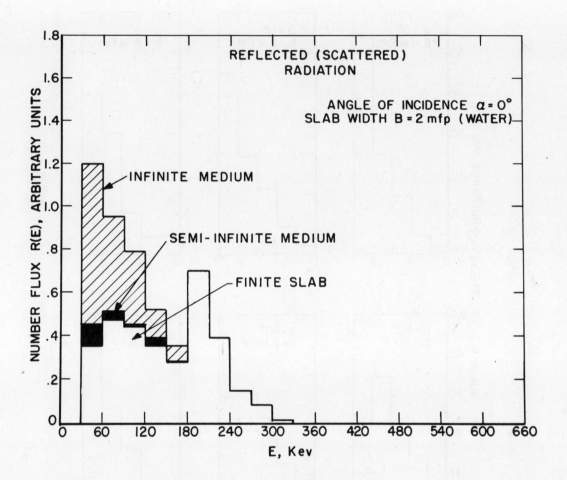

Figure 3.

101

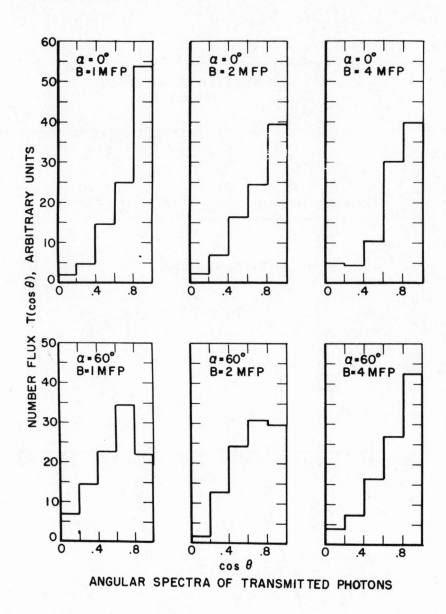

Figure 4.

STOCHASTIC CALCULATIONS OF GAMMA RAY DIFFUSION

L. A. Beach and R. B. Theus

Naval Research Laboratory
Washington 25, D. C.

A B S T R A C T

Results of several exploratory Monte Carlo problems of gamma ray diffusion solved on the NAREC are presented. The problem of plane parallel Cs^{137} radiation normally incident upon water illustrates that a statistically satisfactory Monte Carlo estimate of spectral intensities can be obtained for shallow penetration. For deep penetration several bias techniques were studied for plane parallel 6 Mev photons normally incident upon lead and the results compared to show their relative advantages and disadvantages. Truncated bias distributions may lead to underestimation of the true answer. The exponential transformation has several advantages over a bias technique utilizing arbitrary bias distributions and is able to estimate intensity and spectral distributions for penetration distances as great as 18 mean free paths of the primary radiation.

INTRODUCTION

Monte Carlo techniques represent a basic method of computing gamma ray diffusion problems. Although the moment method can compute penetration through infinite media, stochastic methods may be applied to semi-infinite media, slab geometry and even more complicated geometrical arrangements such as ducts or voids in a finite shield.

Utilizing the NAREC (Naval Research Electronic Computer) several exploratory problems have been solved. A sample problem of plane parallel Cs^{137} radiation through water provided experience in solving a simple Monte Carlo with a fast electronic computer and indicated the limitations of the straight analog method for large penetration distances. Since we were interested in calculating deep penetration problems, several methods of biasing were investigated and evaluated on a trial problem of 6 Mev photons normally incident upon lead.

SHALLOW PENETRATION

Plane parallel Cs^{137} radiation ($E_o = 0.66$ Mev) was normally incident upon a water medium considered both as a semi-infinite medium and slab shields of various thickness. We obtained estimates of the flux reflected from the surface (albedo), and the flux at detecting planes 1, 3 and 5 mean free paths into the medium with and without boundaries at these planes. Histories were not allowed to terminate by photoelectric absorption but were weighted at each collision by the appropriate survival factor. A photon history was terminated when its penetration depth exceeded 7 mean free paths, its energy degraded below 40 Kev, or its accumulated weight factor decreased below .001. When a photon crossed a detecting plane, both the success and its statistical weight were recorded in the proper energy channel. In the albedo and slab geometry cases, the successes were stored in 10° intervals of the angle with respect to the normal.

A total of 635 histories were generated on the NAREC and the resulting estimates are considered satisfactory for shallow penetration. The various energy distributions are shown in Figures 1 - 4, illustrating that more histories are necessary for penetrations exceeding 4-5 mean free paths. Figure 5 shows the angular distribution of the energy flux for the 1 m.f.p. slab shield. A much larger sample would be required for a good estimate of angular distributions. Figure 6 shows the number and energy build-up factors for the cases considered in this problem.

DEEP PENETRATION

Truncated Bias

To obtain a Monte Carlo estimate of the intensity and spectral distribution of gamma radiation at large penetration depths, several methods of biasing have been investigated on a trial problem of 6 Mev gamma rays normally incident upon lead. If the exact physical analogue were used, a prohibitive number of histories would be required for an accurate estimate of the spectrum at a penetration depth of 10 mean free paths.

A first effort to decrease the number of histories employed a type of quota sampling. Path lengths and Compton scattering angles were selected from distributions biased to favor photons with a reasonable chance of success, i.e., those having long path lengths and undergoing small angle scatterings. However, when a photon reached a depth of $u_0 x = 9$, selections of path lengths and scattering angles were made from physically correct distributions. Bias and survival factors are accumulated in the statistical weight of each history. The only criterion for beginning a new history was for the photon energy to become $= 0.25$ Mev.

Figure 7 compares the biased distribution of scattering angles with a typical "normal" distribution, i.e., the Klein-Nishina differential cross-section in probability per unit angle for photons of 2.5 Mev. The biased distribution was chosen constant over two angular intervals with magnitudes such that 90% of scattering angles were between 0° and 20°.

Figure 8 shows the normal and biased distributions of "free path lengths." If histories prohibited by this truncated biased distribution are important, the resulting spectral intensity will be an underestimation. To examine this effect the problem was solved under two biased distributions; the first truncated at 4 free path lengths and the second at 5-1/2 free path lengths.

In Figure 9, a comparison of the two results is shown. For the 5-1/2 truncation study, 53% of 700 histories resulted in success. Truncation at 4 mean free paths reduced the successes to 39%. However, this reduction in spectral intensity does not result from the decrease in successes but from the increase in prohibited path lengths.

Bias Study

In a second problem, an attempt was made to overcome many of the weaknesses of the first. Path lengths were generated from an incomplete gamma function, i.e.,

$$P(\mu\ell) = \alpha(\mu\ell)^4 \, e^{-\mu\ell}$$

where "α" is a normalization constant. This distribution favors large path lengths yet converges rapidly for $\mu\ell > 10$ and excludes no histories.

For scattering angles, the integrand of a β function was selected, i.e.,

$$P(\theta) = b\theta(\pi-\theta)^9$$

where b is a normalization constant. This distribution also favors small angle scattering, but it goes to 0 for $\theta = 0$ in agreement with the physically correct distribution; and it eliminates the abrupt discontinuity at 20°. Figure 10 compares this biased distribution with the normal distribution for 2.5 Mev photons.

In the first study selections from the biased distributions were discontinued at the collision point after crossing the plane at $\mu_0 x = 9$. This point could be considerably past the detecting plane since the last path length was selected from the biased distribution. Not only would the weight recorded for passing the detecting plane be small but any probability of the photon being scattered back to the detector again would be negligible. Therefore, in this second study, whenever a photon reached a depth of $\mu_0 x = 9$, its weight at the 9 mean free path plane was computed and the photon was restarted from this position with its same energy and direction. Path lengths and scattering angles, however, were now selected from the normal distributions. Of those photons exceeding and consequently restarted at $\mu_0 x = 9$ approximately 75% would never reach the detecting plane. Therefore, the statistical weight of each photon was reduced by a factor of 4 and 4 photons were followed until their energy was degraded to less than .25 Mev.

The spectral distribution based upon 500 histories is shown in Figure 11. Of these 500 histories 85% succeeded in reaching the plane at $\mu_0 x = 9$, and 30% of those restarted were counted at the detecting plane.

Exponential Transformation

In the next study of bias techniques, the mathematical analogue suggested by H. Kahn[+] was used.

If $\psi(X, \lambda, E)$ is the density of photons at a penetration distance, X, having direction in an increment about λ , the angle with the normal, the transport equation governing ψ is

$$\cos \lambda \, \frac{\partial \psi}{\partial X}(X, \lambda, E) + \mu(E) \psi(X, \lambda, E) = \int_{E'} \int_{\lambda'} K(E, E', \lambda, \lambda') \psi \, dE' d\lambda' + \text{source}$$

in which $\mu(E)$ is the total absorption coefficient and the integral is the usual scattering term.

Substitution of

$$\overline{\psi} = e^{cx} \psi$$

changes the transport equation to

$$\cos \lambda \, \frac{d\overline{\psi}}{dx} + \overline{\mu} \, \overline{\psi} = \int \int K \, \overline{\psi} \, d\lambda' \, dE' + \text{source}$$

where $\overline{\mu} = \mu(E) - c \cos \lambda$.

If $\overline{\mu}$ is substituted for $\mu(E)$ in the program for arriving at a Monte Carlo estimate of ψ , an estimate of $\overline{\psi}$ is obtained which is exponentially larger than ψ . The only condition on "c" is that it be less than the minimum absorption coefficient. In this problem "c" was chosen to be 9% less than the minimum value of $\mu(E)$. This method automatically favors selection of long path lengths when the photon direction is near the normal.

Figure 12 shows the spectral distributions at penetration distances of $\mu_o x = 6$, 10, 14 and 18. These are based upon 1200 histories but the curves have been normalized to unit source strength.

The buildup factor is plotted in Figure 13 and indicates the increasing importance of the scattered radiation at large penetration distances.

In Figure 14, the spectra resulting from the three bias studies are compared. All show a maximum corresponding

---

[+]Herman Kahn, Nucleonics 6, No. 5, 27, 1950.

to the "window" in the absorption coefficient, and the intensity of the "biased" and "exponential" methods are in rather good agreement for the number of histories used.

Advantages of the exponential substitution are:

1. Estimates of spectral distributions can be obtained at several detecting planes from the same histories.

2. Requires a simpler and shorter program for the digital computer.

3. The choice of scattering angles from physically exact distributions degrades the energy of photons more rapidly resulting in a shorter calculation time per history.

4. The self-contained biasing eliminates guessing biased distributions which favor important histories.

CONCLUSION

In conclusion, it is felt that the Monte Carlo method can be successfully and easily employed for gamma ray shielding problems for penetration distances as large as 20 mean free paths. Since Monte Carlo estimates can be obtained for slab geometries, it can also be applied to two region problems.

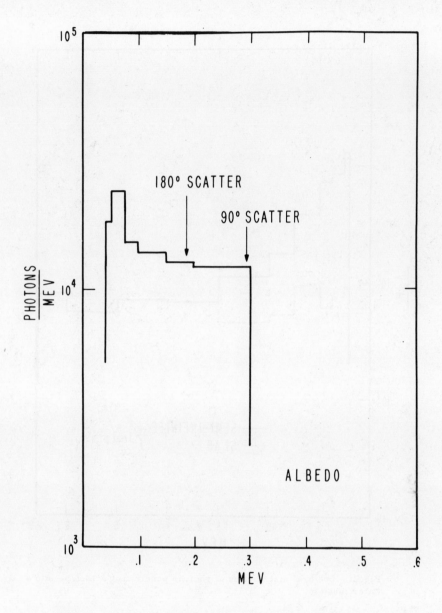

Fig. 1. Spectral distribution of photons reflected from a water medium for plane parallel Cs^{137} radiation normally incident.

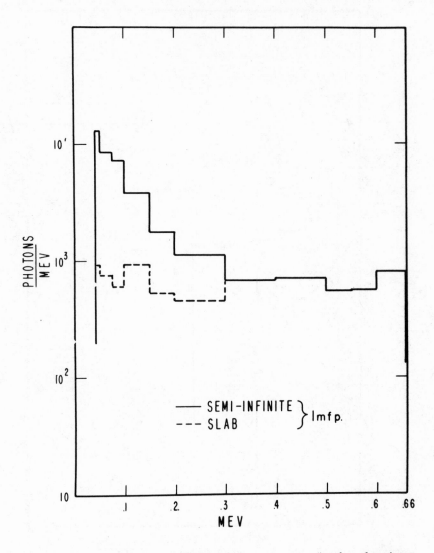

Fig. 2.   Spectral distribution of photons penetrating 1 m.f.p. into a
water medium.

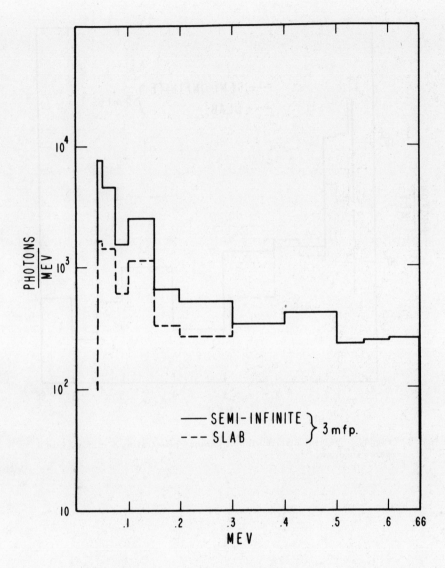

Fig. 3. Spectral distribution of photons penetrating 3 m.f.p. into a water medium.

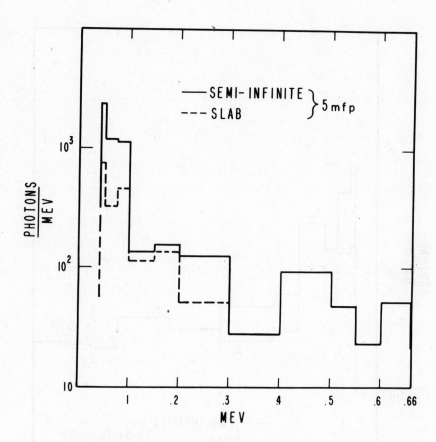

Fig. 4.   Spectral distribution of photons penetrating 5 m. f. p. into a
water medium.

112

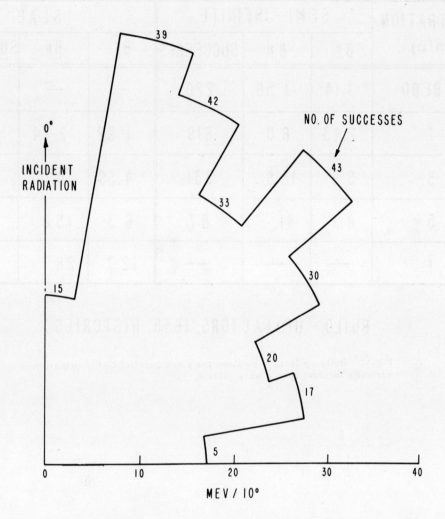

Fig. 5. Angular distribution of photons emerging from a 1 m.f.p. slab shield of water.

PENETRATION (mfp)	SEMI-INFINITE			SLAB		
	B E	B N	SUCCESSES	B E	B N	SUCCESSES
ALBEDO	1.14	1.59	220	—	—	—
1	2.43	6.0	619	1.92	2.74	244
3	5.9	18.8	331	4.56	10.0	176
5	8.1	31.	87	6.3	15.8	49
7	—	—	—	12.7	28.	14

BUILD-UP FACTORS (635 HISTORIES.)

Fig. 6.   Build-up factors obtained for plane parallel Cs^{137} radiation normally incident upon a water shield.

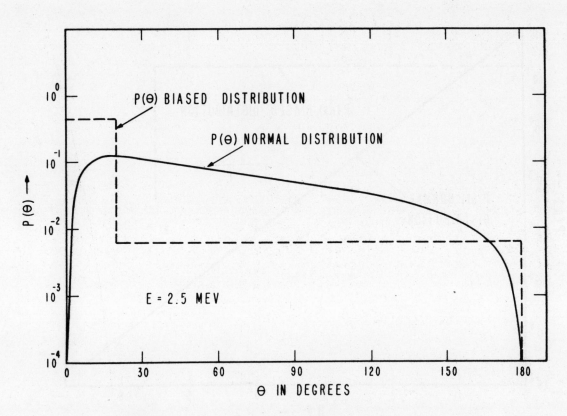

Fig. 7. Comparison of biased distribution of scattering angles with the Klein-Nishina distribution for 2.5 Mev photons.

115

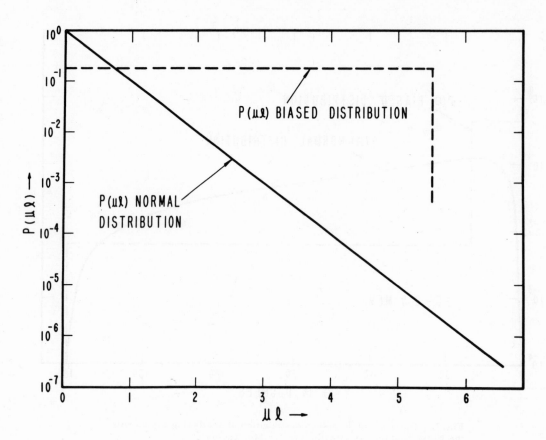

Fig. 8.   The "normal" and biased distributions of "free path lengths."

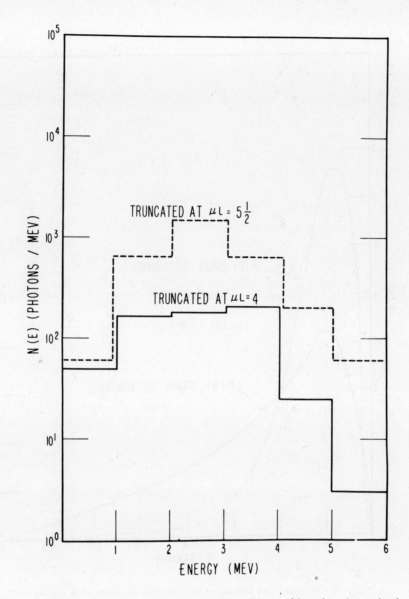

Fig. 9.   Comparison of spectral intensities at 10 m.f.p. into a lead medium for 6 Mev photons normally incident obtained in the two truncated studies.

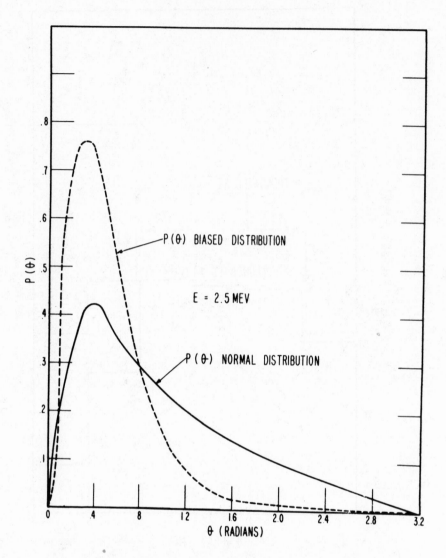

Fig. 10. Comparison of biased distribution of scattering angles with the Klein-Nishina distribution for 2.5 Mev photons.

118

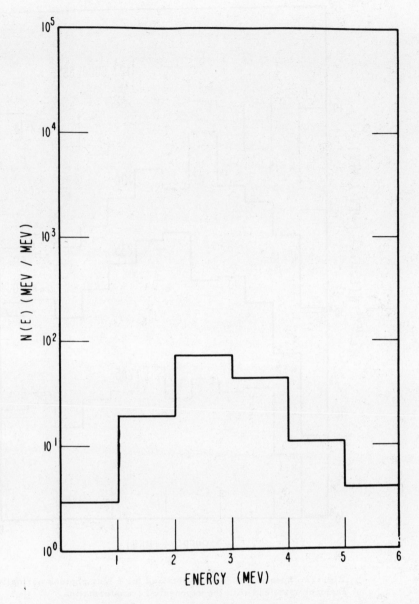

Fig. 11.   Spectral intensity 10 m. f. p. into lead for 6 Mev photons normally incident.

119

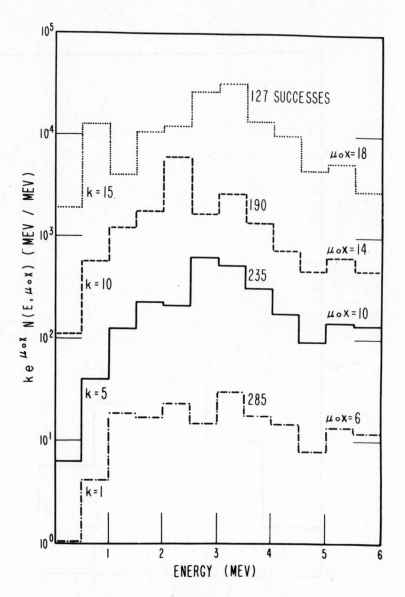

Fig. 12. Spectral intensities obtained for 6 Mev photons normally incident upon lead with the exponential transformation.

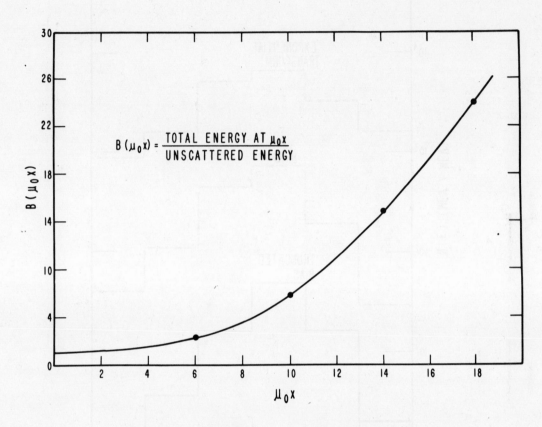

Fig.13. Energy build-up factors for 6 Mev photons normally incident upon lead.

121

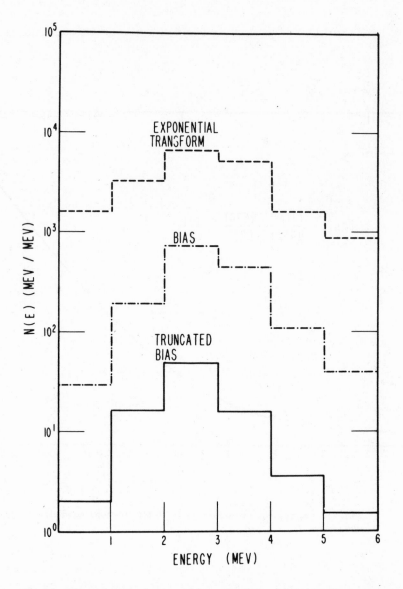

Fig. 14. Comparison of spectral intensities for 6 Mev photons normally incident upon lead obtained in the three studies. BIAS and EXPONENTIAL TRANSFORM intensities have been multiplied by scale factors of 10 and 100, respectively.

122

THE USE OF MULTI-STAGE SAMPLING SCHEMES IN MONTE CARLO COMPUTATIONS

Andrew W. Marshall

The RAND Corporation

I.   INTRODUCTION

One of the available techniques of Monte Carlo computations, importance sampling, can make Monte Carlo computations much more efficient if we are able to choose judiciously the probability distribution from which the sample observations are drawn. The details of this technique will be reviewed below. The difficulty in practice is that one is often not able to specify a priori what the more efficient probability distribution is, or even if a good choice can be made with regard to the parameter class of distributions to be used the parameter values are difficult to determine. In this situation one naturally thinks of using some sort of multi-stage sampling in which information obtained in a preliminary sample is used to determine the way in which the remainder of the sample is to be picked. Some results relating to procedures of this type are described below.

We turn now to the description of the setting of the problem and the technique of importance sampling.

II.   THE SETTING OF THE PROBLEM   [1]

The problem to be discussed is the estimation of ξ , where

$$\xi = \int_{-\infty}^{\infty} g(x)\ f(x,\theta)dx$$

where $g(x)$ is some known function of x; e.g., x, x^2, sin x, $x^2 + 3x^3$, or even

$$g(x) = 0 \qquad x \leq a$$
$$= 1 \qquad x > a .$$

$f(x, \theta)$ is the probability distribution of x, where $\theta = (\theta_1, \ldots, \theta_k)$ is a vector of parameters determining the probability distribution. Frequently the characteristic of the problem that makes Monte Carlo methods preferable to ordinary numerical methods is the complexity of $f(x, \theta)$. Often it is not possible or convenient to write down $f(x, \theta)$ in closed form, but one is able to sample from it.

The general idea of importance sampling is the following: rather than sampling from $f(x)$, suppressing θ in our notation for the moment, it is preferable to sample from another probability distribution $h(x)$ giving

$$\xi = \int_{-\infty}^{\infty} \frac{g(x)\, f(x)}{h(x)}\, h(x)\, dx = \int_{-\infty}^{\infty} g^o(x)\, h(x)\, dx$$

where $h(x)$ is restricted to be a probability distribution such that $h(x) \neq 0$ unless $g(x) f(x) = 0$. There is therefore a wide choice available in choosing $h(x)$ and if we consider the estimate

$$\overline{g^o(x)} = \frac{1}{n} \sum_{i=1}^{n} g^o(x_i)$$

based upon a sample $x_1 \ldots x_n$ from $h(x)$ it is possible to make it a better estimate of ξ by a proper choice of $h(x)$ than $\overline{g(x)}$, where

$$\overline{g(x)} = \frac{1}{n} \sum_{i=1}^{n} f(x_i)$$

when the sample $x_1 \ldots x_n$ is drawn from $f(x)$. Both estimates are consistent, unbiased estimates of ξ. The variance of the estimate $\overline{g^o(x)}$ is equal to

$$\sigma_n^2 = \frac{1}{n} \left[\int_{-\infty}^{\infty} \left[\frac{g(x) f(x)}{h(x)} \right]^2 h(x)\, dx - \xi^2 \right] .$$

It can be shown that the optimal $h(x)$, the $h(x)$ that minimizes the variance of its associated estimate $\overline{g^o(x)}$, is

$$h(x) = \frac{|g(x)|\, f(x)}{\displaystyle\int_{-\infty}^{\infty} |g(x)|\, f(x)\, dx} .$$

124

If $g(x) \geq 0$, $h(x) = \dfrac{g(x)\ f(x)}{\xi}$ is the optimum choice of $h(x)$ and the variance of the associated $\overline{g^o(x)}$ is zero. If $g(x)$ takes on both positive and negative values then a zero variance estimate is not possible unless more complicated procedures are used. It will be pointed out below it is seldom possible, or practical, to achieve these optimum results.

Before going on I wish to discuss a difficulty introduced by the application of importance sampling techniques that is glossed over in the above formulation of the problem. It often is the case that x is a very complicated random variable and that one does not pick an x from $f(x)$ but constructs x as a function of several other random variables. For example, suppose the random variable x is the statistic w_n^2,

$$w_n^2 = \frac{1}{12n} + \sum_{i=1}^{n} \left(y_i - \frac{2i-1}{2n} \right)^2$$

where the y's are drawn from the uniform distribution $(0,1)$ and $y_1 \leq y_2 \leq \cdots \leq y_n$. In this case x is a function of several random variables and we denote this by $x(y_1 \cdots, y_n)$ $= x(y)$. It may then be easier to construct x from the y's than to draw x from $f(x)$, or even this may be the only practical way to obtain sample values of x. The values of x obtained are drawn from $f(x)$ thus

$$\xi = \int_{-\infty}^{\infty} \int \cdots \int \int_{-\infty}^{\infty} g\left[x(y_1, \ \cdots \ y_n \right] \ell(y_1, \ \ldots, \ y_n) dy_1 \cdots dy_n.$$

The importance sampling must enter into the problem by altering the distribution of the y's, choosing them not from $\ell(y_1, \ \ldots, \ y_n)$ but from say $k(y_1, \ \ldots, \ y_n)$ and our estimate of ξ will be

$$\frac{1}{n} \sum_{i=1}^{n} g\left[x(y_1^{(i)}, \ \ldots, \ y_n^{(i)} \right] \frac{\ell\left[y_1^{(i)}, \ \ldots, \ y_n^{(i)} \right]}{k\left[y_1^{(i)}, \ \ldots, \ y_n^{(i)} \right]} ,$$

using superscripts to denote the ith vector of sample values.
This estimate is essentially $g(x_i)$ weighted by the likelihood
ratio of the y's yielding x_i, and this is not necessarily the
same as weighting $g(x_i)$ with $f(x_i)/h(x_i)$. If the same value
of x can arise from many vectors, y, there is no guarantee
that

$$\frac{f[x(y)]}{h[x(y)]} = \frac{\ell(y)}{k(y)} \quad .$$

Picking the y's from the distribution specified by $k(y)$ implies distribution $h(x)$ and it is suggestive to think of the
variance of random variable $g[x(y)]\dfrac{\ell(y)}{k(y)}$ as being composed of

two components: (1) variation in $g[x(y)]\dfrac{f[x(y)]}{h[x(y)]}$ and (2) var-

iation of $\dfrac{\ell(y)}{k(y)}$ from $\dfrac{f[x(y)]}{h[x(y)]}$.

In the following discussion of the problem of finding
good $h(x)$'s through multi-stage sampling procedures the explicit treatment will be in terms that imply one is sampling
from $f(x)$ and $h(x)$ directly. The changes that will be made
when this is not the case are clear and readers should con-
stantly keep in mind the distinction, indicated in the above
paragraph, between the two problems.

In practice, as was indicated above, one does not work
with completely general classes of distribution functions
but confines his choice of $h(x)$ to some parametric family
of distribution functions, often confining selection still
further by using some family of distributions closely related to $f(x, \theta)$. Thus in effect one makes two choices: (1)
the choice of parametric family $h(x, \alpha)$, where α is the
vector of parameters defining particular distributions
within the family, and (2) the choice of some particular
parameter value, α'. It is the latter choice that will concern us most in the remainder of the discussion. The choice
of the class of distributions, $h(x, \alpha)$, is a very difficult
problem and only a few general rules are available for making
this decision. In some problems intuition based upon the
physical structure of the real problem is of help. For the
moment we will consider that the choice of $h(x, \alpha)$ has been
made and our problem is to choose α' in some optimal way.

126

If $h(x, \alpha)$ is a one-parameter family of distribution functions we may illustrate the problem by plotting the variance of the associated estimate of ξ as a function of α. A typical case is shown in Chart I. As shown in Chart I there will be some value of α, α_0, which is associated with the minimum variance estimate of ξ. Also there are often values of α, such as α_1, that are poles of $V(\alpha)$; i.e., $V(\alpha_1) = \infty$. For example,[+] if

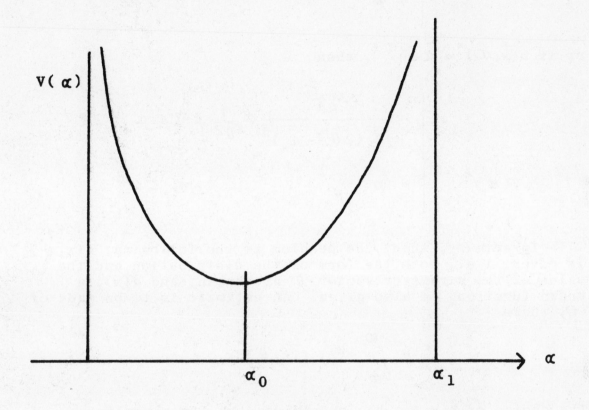

CHART I.

[+]An apology of sorts must be made for the type of examples it is possible to offer in discussions of Monte Carlo methods. In general they are of little interest themselves because the problems of most interest, as far as applications of Monte Carlo methods are concerned, are those that are not analytically tractable. All one can hope for is that the examples are revealing as far as principles are concerned.

$f(x, \theta) = \theta e^{-\theta x}$, $g(x) = x$, and the class distribution functions $h(x)$ is restricted to $h(x, \alpha) = \alpha^2 x e^{-\alpha x}$, then

$$V(\alpha) \begin{cases} = \dfrac{\theta^2}{\alpha^2 (2\theta - \alpha)^2} - \dfrac{1}{\theta^2} & ; \quad 0 < \alpha < 2\theta \\[3mm] = \infty & ; \quad \alpha \geq 2\theta \end{cases}$$

or if $h(x, \alpha) = \alpha e^{-\alpha x}$, then

$$V(\alpha) \begin{cases} = \dfrac{2\theta^2}{\alpha (2\theta - \alpha)^3} - \dfrac{1}{\theta^2} & ; \quad 0 < \alpha < 2\theta \\[3mm] = \infty & ; \quad \alpha \geq 2\theta \quad . \end{cases}$$

In summary, then, the problem is the following: $f(x, \theta)$ is given, i.e., both the form of the distribution and the value of the parameter vector θ are known, and $g(x)$, a known function, is also given. An estimate is to be made of ξ, where

$$\xi = \int_{-\infty}^{\infty} g(x) \, f(x, \theta) \, dx.$$

The choice of $h(x, \alpha)$ has been made, but the parameter α, or rather a good value of it is not known. In order to obtain an estimate of ξ, one simple suggestion would be that a sample, $x_1, \ldots, x_{n_1}$, be drawn from $f(x, \theta)$ and on this basis an estimate be made of α_0, say $\hat{\alpha}_0$, and the sampling then proceed using $h(x, \hat{\alpha}_0)$ as the distribution from which further samples are drawn. Some combined estimate based upon $\hat{\xi}_1$ and $\hat{\xi}_2$, the estimates obtained from this two-stage sampling plan would be used to estimate ξ. Given a fixed cost for computing program we wish to obtain an estimate having optimal characteristics, e.g., minimum variance or minimum risk estimates. The elements at our command are the choice of

128

methods of estimating the best value α and the balance between the size of the initial sample and the second sample; that is, balancing the value of an improved estimate of α_0 against a smaller opportunity to make use of it for estimating ξ. Of course, once the restriction of the sampling scheme to two stages is lifted other possibilities arise.

III. A TWO STAGE SAMPLING PROCEDURE FOR ESTIMATING ξ.

In this section it is proposed to discuss some aspects of the two staged sampling procedure suggested in the paragraph immediately above. The first problem to be treated will be the sampling distribution of an estimate $\hat{\alpha}_0$ of α_0, the value of α for which $V(\alpha)$ takes on its minimum value, in the case where $h(x, \alpha)$ is a single parameter family of distributions.

We have

$$\xi = \int_{-\infty}^{\infty} g(x) \frac{f(x)}{h(x, \alpha)} h(x, \alpha) dx$$

$$V(\alpha) = \int_{-\infty}^{\infty} g^2(x) \frac{f(x)}{h(x, \alpha)} f(x) dx - \xi^2,$$

and (1) assume that we have

$$\frac{\partial V(\alpha)}{\partial \alpha} = \int_{-\infty}^{\infty} g^2(x) \frac{f(x)}{h^2(x, \alpha)} \left[\frac{-\partial h(x, \alpha)}{\partial \alpha} \right] f(x) dx$$

$$= \int_{-\infty}^{\infty} \psi(x, \alpha) f(x) dx,$$

$$\frac{\partial^2 V(\alpha)}{\partial \alpha^2} = \int_{-\infty}^{\infty} \frac{\partial \psi(x, \alpha)}{\partial \alpha} f(x) dx,$$

and

$$\frac{\partial^3 V(\alpha)}{\partial \alpha^3} = \int_{-\infty}^{\infty} \frac{\partial^2 \psi(x, \alpha)}{\partial \alpha^2} f(x) dx .$$

129

This assumes, in effect, that for almost all x, the derivatives $\frac{\partial h}{\partial \alpha}$, $\frac{\partial^2 h}{\partial \alpha^2}$, and $\frac{\partial^3 h}{\partial \alpha^3}$ exist for every α belonging to a non-degenerate interval A.

(2) For every α in A, it is also assumed that $\left| \frac{\partial^2 \psi(x, \alpha)}{\partial \alpha^2} \right| < H(x)$ and $\int_{-\infty}^{\infty} H(x)f(x)dx < M$, where M is independent of α.

(3) For every α in A, the integral $\int_{-\infty}^{\infty} \psi^2(x,\alpha)f(x)dx = E_f\left[\psi^2(x, \alpha_0)\right]$ is finite and positive.[+]

If we denote α_0 as the value of α for which $\left. \frac{\partial V(\alpha)}{\partial \alpha} \right|_{\alpha_0} = 0$, or the minimizing value of α, an estimate of α_0 is $\hat{\alpha}_0$ the solution of the equation

$$\frac{1}{N} \sum_{i=1}^{n} \psi(x_i, \alpha) = 0.$$

By now the whole analogy to maximum likelihood estimation is obvious [2], although only in terms of the asymptotic distribution theory and its proof. $\hat{\alpha}_0$ is obviously a consistent estimate α_0 and we are concerned here only with its distribution. In order to investigate the asymptotic distribution of $\hat{\alpha}_0$ we expand $\psi(x, \alpha)$ about α_0 and obtain

$$\psi(x, \alpha) = \psi(x, \alpha_0) + \frac{\partial \psi(x, \alpha_0)}{\partial \alpha}(\alpha - \alpha_0) + \frac{1}{2}\phi H(x)(\alpha - \alpha_0)^2$$

where $|\phi| < 1$. Thus the equations determining $\hat{\alpha}_0$ may be written as

---

[+]We denote by $E_f(y)$ the expected value of the random variable y with respect to the probability density function f, thus we might write $\xi = E_f\left[g(x)\right]$.

$$\frac{1}{N} \sum_{i=1}^{N} \psi(x_i, \hat{\alpha}_0) = \frac{1}{N} \sum_{i=1}^{N} \psi(x_i, \alpha_0) + \frac{1}{N} \sum_{i=1}^{N} \frac{\partial \psi(x_i, \alpha_0)}{\partial \alpha}(\hat{\alpha}_0 - \alpha_0)$$

$$+ \frac{1}{2} \phi \sum_{i=1}^{N} H(x_i)(\hat{\alpha}_0 - \alpha_0)^2 = 0$$

$$\frac{1}{N} \sum_{i=1}^{N} \psi(x_i, \hat{\alpha}_0) = B_0 + B_1(\hat{\alpha}_0 - \alpha_0') + \frac{1}{2}\phi B_2(\hat{\alpha}_0 - \alpha_0)^2 = 0.$$

The B's are random variables, being functions of random variables $x_1 \ldots, x_N$. By Khintchine's theorem B_0 converges in probability to zero, B_1 converges in probability to $\dfrac{\partial^2 V(\alpha_0)}{\partial \alpha^2}$, and B_2 converges to the non-negative value $E\left[H(x)\right] < M$. Thus when we rewrite the above equation as

$$\sqrt{N} \, (\hat{\alpha}_0 - \alpha_0) = \frac{\dfrac{1}{\sqrt{N}} \sum_{i=1}^{N} \psi(x_i, \alpha_0)}{-\left[B_1 + \dfrac{1}{2}\phi B_2(\hat{\alpha}_0 - \alpha_0)\right]}$$

we see that the denominator converges to $\dfrac{-\partial^2 V(\alpha_0)}{\partial \alpha^2}$ and that the numerator is essentially the sum of independent random variables each with mean zero, variance $E_f\left[\psi^2(x, \alpha_0)\right]$, thus the central limit theorem applies and the sum $\sum_{i=1}^{N} \psi(x_i, \alpha_0)$ is asymptotically normal with mean zero and variance $N E_f\left[\psi^2(x, \alpha_0)\right]$. Therefore, $\sqrt{N} \, (\hat{\alpha}_0 - \alpha_0)$ is asymptotically normal with mean zero and variance

$$\frac{E_f\left[\psi^2(x, \alpha_0)\right]}{\left[\dfrac{\partial^2 V(\alpha_0)}{\partial \alpha^2}\right]^2}$$

In the case where α is a vector of parameters $(\alpha_1, \ldots, \alpha_k)$ similar results on the joint distribution of sample estimates can be obtained in a straightforward way.

We turn now to a description of an estimation procedure for ξ : a sample of size n_1 is drawn from the $f(x, \theta)$ and estimates $\hat{\xi}_1$ and $\hat{\alpha}_0$ are produced,

$$\hat{\xi}_1 = \frac{1}{n_1} \sum_{i=1}^{n_1} g(x_i)$$

then a sample of size n_2 is drawn from $h(x, \hat{\alpha}_0)$ and an estimate $\hat{\xi}_2$ computed,

$$\hat{\xi}_2 = \frac{1}{n_2} \sum_{i=1}^{n_2} g(x_i) \frac{f(x_i, \theta)}{h(x_i, \hat{\alpha}_0)}$$

and finally the two estimates of ξ are combined to form $\hat{\xi}$,

$$\hat{\xi} = \hat{w}_1 \hat{\xi}_1 + \hat{w}_2 \hat{\xi}_2$$

where the weights $\hat{w}_1$ and $\hat{w}_2$ are perhaps given by

$$\hat{w}_1 = \frac{\hat{\sigma}_2^2 / n_2}{\dfrac{\hat{\sigma}_1^2}{n_1} + \dfrac{\hat{\sigma}_2^2}{n_2}}$$

$$\hat{w}_2 = 1 - \hat{w}_1$$

and

$$\hat{\sigma}_1^2 = \frac{1}{n_1} \sum_{i=1}^{n} g^2(x_i) - \hat{\xi}_1^2$$

$$\hat{\sigma}_2^2 = \frac{1}{n_2} \sum_{i=1}^{n} g^2(x_i) \frac{f^2(x_i, \theta)}{h^2(x_i, \alpha)} - \hat{\xi}_2^2 \ .$$

If one were able to estimate before sampling the values of σ_1^2 and σ_2^2 as function of n_1 and n_2 a reasonable choice of n_1 and n_2 could, perhaps, be based upon the loss function $L(\xi, \hat{\xi}) = \lambda(\xi - \hat{\xi})^2$. In this case one would try to minimize by proper choice of n_1 and n_2 the expected loss (risk) $E\left[L(\xi, \hat{\xi})\right] = \lambda \, \mathrm{Var}(\hat{\xi}) = R(n_1, n_2)$, the expectation being taken relative to the probability distribution of $\hat{\xi}$, subject to the condition $(c_0 + c_1 n_1 + c_2 n_2) = c$, where

c_0 = initial cost of programming and cost of computing estimate $\hat{\alpha}_0$, etc., in other words all fixed costs given that two stages of sampling are done

c_1 = cost per observation from $f(x, \theta)$,

c_2 = cost per observation from $h(x, \hat{\alpha}_0)$.

In general it will not be possible to evaluate $E\left[L(\xi, \hat{\xi})\right] = V(\hat{\xi}) = R(n_1, n_2)$ beforehand because the values of the required expected values, etc., will not be known. In any case $V(\hat{\xi})$ will be quite a complicated expression since $\hat{\xi}_1$, $\hat{\sigma}_1^2$, $\hat{\xi}_2$, and σ_2^2 are not independent of one another. Although $E(\hat{\xi}_2 | \hat{\alpha}_0) = \xi$, the mean value of $\hat{\xi}$ is not ξ, in general, because of the bias introduced by the various covariance between $\hat{\xi}_1$, $\hat{\sigma}_1^2$, $\hat{\xi}_2$ and $\hat{\sigma}_2^2$ [+]. An additional difficulty is

---

[+]This bias in the estimate $\hat{\xi}$ can be removed by the use of a sampling technique called hybrid-splitting. This technique requires that two two-staged samples be taken, with n_1 and n_2 the same in each, and the weights $\hat{w}_1$ and $\hat{w}_2$ of one of the two-staged samples be used to combine the estimates $\hat{\xi}_1$ and $\hat{\xi}_2$ of the other two-staged sample. In this way the weights and the estimates are independent and the resulting weighted estimates $\hat{\xi}^{(1)}$ and $\hat{\xi}^{(2)}$ are both unbiased estimates of ξ of equal value a priori. Thus $1/2 \, \hat{\xi}^{(1)} + 1/2 \, \hat{\xi}^{(2)}$ is a reasonable pooled estimate, also unbiased. The removal of bias via this means is not always, or usually, costless in terms of the variance of the final estimate of ξ and these costs must be balanced against the value of the reduction of bias obtained.

that in many cases $E_p\left[V[\hat{\xi}_2(\hat{\alpha}_0)]\right]$ is unbounded. This is easily illustrated in the case of the examples given earlier where there is always a positive, but small, probability of $\hat{\alpha}_0 \geq 2\theta$ for any finite value of n_1. The situation is illustrated on Chart II, where $P\left[\hat{\alpha}_0(n_1)\right]$ is the probability density function of $\hat{\alpha}_0$, $n_1' > n_1$. As n_1 becomes large the probability approaches one that sampling from $h(x, \hat{\alpha}_0)$ is preferable to sampling from $f(x, \theta)$. Nonetheless $E_p\left[V[\hat{\xi}_2(\hat{\alpha}_0)]\right]$ is unbounded. No reasonable man would forego the advantages of sampling from $h(x, \hat{\alpha})$ if the probability is near enough to one that it will improve his estimate of ξ despite the resulting unbounded expected value of the variance of the estimate obtained from $h(x, \hat{\alpha}_0)$. Of course, since the weight given to the estimate derived from

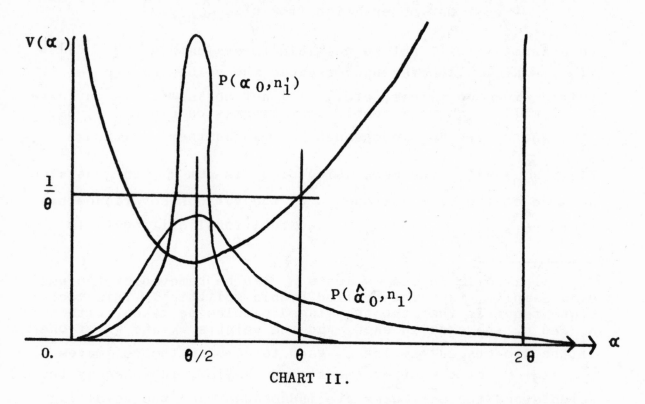

CHART II.

the second sample tends to zero when its variance is large the expected or average variance of $\hat{\xi}$ is not infinite but is essentially σ_1^2/n_1. This implies that one's loss function is not really $\lambda(\xi - \hat{\xi})^2$ and as a convenient alternative

I suggest that $V(\hat{\alpha})$ be replaced by a quadratic approximation about α_0 and further that the expected loss, $R(n_1, n_2)$ be simplified to

$$R(n_1, n_2) = w_1^2 V(\hat{\xi}_1) + w_2^2 V_{Approx}(\hat{\xi}_2) = \frac{w_1^2 \sigma_1^2}{n_1} +$$

$$\frac{w_2^2}{n_2} \left[V(\alpha_0) + \frac{E\left[\psi^2(x, \alpha_0)\right]}{2n_1 \dfrac{\partial^2 V(\alpha_0)}{\partial \alpha^2}} \right] .$$

This amounts to ignoring terms for the sampling variation in the weights and the complicated covariance terms involving the variables $\hat{\xi}_1$, $\hat{\sigma}_1^2$, $\hat{\xi}_2$, and $\hat{\sigma}_2^2$. The average variance of $\hat{\xi}_2$ is approximated by taking the expected value of the quadratic approximation of $V[\alpha_0(n_1)]$ relative to the asymptotic distribution of $\hat{\alpha}_0(n_1)$, which must introduce another approximation error for finite n_1, thus we have

$$V(\hat{\alpha}_0) \approx V(\alpha_0) + \frac{\partial V(\alpha_0)}{\partial \alpha}(\hat{\alpha}_0 - \alpha_0) + \frac{1}{2}\frac{\partial^2 V(\alpha_0)}{\partial \alpha^2}(\hat{\alpha}_0 - \alpha_0)^2$$

and

$$\int_{-\infty}^{\infty} V(\hat{\alpha}_0) P\left[\hat{\alpha}_0(n_1)\right] d\hat{\alpha}_0(n_1) \approx V(\alpha_0) + \frac{1}{2}\frac{\partial^2 V(\alpha_0)}{\partial \alpha^2} V\left[\hat{\alpha}_0(n_1)\right]$$

since $\dfrac{\partial V(\alpha_0)}{\partial \alpha} = 0$. In evaluating the weights w_1^2 and w_2^2, σ_2^2 must also be replaced by the approximation expression given above.

All one can suggest is that this is a reasonable thing to look at when deciding upon sampling designs. If possible, one would choose n_1 and n_2 such that

$$E\left[L(n_1, n_2)\right] = R(n_1, n_2)$$

is minimized subject to the constraint $(c_0 + c_1 n_1 + c_2 n_2) = c$.

Care should be taken in any case that the n_1 is large enough for the asymptotic variance to be a reasonable approximation.

IV. AN ASYMPTOTIC MINIMUM EXPECTED LOSS, SEQUENTIAL PROCEDURE FOR ESTIMATING ξ

It is completely unlikely that optimization of two stage sampling schemes could, or should, be carried out along the lines suggested above for the reasons just mentioned. In addition, to assume that one can evaluate $R(n_1, n_2)$ implies in practical situations that one can directly compute ξ , in which case there would be no problem, or at least no Monte Carlo problem. These difficulties suggest using knowledge obtained from the initial sample observations from $f(x, \theta)$ to decide when to change over to sampling from $h(x, \hat{\alpha}_0)$, as well as determining $\hat{\alpha}_0$. A sequential scheme for accomplishing this is described below. One can think of sampling procedures that are sequential in different ways; the one discussed here is a sampling procedure sequential for the determination of the best point in the sampling for the changeover from $f(x, \theta)$ to $h(x, \hat{\alpha}_0)$. The procedure is very much like Wald's suggestion for sequential point estimation [3].

The procedure would be as follows. Choose an initial sample of size n_0, where n_0 is large enough for the asymptotic approximations involved to be reasonably accurate, and choose the value of n, the incremental sample sizes. Take a sample of size n_0 from $f(x, \theta)$ and form

$$R\left[n_0, \; n_2(n_0)\right] \; - \; R\left[n_0 + n, \; n_2(n_0 + n)\right] \; = \Delta(n_0),$$

where

$$n_2(n') \; = \; \frac{C - C_0 - C_1 n'}{C_2}$$

using sample estimates of σ_1^2, $V(\alpha_0)$, $E_f\left[\psi^2(x, \alpha_0)\right]$, and $\dfrac{\partial^2 V(\alpha_0)}{\partial \alpha^2}$ to evaluate these expressions. The sample estimates would be

136

$$\hat{\sigma}_1^2 = \frac{1}{n_0} \sum_{i=1}^{n_0} g^2(x_i) - \overline{g(x_i)^2}$$

$$\hat{v}(\alpha_0) = \frac{1}{n_0} \sum_{i=1}^{n_0} g^2(x_i) \frac{f(x_i, \theta)}{h(x_i, \hat{\alpha}_0)} - \overline{g(x_i)^2}$$

$$\hat{E}_f\left[\psi^2(x, \alpha_0)\right] = \frac{1}{n_0} \sum_{i=1}^{n_0} \psi^2(x_i, \hat{\alpha}_0)$$

$$\frac{\partial^2 v(\hat{\alpha}_0)}{\partial \alpha^2} = \frac{1}{n_0} \sum_{i=1}^{n_0} \frac{\partial \psi(x_i, \hat{\alpha}_0)}{\partial \alpha}$$

where $\hat{\alpha}_0$ is, of course, the solution of

$$\frac{1}{n_0} \sum_{i=1}^{n_0} \psi(x_i, \alpha) = 0$$

If $\Delta(n_0) > 0$: Continue sampling from $f(x, \theta)$ and take a sample of size n, and test again using $\Delta(n_0 + n)$

$\Delta(n_0) \leq 0$: Take sample of size $n_2(n_0)$ from $h\left[x, \hat{\alpha}_0(n_0)\right]$.

Sampling is to proceed by repeated application of this test until the decision has been made to sample from $h(x, \hat{\alpha})$, at say the mth step when $\Delta(n_0 + mn) < 0$; then sampling will proceed from $h\left[x, \hat{\alpha}_0(n_0 + mn)\right]$. The final estimate of ξ is to be made as before.

If the total sample size is large (it can then be shown that the best value of n_1 will usually be large) and if the cost of making the sequence of decisions is negligible relative to the other costs of computations then this procedure should be nearly optimal, in the sense that it minimized the expected loss (risk) for fixed total cost of computation.

137

V. SOME EXAMPLES

Some examples have been worked out in order to determine the optimal balance of n_1 and n_2. Of course, the examples are not themselves of direct interest but one would hope that they shed some light upon the best choice of n_1 and n_2 in other more difficult problems where $g(x)$ and $f(x, \theta)$ are very similar but one cannot evaluate the required expressions. This is the most one can expect of analytical examples in Monte Carlo problems; that is, that they can be suggestive of how to proceed in the more difficult cases encountered in practice.

The examples are the following: As before let

$$f(x, \theta) = \theta \, e^{-\theta x}$$

$$g(x) = x$$

so that $\xi = \int_0^\infty g(x) f(x, \theta) dx = 1/\theta$.

We will examine two different choices of $h(x)$: $h(x, \alpha) = \alpha e^{-\alpha x}$ and $h(x, \alpha) = \alpha^2 x e^{-\alpha x}$. In the case of the first of these we find that

$$\left[v(\alpha_0) + \frac{E_f \left[\psi^2(x, \alpha_0) \right]}{2n_1 \dfrac{\partial^2 v(\alpha_0)}{\partial \alpha^2}} \right] = \frac{1}{\theta^2} \left[.185 + \frac{.356}{n_1} \right]$$

and $\alpha_0 = \theta/2$. If we let $k_1 = c_2/c_1$ and let $(c - c_0) = k_2$ then

$$R \left[n_1, \ n_2(n_1) \right] = \frac{1}{\theta^2} \left[\frac{\left[.185 + \dfrac{.356}{n_1} \right]}{.185 n_1 + .356 + \dfrac{k_2 - n_1}{k_1}} \right] .$$

From this we find optimal n_1' S, as a function of k_1 and k_2. These values are given in Table 1.

Table 1 $(k_2 = 1000)$

Optimal Values of n_1, n_2, given k_1	k_1	Value of $\theta^2 R(n_1, n_2)$ for optimal choice of n_1, n_2
$n_1 = 47$, $n_2 = 953$	1	.0002
53 474	2	.0004
64 312	3	.0006
85 229	4	.0008
158 128	5	.0010

These are to be compared with $\theta^2 R(1000, 0) = .0010$, the value for simple random sampling. We see that for $k_1 > 5$ the two staged sampling, even if optimal, would be worse than simple random sampling, because of the high relative cost of sampling from $h(x, \alpha)$.

In the case of $h(x, \alpha) = \alpha^2 x e^{-\alpha x}$ we find that since $\alpha_0 = \theta$

$$\left[V(\alpha_0) + \frac{E_f\left[\psi^2(x, \dot{\alpha}_0) \right]}{2n_1 \dfrac{\partial^2 V(\alpha_0)}{\partial \alpha^2}} \right] = \frac{1}{\theta^2}\left[\frac{1}{n_1} \right] \quad .$$

Defining k_1 and k_2 as before; then

$$R\left[n_1, \; n_2(n_1) \right] = \frac{1}{\theta^2}\left[\frac{k_1}{n_1\left[k_1 + k_2 - n_1 \right]} \right] \quad .$$

If $k_2 = 1000$ we find that the optimal n_1, and n_2 as functions of k_1 are such that

139

$$n_1 = \frac{1000 + k_1}{2} \approx 500$$

$$n_2 = \frac{500}{k_1} - 1/2 \approx \frac{500}{k_1}$$

so that n_1 does not depend to any great extent upon k_1.

Table 2 gives the values of $\theta^2 R(n_1, n_2)$ for optimal choices of n_1 and n_2.

Table 2 ($k_2 = 1000$)

Optimal Values of n_1, n_2, given k_1		k_1	Value of $\theta^2 R(n_1, n_2)$ for optimal choice of n_1, n_2
$n_1 = 501$,	$n_2 = 499$	1	.000004
501	250	2	.000008
502	150	3	.000012
502	112	4	.000016
503	89	5	.000020

These again are to be compared with the simple random sampling value for $\theta^2 R(1000, 0)$ of .0010. For no reasonable value of k_1 is simple random sampling better than a two staged sampling procedure (if optimal).

BIBLIOGRAPHY

[1] H. Kahn and A. W. Marshall, "Methods of Reducing Sample Size in Monte Carlo Computations," Journal of the Operations Research Society of America, Vol. I, 5, pp. 263-278.

[2] H. Cramér, Mathematical Methods of Statistics, 1946, pp. 500-504.

[3] A. Wald, "Asymptotic Minimax Solutions of Sequential Point Estimation Problems." Second Berkeley Symposium on Probability and Mathematical Statistics: I-II, 1951.

QUESTIONABLE USEFULNESS OF VARIANCE FOR MEASURING ESTIMATE ACCURACY IN MONTE CARLO IMPORTANCE SAMPLING PROBLEMS

John E. Walsh

U. S. Naval Ordnance Test Station

INTRODUCTION

Let us consider situations where the problem is to estimate the value of

$$\xi = \int_{-\infty}^{\infty} g(x)f(x)dx.$$

Here f(x) is a probability density function (pdf) and x may be a vector. The importance sampling procedure consists in introducing another pdf, h(x), which appears to be preferable for sampling purposes. Then

$$\xi = \int_{-\infty}^{\infty} \frac{g(x)f(x)}{h(x)} h(x)dx = \int_{-\infty}^{\infty} g^+(x)h(x)dx.$$

The estimate of ξ is

$$\hat{\xi} = \frac{1}{n} \sum_{i=1}^{n} g^+(x_i),$$

where $x_1, \ldots, x_n$ is a random sample from the population with pdf h(x). Then the usual method of measuring the estimate accuracy of $\hat{\xi}$ consists in examining its variance; that is, $E(\hat{\xi} - \xi)^2$. The preferable h(x), of the class considered, is the one which minimizes the variance of $\hat{\xi}$.

The purpose of this note is to show that cases exist where the variance is not a useful measure of the estimate accuracy of $\hat{\xi}$. An example is presented which appears to be reasonable from an application viewpoint but where the variance of $\hat{\xi}$ is infinite for all h(x) of the class considered. In spite of this infinite variance, $\hat{\xi}$ is a consistent estimate of ξ for all h(x) of the class. Moreover, if other criteria which appear to be intuitively as

141

acceptable as the variances are used, a preferable h(x) can be determined.

The mean deviation, $E\left[\hat{\xi} - \xi\right]$, is a measure of the estimate accuracy of $\hat{\xi}$ which is always useable as well as intuitively acceptable. Unfortunately this quantity is difficult to estimate from the sample values $x_1, \ldots, x_n$. Another possible measure which is always useable and appears to be intuitively acceptable is the mean difference

$$E\left[g^+(x) - g^+(y)\right] = \int_{-\infty}^{\infty} \int_{-\infty}^{\infty} \left[g^+(x) - g^+(y)\right]h(x)h(y)dxdy.$$

The statistic

$$\frac{2}{n(n-1)} \sum_{i>j=1}^{n} \left[g^+(x_i) - g^+(x_j)\right]$$

furnishes an unbiased and consistent estimate of $E\left[g^+(x) - g^+(y)\right]$. Other more readily computed estimates also can be obtained.

EXAMPLE

Sample values from a normal or truncated normal distribution are readily obtained by use of existing tables. Thus selecting h(x) from a class consisting of normal and/or truncated normal distributions has computational advantages in many cases. For situations where a Monte Carlo approach seems appropriate, the properties and shape of g(x)f(x) are seldom more than vaguely known. Often the only knowledge is an evaluation of g(x)f(x) at a few values of x. When this lack of information exists, the use of a class of normal and/or truncated normal distributions which have the same general shape as g(x)f(x) seems to be a procedure which is as reasonable and easily applied as any other.

Let us consider a special case where the normal and/or truncated normal choice for h(x) is used and where analytical results are easily obtained. Let g(x) = x and

142

$$f(x) = \begin{cases} ac^{-ax} & \text{for } x \gtreqless 0 \ (a > 0), \\ 0 & \text{for } x < 0. \end{cases}$$

Evidently the shape of xac^{-ac} can be at least roughly approximated by a special class of truncated normal distributions; this class consists of distributions which are only truncated from below and at a value which is at least zero. Consequently the possible $h(x)$ distributions are taken to consist of this special class. Using the specified choice, it is easily verified that the variance of $\hat{\xi}$ is infinite for every $h(x)$ of the class considered.

MEAN DIFFERENCE APPLICATION EXAMPLE

To illustrate application of the mean difference as a method of selecting the optimum $h(x)$ of the class considered, an example is analyzed. This example has the property that $E(\hat{\xi} - \xi)^2$ is infinite. The problem is to select $h(x)$, subject to stated limitations, so that the value of $E|g^+(x) - g^+(y)|$ is minimized.

Let

$$h(x) = \begin{cases} \left[\int_{-\infty}^{\mu} e^{-x^2/2} dx\right]^{-1} e^{-\frac{1}{2}(x-\mu)^2}, & 0 \leqq x < \infty \\ \\ 0 & , \quad \text{otherwise}, \end{cases}$$

where $\mu \leqq -1/10$,

$$f(x) = \begin{cases} e^{-x}, & 0 \leqq x < \infty \\ 0 , & \text{otherwise}, \end{cases}$$

while $g(x) = e^{9x/10}$. Then

$$g^+(x) = e^{\frac{1}{2}(x-\mu)^2 - x/10}$$

and $E|g^+(x) - g^+(y)|$ has the value

143

$$\left[\int_{-\infty}^{\mu} e^{-x^2/2} dx\right]^{-2} \int_0^{\infty}\int_0^{\infty} \left| e^{\frac{1}{2}(x-\mu)^2 - x/10} - e^{\frac{1}{2}(y-\mu)^2 - y/10} \right| \cdot$$

$$e^{-\frac{1}{2}\left[(x-\mu)^2 + (y-\mu)^2\right]} dy\,dx$$

$$= e^{-\frac{1}{10}(\mu+1/20)}\left[\int_{-\infty}^{\mu} e^{-x^2/2} dx\right]^{-2} \int_{-\infty}^{\mu}\int_{-\infty}^{\mu} \left| e^{\frac{1}{2}(x+1/10)^2} - \right.$$

$$\left. -e^{\frac{1}{2}(y+1/10)^2} \right| e^{-\frac{1}{2}(x^2+y^2)} dy\,dx$$

$$= 2e^{-\frac{1}{10}}\left[\int_{-\infty}^{\mu} e^{-x^2/2} dx\right]^{-2} \int_{-\infty}^{\mu}\int_{-\infty}^{x} \left[e^{\frac{1}{2}(y+1/10)^2} - \right.$$

$$\left. -e^{\frac{1}{2}(x+1/10)^2} \right] e^{-\frac{1}{2}(x^2+y^2)} dy\,dx$$

$$= 20\left[\int_{-\infty}^{\mu} e^{-x^2/2} dx\right]^{-2} \left[2e^{-\frac{1}{10}(\mu-1/20)} \int_{-\infty}^{\mu-1/10} e^{-x^2/2} dx - \right.$$

$$\left. \int_{-\infty}^{\mu} e^{-x^2/2} dx\right] \quad .$$

Examination shows that this is a decreasing function of μ.
Thus, the optimum h(x) is obtained by setting $\mu = -1/10$,
the maximum allowable value of μ.

144

EXPERIMENTAL DETERMINATION OF EIGENVALUES AND DYNAMIC INFLUENCE COEFFICIENTS FOR COMPLEX STRUCTURES SUCH AS AIRPLANES

C. W. Vickery[+]

Fairchild Aircraft Corporation
Hagerstown, Maryland

ABSTRACT

This paper describes a simple experimental technique for determining eigenvalues and dynamic influence coefficients applicable to airplanes. A dynamic influence coefficient μ_{ij} is defined as the response of the system at station i to a unit impulse at station j. The dynamic influence coefficients so defined are complex functions. These dynamic influence coefficients completely characterize the vibrational properties of the system. (Author's Introduction).

[+]In the absence of Mr. Vickery, this paper was read by Henry E. Fettis, Wright Air Development Center.

USE OF DIFFERENT MONTE CARLO SAMPLING TECHNIQUES[+]

Herman Kahn

The RAND Corporation, Santa Monica, California

When doing a Monte Carlo problem one focusses attention on three main topics. They are:

1. Choosing or analogizing the probability process

2. Generating sample values of the random variables on a given computing machine

3. Designing and using variance reducing techniques.

This paper will discuss only the last topic. It is, of course, true that in actual problems one cannot isolate variance reduction from the first two topics. The methods which can be used to reduce variance are often sharply dependent upon the probability model and in some cases on the techniques used to generate values of the random variables. Also, the greatest gains in variance reduction are often made by exploiting specific details of the problem, rather than by routine application of general principles. However, there do seem to be some general ideas on reducing variance which can be used in many problems. In particular, six techniques seem to be most useful. They are:

[+] This paper is a revision of the second chapter of a larger report being prepared by the author. I would also like to express my thanks to I. Mann, A. Marshall, and N. Shapiro who read and commented on a first draft. While the author is fundamentally responsible for any mistakes, he would like to point out that under the legal doctrine "of the last clear chance" the foregoing should be sued.

[++] Published with permission of The RAND Corporation.

1. Importance Sampling

2. Russian Roulette and Splitting

3. Use of Expected Values (combination of analytic and probabilistic methods)

4. Correlation and Regression

5. Systematic Sampling

6. Stratified Sampling (Quota Sampling).

While all of these techniques can be used in standard statistical sampling problems, the first three seem to have found particular and specialized usefulness in Monte Carlo applications as differentiated from the usual applications in ordinary sampling. This is mainly due to the fact that in a Monte Carlo problem the experimenter has complete control of his sampling procedure. If for example he wanted a green-eyed pig with curly hair and six toes and if this event had a non zero probability, then the Monte Carlo experimenter, unlike the agriculturist, could immediately produce the animal.

In order to illustrate the general nature of the techniques, we will first apply them to a very simple example--so simple, in fact, that the reader will have to exercise his imagination in order to pretend there is any problem. After we have gone through the elementary exercise, we will discuss, in some detail, how the six techniques can be applied to the Monte Carlo evaluation of definite integrals. The integral is used for the serious example, not because it is the main application of the technique--it is not (except in the generalized sense that any expected value can be calculated by an integral)--but rather because it is the application in which the ideas are most clearly exposited.

The simple example we will use is the problem of calculating the probability of obtaining a total of three when one tosses two ordinary dice. Each die is of the standard sort with six faces labeled from one to six and constructed so that each face has the same probability (1/6) of being on top.

The problem can, of course, be solved analytically. Any particular combination of the dice has a probability equal to 1/6 times 1/6 of occurring. Since there are two combinations which make three (one-two and two-one), the probability of getting a three in a random toss of the dice is 2/36 or 1/18.

In doing the above problem by Monte Carlo one would simply toss the dice[+] N times, count the number (n) of successes (threes) and then estimate the probability (p) of success by

$$\hat{p} = \frac{n}{N} \tag{1}$$

Typically, $\hat{p}$ differs from p; that is, the estimate has a statistical error. This statistical error is usually measured[++] by the standard deviation σ, where

$$\sigma = \sqrt{\frac{p(1-p)}{N}} \tag{2}$$

The percent error is then given by

$$\frac{100\sigma}{p} = 100\sqrt{\frac{1-p}{Np}} \tag{3}$$

As is well known, and as is shown by the above formula, this error goes down as the number of trials is increased. It is the purpose of Part One to illustrate other ways in which the error can be decreased.

[+] Usually one would not toss physical dice, but simulate the tosses with the aid of a table of random numbers.

[++] In Monte Carlo problems the error has statistical properties which can usually be described in the following manner. The probability that the absolute value of the error will be larger than mσ is given by the following table:

m	Prob.
.67	.50
1.00	.32
2.00	.05

σ is called the standard deviation and σ^2 the variance. The latter is usually denoted by V. A more complete explanation of statistical errors can be found in almost any elementary book on statistics.

PART ONE

THE TRIVIAL EXAMPLE

1. Importance Sampling

If by some method we can increase the effective value
of p, equation (3) shows that the percent error will be
reduced. This increase in the effective value of p can be
obtained very easily. We could, for example, bias the
dice so that the probability that a one or a two would come
up is twice as great as usual, that is 1/3 rather than 1/6.
This could be done with physical dice by "loading" them, or
by mathematically simulated dice by using a biased table of
random numbers. If this is done then the probability of
getting a three, instead of being 1/18, is four times as
great or 2/9. The percent error is then cut by slightly
more than a factor of two. Of course, equation (1) can no
longer be used to estimate p, but

$$\hat{p} = \frac{1}{4} \frac{n}{N} \qquad\qquad (4)$$

must be used instead. The 1/4 in equation (4) is called a
weighting factor. By using it, the distortion introduced
by the biased sampling is removed.

This illustrates the general idea of Importance Samp-
ling--which is to draw samples from a distribution other
than the one suggested by the problem and then to carry
along an appropriate weighting factor which, when multiplied
into the final results, corrects for having used the wrong
distribution. The biasing is done in such a way that the
probability of the sample's being drawn from an "interesting"+ region is increased; the probability that it comes
from an "uninteresting" region is correspondingly decreased.
The reader should verify for himself that it would be correct to carry the bias to the limit; that is, the probability
of getting a one or a two could be increased by a factor of
three, making the probability of obtaining one of these numbers 1/2 and making the probability of obtaining any other
number zero.

+ As discussed later, the words "interesting" and
"uninteresting" refer to the amount of effort or interest
the sensible calculator would show in the region.

The above limit is not the ultimate limit. For example, if we tossed the dice one at a time, then we might want to bias the second die differently from the first one. In particular, if we were willing to let the biasing of the second die depend on the outcome of the first throw, we might consider the following scheme.

1. Increase the probability of getting a one or a two on the first die by a factor of three. This means, of course, that there will be a zero probability of getting any other numbers.

2. If the first die comes up one, increase the probability of the second die coming up two by a factor of six; if the first die comes up two, increase the probability of the second die coming up one by a factor of six.

If this scheme is followed every toss of the dice will yield a three so that the number of successes (n) will be equal to the number of trials (N). The weighting factor will be 1/3 times 1/6 or 1/18 and the estimate will be

$$\hat{p} = \frac{n}{18N} \tag{5}$$

$$= \frac{1}{18}$$

which is exactly equal to p. We have devised a sampling procedure which has zero variance. In principle, though not in practice, it is always possible to design an Importance Sampling Scheme that has zero variance.

2. Russian Roulette and Splitting[+]

Let us assume that the dice are tossed one at a time and that the cost of the problem is measured by the total number of tosses. Now, it is immediately clear that if the first die is tossed and if it happens to come up three or greater, it will be impossible to get a total of three, no matter how the second die comes up. Under these circumstances, there is no point in making the second toss and we can simply record a zero for the experiment. This makes it unnecessary to toss the second die 2/3 of the time. Therefore on the average we will do 1/3 fewer tosses in an experiment.

[+] Both the idea and the name are due to J. von Neumann and S. Ulam.

Generally in more complicated examples where the sampling is done in stages, it is often possible to examine the sample at each stage and classify it as being in some sense "interesting" or "uninteresting." The sensible calculator is willing to spend more than an average amount of work on the "interesting" ones and contrariwise wants to spend less effort on the "uninteresting" ones. This can be done by splitting the "interesting" samples into independent branches, thus getting more of them, and by killing off some percent (in the above example 100%) of the "uninteresting" ones. The first process is Splitting and the second Russian Roulette.

The "killing off" is done by a supplementary game of chance. If the supplementary game is lost the sample is killed; if it is won the sample is counted with an extra weight to make up for the fact that some other samples have been killed. The game has a certain similarity to the Russian game of chance played with revolvers and foreheads-- whence the name.

The idea of Russian Roulette and Splitting is similar to the sequential sampling schemes of quality control, though quite different in detail. It was first thought of in connection with particle diffusion problems. Particles which get into interesting regions are split into n independent sub-particles, each with one n'th of the weight of the original particle. Particles which get into uninteresting regions are, in effect, amalgamated into a fewer number of heavier particles. In this way the calculator achieves his goal of allocating his effort sensibly.

3. Use of Expected Values

If the sampling is being done in two stages, then even if we aren't clever enough to calculate the combinatories of the whole problem, we still might be clever enough to notice that there is no point in tossing the second die; that is, once the first die is tossed, it is trivially easy to calculate the probability of obtaining a total of three. For example, when the first die comes up one, the only way we can get the three total is for the second die to come up two. This event obviously has a probability of 1/6. Similarly if the first die comes up two, the only way to get three is for the second die to be one. This event has a probability of 1/6. Finally, all the other possibilities for the first die (three to six) have a zero probability of giving three.

151

If we record the probabilities rather than toss the second die, then it is a fact that the average of these probabilities is an estimate of p. This method of doing the problem simultaneously reduces the number of tosses we need by a factor of two and decreases the variance, so that the tosses we do make are more effective.

The illustration is not artificial. In many probabilistic problems, it turns out that much of the variance or fluctuation is introduced by a part of the probabilistic problem which can be calculated analytically; the probabilistic part which is hard to calculate analytically may, in fact, not introduce much fluctuation. In these cases the sensible calculator combines analytic and probabilistic methods--calculating analytically that which is easy and Monte Carloing that which is hard.

The three techniques discussed above can be fantastically effective in realistic applications. The author is familiar with applications in which each technique has, by itself, decreased the effective variance by factors of the order of 10^4 to 10^6. In most cases this means changing the problem from one which cannot be done because it would be too expensive or lengthy to one which is easily done on modern computing machines or even by hand computers.

The three techniques which we are now going to discuss are, in general, not as effective as the three already mentioned. However, they often are very easy to use and may yield substantial improvements.

4. Correlation and Regression

In order to illustrate this technique, it will be necessary to change the example slightly. Assume, for instance, that the proprietor of one of the gaming establishments in Las Vegas wishes to change the rules in force at his dice tables. Under the current rules, if a player tosses a 2, 3, or 12, on the first throw of the dice, the player loses. If he tosses a 7 or 11, he wins, and if he tosses a 4, 5, 6, 8, 9 or 10, he will win or lose, depending on whether or not that number or a 7 comes up first in his subsequent throws.

Now let the rule change being considered be the interchange of the roles of 3 and 4 and assume that, unlike most of the proprietors in Las Vegas, the one we are considering is unsophisticated and wishes to determine by sampling what the change in his revenue will be. The obvious way to do this is to run two sets of experiments, one with the old rules and one with the new rules, and then compare the two experimentally-determined revenues. Under these circumstances, one is subtracting two relatively large, fluctuating quantities to determine a small quantity. In general, this yields a process with a large percent error.

There is a better way to do this problem. Instead of running two independent games, the proprietor could run only one game and apply both sets of rules simultaneously to this game. In fact, he can choose to estimate the difference in revenue directly rather than the revenue that would be achieved under each set of rules.

This can be done by playing the following game:

1. Whenever a 3 comes up, continue to toss the dice until either a 3 or a 7 comes up. In the first happenstance, record a minus two, since under the old rules the customer would have lost a dollar, but under the new rules he wins one; in the second happenstance, record a zero because under both sets of rules the customer loses.

2. Follow a similar process if a 4 comes up.

3. If a number other than 3 or 4 comes up terminate the play then and there and record a zero. (Because of this rule, the effects of chance fluctuations in the proportionate number of times that the numbers 2 and 5 to 12 come up are eliminated from the comparison.)

It should be noticed that the specific game that is played is quite different from the two games that are being compared. As usual, this causes a double saving of efficiency; first because only one set of games is played, and second because the number and kinds of chance fluctuations that can affect the results are greatly reduced.

It is in fact generally true that if we wish to compare two or more situations, we can, by combining this comparison into a single problem, reduce the work substantially. Only one problem, rather than several, has to be done, and the direct estimate of the difference can usually be made more accurately than estimates of separate individual quantities.

This is a substantial virtue of the Monte Carlo method. In many complicated problems we are not actually interested in absolute values but only in comparisons. We may wish, for example, to know if Strategy A is better than Strategy B, or if Engineering Design A is better than Engineering Design B. We might, in fact, not even believe the absolute values because the idealizations are so rough, but we do believe the qualitative features implied by differences. Monte Carlo can then be used to estimate the thing which we actually desire to know and which we believe, and we can bypass the estimate of irrelevant quantities. Usually, however, we can obtain these also, but at some extra cost.

Correlated Sampling can also often be used to test the accuracy of an approximate theory. If the approximate theory happens to be an exact treatment of an idealized situation, and if the idealized situation happens to be "structurally" similar to the unidealized situation, then it is often possible to design very efficient sampling schemes to calculate the difference between the idealized and unidealized situations. The answer to the problem posed by the unidealized situation can then be obtained by adding together the results of the approximate analytic calculation and the Monte Carlo difference calculation.

5. Systematic Sampling

If we are doing a multi-stage sampling problem, it often turns out to be very easy to do the first stage systematically. For example, in our problem, if we are going to toss the dice one at a time then there is really no point in actually tossing the first die. If, for example, we were planning on getting 600 samples, we would expect on the average that each die would come up one about 100 times, two another 100, and so on. It is easy to show that we do not bias the results if we assume that the first 100 tosses of the first die actually do come up one, the second 100 tosses of this die come up two, etc. and so only toss the second die. The main advantage in doing this is that we have eliminated the error caused by the fluctuation in the proportions of ones, twos, etc. which would result if the first toss was random.

In practice, however, doing the first stage of the sampling systematically does not usually lead to substantial improvements in efficiency. Generally, in fact, it will only reduce the number of samples required by a relatively few percent -- say 5 to 30. However, it ordinarily does not cost anything to apply this technique, so that there is no point in not using it. About the only time we may not be able to use it conveniently is when we do not know in advance how big a sample we will want.

6. <u>Stratified</u> <u>Sampling</u>

This last technique is a sort of combination of Importance Sampling and Systematic Sampling. For example, if we were only a little bit sophisticated and were doing the systematic sampling described above, we would soon notice that there is no point in considering the 400 tosses in which we had assigned the values three to six for the first toss of the die, since under these circumstances, we can never get a total of three. Therefore, we might systematically divide the sample into halves rather than sixths. In the first half we would say that the first die came up one, and in the second half that the first die came up two.

In theory, this method could be as powerful as Importance Sampling. In actual practice, the fact that you have to sample systematically turns out to decrease sharply the number of places in which it can be used. However, where it can be used, it is usually better than Importance Sampling and in any case never worse. Therefore whenever the costs of the two techniques are comparable, Stratified Sampling is preferable to Importance Sampling.

PART TWO

THE EVALUATION OF DEFINITE INTEGRALS[+]

The second part of the paper is concerned with the evaluation of definite integrals. Formulae will be derived which can, in principle, be used in a direct way to design sampling schemes. In practice, however, these formulae can rarely be used explicitly, because usually the Monte Carlo designer cannot obtain accurate numerical values of the variables that appear in them. It turns out though that if the Monte Carlo experimenter uses approximate values in the formulae, then the effect of using these approximations is not to bias the estimating procedure, but only to increase

---

+ While Part Two requires somewhat more mathematical maturity to read than Part One, it does not require as much more as the casual reader is likely to think at first glance. However some skipping or a preliminary skimming may be helpful to the novice.

the statistical error of the calculation as compared with what would have been obtained if correct values had been used. Usually though the statistical error will have been decreased, at least as compared with what would be obtained if no design at all were attempted.

Perhaps the best way to describe the situation is to say that the formulae are a powerful guide to one's intuition in designing useful sampling schemes but can rarely be used in a routine way. They are suggestive and normative rather than explicitly directive. It is, however, often possible to do subsidiary studies--Monte Carlo, analytic, or numerical--which can be used with the formulae to guide intuition.

It is probably advisable at this point to add a few words of caution. Techniques described under the headings of Importance Sampling, Russian Roulette and Splitting, and Stratified Sampling have the property that in many calculations they will give a tremendous increase in efficiency if properly used; if, however, the intuition of the calculator is faulty and he does not use a reasonable design, then they can be very unreliable and actually increase the variance. The other techniques are more stable in that it is almost impossible for the experimenter to worsen the sampling variance by misusing them, even if he has a bad intuition.

We will not discuss in this paper how the experimenter can protect himself from trouble, except to say that the usual method of estimating error (calculating the sample variance and then appealing to the Central Limit Theorem) is usually satisfactory; however, it can give trouble in semi-pathological though real cases.

The six techniques will be illustrated by considering the problem of estimating the integral

$$\iint\limits_{S} z(x,y)f(x,y)dxdy = \overline{z(x,y)} = \overline{z} \tag{6}$$

by random sampling. z(x,y) is arbitrary and

$$f(x,y) \geq 0 \text{ for } (x,y) \text{ in } S \tag{7}$$

$$\iint\limits_{S} f(x,y)dxdy = 1$$

Two independent variables are shown; actually most of the discussion is unchanged if x and y are multi-dimensional variables or if one of the variables is eliminated.

156

$\bar{z}$ is defined as the expected value of $z(x,y)$ with respect to $f(x,y)$. $f(x,y)$ is a probability density function (to be abbreviated p.d.f.) over the space S. Mathematically speaking, this statement is equivalent to conditions (7). Roughly $f(x,y)$ can be thought of as being proportional to the joint probability that $X = x$ and $Y = y$. More properly, $f(x,y)dxdy$ is the probability that $x \leq X \leq x + dx$ and $y \leq Y \leq y + dy$.

The representation of the integral as an expected value does not in any way limit the generality of the problem; such a representation can be made for any integral.

An estimate of $\bar{z}$ can be obtained very simply by Monte Carlo. A number (N) of sample values (x_i, y_i) are picked from the p.d.f., $f(x,y)$,[+] the function $z(x,y)$ is evaluated for each (x,y) sample, and the arithmetical average

$$\hat{z} = \frac{1}{N} \sum_{i=1}^{N} z(x_i, y_i) \tag{8}$$

of the N numbers $z(x_i, y_i)$ is calculated.

This sample average $\hat{z}$ is an estimate of $\bar{z}$. As has been mentioned (note [++] on page 148) any statistical estimate has an error which is described in terms of the variance. The variance is defined as:

$$V = \frac{1}{N} \iint \left[z(x,y) - \bar{z} \right]^2 f(x,y)dxdy \tag{9}$$

$$= \frac{1}{N} \overline{\left[z(x,y) - \bar{z} \right]^2}$$

$$= \frac{1}{N} \left[\iint z^2(x,y) f(x,y)dxdy - \bar{z}^2 \right]$$

$$= \frac{1}{N} \left(\overline{z^2} - \bar{z}^2 \right)$$

The square root of the variance is called the standard deviation and will be denoted by σ. We will loosely refer to either σ or V as the error. Let us now investigate what happens to this error in the six techniques.

[+] Butler's paper in this book describes ways to pick from a p.d.f.

1. Importance Sampling

If the integrand is multiplied and divided by an arbitrary p.d.f., $f^+(x,y)$, $\bar{z}$ is written

$$\bar{z} = \iint z(x,y)\, \frac{f(x,y)}{f^+(x,y)}\, f^+(x,y)\,dxdy \qquad (10)$$

One can now pick from $f^+(x,y)$ instead of $f(x,y)$, and $z(x,y)f(x,y)/f^+(x,y)$ plays the role that $z(x,y)$ played previously. Therefore for (x_i, y_i) picked from $f^+(x,y)$ the estimate of $\bar{z}$ becomes

$$\hat{z}_1 = \frac{1}{N} \sum_{i=1}^{N} z(x_i, y_i)\, \frac{f(x_i, y_i)}{f^+(x_i, y_i)} \qquad (11)$$

instead of $\hat{z}$ as given by equation (8). In addition to being a p.d.f., $f^+(x,y)$ is subject to the condition that it can be zero only when $z(x,y)$ or $f(x,y) = 0$. The expected value of $\hat{z}_1$ is, of course, the same as that of $\hat{z}$. Even though the expected value has not been changed, the errors of the two estimates are quite different. The variance of $\hat{z}_1$ is obtained by modifying equation (9) in the obvious way $\big[\, z(x,y)f(x,y)/f^+(x,y)$ for $z(x,y)$ and $f^+(x,y)$ for $f(x,y)\, \big]$:

$$V_1 = \frac{1}{N}\, \iint \left[z(x,y)\, \frac{f(x,y)}{f^+(x,y)} \right]^2 f^+(x,y)\,dxdy$$

$$= \frac{1}{N} \left[\iint \frac{z^2(x,y)f^2(x,y)}{f^+(x,y)}\,dxdy - \bar{z}^2 \right] \qquad (12)$$

and this is in general different from V given in equation (9). It is easily shown[+] that V_1 is minimized when

$$f^+(x,y) = \frac{|z(x,y)|\,f(x,y)}{\iint |z(x,y)|\, f(x,y)\,dxdy} \qquad (13)$$

[+] One applies the standard Calculus of Variations techniques to the expression

$$\iint \frac{z^2(x,y)\, f^2(x,y)}{f^+(x,y)}\,dxdy + \lambda \int f^+(x,y)\,dxdy$$

When z(x,y) is non-negative and the optimal $f^+(x,y)$ is used, a zero variance estimate is obtained. This can be verified by substituting $f^+(x,y) = z(x,y)f(x,y) / \bar{z}$ into equation (12) or more simply by noticing that the separate estimates $z(x_i,y_i)f(x_i,y_i) / f^+(x_i,y_i)$ are actually constant and equal to $\bar{z}$ independently of what (x_i,y_i) were picked.

Of course before the optimum $f^+(x,y)$ can be obtained, $\bar{z}$ must be known. In more complicated problems even more than just the answer must be known before a zero variance sampling scheme can be designed. Under such circumstances zero variance is not a miraculous result.

The significance of the existence of zero variance estimates lies not in the possibility of actually constructing them in practice but in that they demonstrate there are no "Conservation of Cost" laws. That is, if the designer is clever, wise, or lucky he may, in choosing from the infinite number of sampling schemes available, be able to choose a very efficient one. This is in some contrast to the situation in ordinary numerical analysis. It is usually true there that once a fairly good method of doing a problem has been found, that further work or additional transformations do not reduce the cost very much, if at all. In Monte Carlo problems however we are assured that there is always a better way until we reach perfection.

When z(x,y) changes sign in the area of integration, a perfect sampling scheme cannot be devised using simple Importance Sampling alone. The minimum variance using simple Importance Sampling is found to be

$$V_2 = \frac{4}{N}\left[\iint\limits_{S_1}|z(x,y)|f(x,y)\,dxdy\right]\left[\iint\limits_{S_2}|z(x,y)|f(x,y)\,dxdy\right] \qquad (14)$$

where z(x,y) is positive in S_1 and negative in S_2. This V_2 may be, but is not necessarily small.

It is still possible, in principle, to design a perfect sampling scheme for a general z(x,y) by using correlation in addition to Importance Sampling. Since the author does not know of any practical application of this idea to functions z(x,y) which change sign, there will be no more discussion on this point.

The name Importance Sampling was suggested by the possibility of sampling proportional to importance as shown by the theoretical zero variance estimates. In the simple case just considered, $|z(x,y)|f(x,y)$ measures the importance of the point (x,y) in the sense that it is proportional to the amount that this point contributes to $\bar{z}$, the quantity being calculated. It will turn out that this result is not general and that our use of the word, "importance", will usually carry a somewhat different connotation.

If $z(x,y) \geq 0$, the optimum Importance Sampling for $\bar{z}$ will also reduce the variance for the estimate of the higher moments, $\overline{z^n}$. But this is not necessarily true of just any $f^+(x,y)$ which reduces the variance of the estimate $\bar{z}$.

The central idea in Importance Sampling can be exploited in many different ways. Two possibilities will be mentioned. The following definitions will be needed in the discussion.

$$f(x) = \int f(x,y)dy,$$
     the p.d.f. of the random variable x averaged over y, the so-called marginal p.d.f.

$$g(y:x) = \frac{f(x,y)}{f(x)},$$
     the p.d.f. of y given that X = x, the so-called conditional p.d.f.

$$\bar{z}(:x) = \int z(x,y)g(y:x)dy,$$
     the expected value of $z(x,y)$ given that X = x.

$$\overline{\bar{z}(:x)} = \int \bar{z}(:x) f(x)dx = \bar{z},$$
     an obvious formula

$$\overline{z^2}(:x) = \int z^2(x,y)g(y:x)dy,$$
     the expected value of $z^2(x,y)$ given that X = x.

$$\overline{\overline{z^2}(:x)} = \overline{z^2},$$
     follows as before.

Importance Sampling in the x space only

$\bar{z}$ can also be written

$$\bar{z} = \iint z(x,y) \frac{f(x)}{f^+(x)} g(y:x) f^+(x)dxdy \qquad (15)$$

If the (x_i, y_i) are picked out of $f^+(x,y) = g(y:x)f^+(x)$, an estimate of $\bar{z}$ is

$$\hat{z}_{11} = \frac{1}{N} \sum_{i=1}^{N} z(x_i, y_i) \frac{f(x_i)}{f^+(x_i)} \qquad (16)$$

The variance of this estimate is

$$V_{11} = \frac{1}{N} \left\{ \iint \left[z(x,y) \frac{f(x)}{f^+(x)} \right]^2 f^+(x)g(y:x)dxdy - \bar{z}^2 \right\}$$

$$= \frac{1}{N} \left[\iint \frac{z^2(x,y) \, f^2(x)}{f^+(x)} \, g(y:x)dxdy - \bar{z}^2 \right] \qquad (17)$$

$$= \frac{1}{N} \left[\int \frac{\overline{z^2(:x)} \, f^2(x)}{f^+(x)} \, dx - \bar{z}^2 \right]$$

The minimizing $f^+(x)$ is given by

$$f^+(x) = \frac{f(x)\sqrt{\overline{z^2(:x)}}}{\int \sqrt{\overline{z^2(:x)}} \, f(x)dx} \qquad (18)$$

$$= \frac{f(x) \sqrt{\overline{z^2(:x)}}}{\sqrt{\overline{z^2(:x)}}}$$

If this f^+ is used, the variance becomes

$$V_{11} = \frac{1}{N} \left[\sqrt{\overline{\overline{z^2(:x)}}}^2 - \bar{z}^2 \right] \qquad (19)$$

The difference between this variance and that obtained by straightforward sampling is

$$V - V_{11} = \frac{1}{N} \overline{\left[\sqrt{\overline{z^2(:x)}} - \sqrt{\overline{z^2(:x)}} \right]^2} \qquad (20)$$

and the variance has been reduced.

Sampling only from the x space is significant because it is common in practice to break the problem into two or more parts or stages. If this is done we must define the term "interesting" regions in a more general fashion than we did previously. Thinking of X = x as a "cut" or region of the x space, equation (18) implies that we should sample such regions with a frequency proportional to $f(x)\sqrt{\overline{z^2}(:x)}$. In other words, optimum Importance Sampling means that the a priori probability $f(x)$ of getting into a region x should be modified by the factor $\sqrt{\overline{z^2}(:x)}$.

When Importance Sampling is done in the entire space this factor is $|z(x,y)|$. In this case the word "importance" is used in the natural sense--that is, those regions are called important that make large contributions to the answer being calculated. However the natural analogue of $|z(x,y)|$, $|\overline{z}(:x)|$, is not the correct factor for optimum Importance Sampling in the x space alone. In a rough way we can say that the correct factor $\sqrt{\overline{z^2}(:x)}$ is proportional to the error rather than importance (used in the ordinary sense).

In some problems, the difference between the two definitions of importance is not as great as we may have implied, for

$$\overline{z^2}(:x) = \sigma^2(:x) + \overline{z}^2(:x) \tag{21}$$

where $\sigma^2(:x) = \overline{z^2}(:x) - \overline{z}^2(:x)$ measures the variance left in the y space.

If this variance is small compared to $\overline{z}^2(:x)$, then

$$\sqrt{\overline{z^2}(:x)} \approx \overline{z}(:x) \tag{22}$$

In many situations we may not have even a rough idea of what $z^2(:x)$ is like, but may have a very good estimate of or approximation to $\overline{z}(:x)$. For this reason one often uses $\overline{z}(:x)$ rather than $\sqrt{\overline{z^2}(:x)}$. If this is done, then (for $\overline{z}(:x) > 0$)

$$f^+(x) = \frac{f(x)\ \overline{z}(:x)}{\overline{z}} \tag{23}$$

162

and the variance becomes

$$V_{12} = \frac{1}{N}\left\{ \overline{z}\left[\overline{\frac{\overline{z^2}(:x)}{\overline{z}(:x)}}\right] - \overline{z}^2 \right\} = \frac{1}{N}\,\overline{z}\left[\overline{\frac{\sigma^2(:x)}{\overline{z}(:x)}}\right] \quad (24)$$

While V_{12} is ordinarily much less than V it is easy to see that it can be large and in fact disasters are possible if care is not taken.

The problem of estimating $\overline{z^2}(:x)$ or $\overline{z}(:x)$ is crucial if Importance Sampling is to be done. It is not necessarily difficult. Previous Monte Carlo calculations, new ones perhaps, experiments, approximate calculations, or intuition can all be used to get the information. In any case the designer needs to know only the relative importance of different regions and not the absolute values. This may make the problem much easier. If one does not have the information it is usually worthwhile to go to some effort to get reasonable estimates of $\overline{z^2}(:x)$ or $\overline{z}(:x)$.

Importance Sampling with a parameter

A second variation of Importance Sampling worth mentioning is restriction of the $f^+(x,y)$ to a single family of p.d.f's. This may be desirable to do for either computing or theoretical convenience. If such a family is represented by $h(x,y,\alpha)$, then it is desired to determine α to minimize the variance. Since $\overline{z}$ is fixed this is equivalent to minimizing (see Equation 12):

$$\iint \left[\frac{z(x,y)f(x,y)}{h(x,y,\alpha)}\right]^2 h(x,y,\alpha)\,dxdy = \iint \frac{z^2(x,y)f^2(x,y)}{h(x,y,\alpha)}\,dxdy$$

$$(25)$$

$h(x,y,\alpha)$ is, of course, subject to the usual conditions for being a p.d.f. If the form of $h(x,y,\alpha)$ is such that these conditions are satisfied for all values of α, then the optimal α is determined by

$$\iint \frac{z^2(x,y)\,f^2(x,y)}{h^2(x,y,\alpha)}\,\frac{\partial h(x,y,\alpha)}{\partial \alpha}\,dxdy = 0 \quad (26)$$

One way to solve such an equation is to do a preliminary study by Monte Carlo. The function to be minimized is

163

$$I(\alpha) = \iint \frac{z^2(x,y)\ f^2(x,y)}{h(x,y,\alpha)}\ dxdy \qquad (27)$$

It is of course possible to evaluate (27) by Monte Carlo. It is not necessary, as might be supposed, to sample from $h(x,y,\alpha)$ when doing this evaluation because $I(\alpha)$ can be written

$$I(\alpha) = \iint \frac{z^2(x,y)\ f^2(x,y)}{h(x,y,\alpha)f^+(x,y)}\ f^+(x,y)dxdy \qquad (28)$$

so that an estimate of $I(\alpha)$ is

$$I(\alpha) = \frac{1}{N}\sum_{i=1}^{N} \frac{z^2(x_i,y_i)\ f^2(x_i,y_i)}{h(x_i,y_i,\alpha)f^+(x_i,y_i)} \qquad (29)$$

where the (x_i,y_i) are picked out of $f^+(x,y)$. The chief application of formula (29) is when $f^+(x,y) = h(x,y,\alpha_1)$ and we wish to evaluate $I(\alpha)$ for a series of α's, say $\alpha_1, \alpha_2, \alpha_3$.

In principle, if we chose $\alpha_2 < \alpha_1$ and $\alpha_3 > \alpha_1$ we could observe $I(\alpha_j)$ for these three values. We might then be able to see how α should be changed in order to decrease the sampling variance. We might even program this adjustment of α so that it is done automatically by the computing machine. The procedure can be dangerous, however, (see Marshall's paper) and as far as I know has never been done in this automatic fashion. The idea, however, is so intriguing that it seems worth mentioning.

It should also be clear that if we can evaluate any derivatives of $h(x,y,\alpha)$ then we could evaluate $\frac{\partial I}{\partial \alpha}$ and even maybe $\frac{\partial^2 I}{\partial \alpha^2}$ directly by Monte Carlo and use these quantities to estimate what α should be used in a subsequent calculation.

Examples

In the examples which follow here and later we will be discussing situations which may not lend themselves to being expressed in a simple fashion as integrals. More typically one would tend to describe these situations in terms of integral equations. Despite the fact that the theory of Monte Carlo applied to integral equations is in some sense richer than the one we are discussing, we draw from both for examples because most realistic examples come from the former field and because the ideas carry over at least qualitatively.

One of the major problems on which Monte Carlo can be used is to calculate the probability that nuclear particles will penetrate shields. In such a problem, the particle starts at one side of the shield and has collisions of different types with the material inside the shield, finally being either reflected backwards, absorbed in the shield, or transmitted. The calculation can be done by Monte Carlo by simulating the particle histories with the aid of random numbers. The simulation should not be faithful. For example the following types of random events increase the probability of penetration and should be emphasized at the expense of equally probable, but less "important," ones:

a. collisions resulting in a forward direction
    of motion

b. in most problems collisions which result in
    small energy losses

c. long forward jumps and short backward jumps
    (the exponential transformation discussed
    in the paper by Beach and Theus does this)

d. survival vs. absorption (if carried to the
    limit, this can be looked on as an applica-
    tion of Use of Expected Values).

The calculator is, of course, confronted with the problem of how far to go quantitatively in biasing the sampling. In deciding this he must fall back on trying to estimate the formulae we have just derived.

Another important application of Monte Carlo is in the design or analysis of reactors. Here again we are studying the various ways in which nuclear particles—particularly neutrons—behave in matter. It is found that those which wander away from the center of the re-actor will not contribute much of interest to the process.

On the contrary, those neutrons which wander back toward the fissionable material are the ones which contribute most to the answer. The sampling must then be designed to sample more frequently among the second type of neutrons and less frequently among the first type of neutrons.

Applications can also be made to Operations Research problems. In one typical problem of this type we might try to calculate the vulnerability of a piece of equipment or of an airfield to some type of offensive weapon. In such cases, one often Monte Carlos, for example, the error of the missile which is doing the destruction. The distribution of errors is determined by a parameter called the CEP. Since the thing we are interested in here is destruction, if we Monte Carlo from a distribution defined from a smaller CEP than that which obtains in the real world we will find that more of the interesting processes (hits) happen in the simulated experiment than would happen naturally. The less interesting processes (misses) are then discriminated against. This is, of course, the right kind of Importance Sampling, and is one way to do Importance Sampling with a parameter--the parameter in this case being the sampling CEP.

For another example in the same field one might consider queuing problems. In these problems one is often interested in the mean and variance of the waiting time. One then wishes to bias the sampling to emphasize long waits. This could be done by sampling from f^+'s which simulate increased traffic, increased servicing time, or increased servicing requirements.

It is worth noting that any set of samples obtained with the use of Importance Sampling is less effective in estimating certain quantities than a set that has been obtained in a straightforward fashion. For instance in the shielding problem, a sampling design which leads to an accurate estimate of the probability of penetration will be very poor for estimating the probability of reflection; in the reactor problem the suggested sampling would not be good at estimating leakage; in the vulnerability problem we will lose information about light damage and the location of misses; and finally in the queuing problem we will not get a good estimate of the idle time of the servicing facilities.

It is in fact usually (but not always) true that to design an efficient Monte Carlo calculation one must focus attention on those things one is really interested in and ignore other aspects of the problem. It may even be better to do more than one calculation than to compromise the goals of any particular design. This can be a serious disadvantage if the computation is lengthy, as the decision about what aspects to concentrate on must be made early and therefore may easily be made wrongly.

2. Russian Roulette and Splitting

This technique is essentially a sequential sampling scheme which can be used when the sampling is done in stages; in our case when first an x value is picked and then a y. For some regions of x the error is small enough or the expense of picking y and evaluating $z(x,y)$ large enough that it isn't efficient to pick a y and evaluate a $z(x,y)$ for every such x that has been sampled, but only for a portion of them. In other regions of the x space, the error in the y space is large enough or the additional cost small enough that it pays to sample many values of y for each x value that has been picked. It may be that every x value can be classified as belonging to one region or the other.

To state the problem explicitly, we wish to determine the following:

a. Regions R_1 and R_2 which are mutually exclusive and exhaust the x space. In R_1 we are going to sample a y and evaluate $z(x,y)$ for only a portion of the x's sampled. In R_2 we are going to sample one or more y values for each x value picked.

b. The sampling in R_1 is called Russian Roulette and is done as follows. Every time a chosen x_i is in R_1 a function $q(x_i)$ is evaluated and a supplementary game of chance played. With probability $q(x_i)$ this supplementary game is won and a y_i picked and $z(x_i,y_i)$ evaluated; with probability $1 - q(x_i)$ the game is lost and no y_i is picked.

Corresponding to the two possible outcomes
of the game, the ith sample estimate becomes

$$z_{2i} = \begin{cases} \dfrac{z(x_i,y_i)}{q(x_i)} & \text{for a win} \qquad (30) \\ \\ 0 & \text{for a loss.} \end{cases}$$

It is easy to see that the expected value of z_{2i}
for fixed x_i is $\bar{z}(:x_i)$.

The variance of z_{2i} for fixed x_i is

$$\sigma_2^{\,2}(:x_i) = \frac{\overline{z^2}(:x_i)}{q(x_i)} - \bar{z}^2(:x_i) \qquad (31)$$

c. The sampling in R_2 is called Splitting. When
an x_i is picked from R_2, a positive integral-
valued function $n(x_i)$ is evaluated which gives
the number of y samples to be picked. The ith
sample estimate then becomes the arithmetical
average of the $n(x_i)$ values of $z(x_i,y_j)$, $j = 1$,
$2, \ldots, n(x_i)$:

$$z_{2i} = \frac{1}{n(x_i)} \sum_{j=1}^{n(x_i)} z(x_i,y_j) \qquad (32)$$

Again the expected value of z_{2i} is $\bar{z}(:x_i)$.

The variance in this case is

$$\sigma_2^{\,2}(:x_i) = \frac{\sigma^2(:x_i)}{n(x_i)} \qquad (33)$$

d. R_1, R_2, $q(x)$ and $n(x)$ are chosen to minimize the
total cost of the problem for a fixed level of
error. This is equivalent to minimizing the
product of the average cost of a sample and the

168

variance. This can be seen as follows.
If the average cost is C then the total
cost is NC. If the fixed error is denoted by ϵ then

$$N = \frac{V_2}{\epsilon^2} \tag{34}$$

and the total cost becomes

$$NC = \frac{CV_2}{\epsilon^2} \tag{35}$$

Since ϵ is constant the total cost is minimized when CV_2 is minimized.

If ordinary sampling were used the variance can be
written in the form

$$V = \overline{\left[\, \overline{z}(:x) - \overline{z}\, \right]^2} + \overline{\sigma^2(:x)} \tag{36}$$

Only the last term is affected by the Russian Roulette
and Splitting with $\sigma^2(:x)$ replaced by $\sigma_2^{\,2}(:x)$ as defined in
equations (31) and (33). V_2 then becomes

$$V_2 = A + \int_{R_1} \frac{\overline{z^2}(:x)}{q(x)}\, f(x)\,dx + \int_{R_2} \frac{\sigma^2(:x)}{n(x)}\, f(x)\,dx \tag{37}$$

where

$$A = \int_{R_2} \overline{z}^2(:x)f(x)\,dx - \overline{z}^2$$

The expected cost of a sample is given by

$$C = C_0 + \int_{R_1} C_1(x)q(x)f(x)\,dx + \int_{R_2} C_1(x)n(x)f(x)\,dx \tag{38}$$

169

where C_O is the expected cost of picking an x (by definition independent of y) and $C_1(x)$ is the average additional cost of picking y and evaluating $z(x,y)$ for that x.

The R_1, R_2, $q(x)$ and $n(x)$ which minimize CV_2 are determined[+] by the set of simultaneous conditions:

$$q(x) = \frac{\lambda \sqrt{\overline{z^2}(:x)}}{\sqrt{C_1(x)}} \leq 1 \qquad \text{for x in } R_1$$

(39)

$$n(x) = \frac{\lambda \, \sigma(:x)}{\sqrt{C_1(x)}} \qquad \text{for x in } R_2$$

R_1 and R_2 mutually exclusive and exhaustive

where $\lambda = \sqrt{C/V_2}$.

If one substitutes equations (39) into (37) and (38), one finds that

$$\lambda = \sqrt{\frac{C_O}{A}}$$

(40)

At first sight finding the R_1, R_2, $q(x)$, and $n(x)$ which satisfy conditions (39) appears difficult. There is however an iterative procedure which will converge rapidly:

1. Take A as being equal to $\int_{R_1+R_2} \overline{z}^2(:x)f(x)dx - \overline{z}^2$

rather than $\int_{R_2} \overline{z}^2(:x)f(x)dx - \overline{z}^2$ and call this

approximation A'. A' is too large by an amount

$\int_{R_1} \overline{z}^2(:x)f(x)dx$, but this is usually unimportant.

[+] Calculus of Variations again. Also, the requirement that $n(x)$ be integral has been temporarily ignored.

One reason is because R_1 is defined as the region where $\overline{z^2}(:x)$ is small and wherever $\overline{z^2}(:x)$ is small, $\overline{z}^2(:x)$ is also small.

2. An approximate λ can now be estimated by using A' for A in equation (40) (or by any other reasonable method).

3. Equations (39) can now be used to define the functions $q(x)$ and $n(x)$ for the entire x space and not just the appropriate regions. Because

$$\overline{z^2}(:x) \geq \sigma^2(:x) \tag{41}$$

the everywhere defined $q(x)$ is greater than $n(x)$. If therefore we define approximate regions R_1 and R_2 by the conditions

$$x \text{ in } R_1 \text{ if } q(x) \leq 1 \tag{42}$$

$$x \text{ in } R_2 \text{ if } n(x) \geq 1$$

R_1 and R_2 will be mutually exclusive. It can be shown that it is best to put anything left over into R_2.

4. A new A' approximation to A can now be computed by using the approximate R_2 as the region of integration in the definition of A and a new λ estimated.

5. Steps 3-4 are repeated until reasonable convergence is obtained.

We can estimate (but only roughly) the improvement over straightforward sampling that is gained when optimum Russian Roulette and Splitting is used. In most problems, $C_1(x)$ is not a sensitive function of x and can be taken equal to an average C_1'. Similarly (as already mentioned) there is very little error introduced if A is taken equal to $\overline{\left[\overline{z}(:x) - \overline{z}\right]^2}$ (which we will represent by A'). Lastly we make the dubious approximation that in R_1

$$\overline{z^2}(:x) = \sigma^2(:x) \tag{43}$$

We can now write that

171

$$V_2 \approx A' + \overline{\sigma(:x)} \sqrt{\frac{C_1' \, A'}{C_o}} \tag{44}$$

$$C \approx C_o + \overline{\sigma(:x)} \; \frac{C_o C_1'}{A'} \tag{45}$$

$$CV_2 \approx C_o A' + 2\overline{\sigma(:x)} \sqrt{C_o C_1' \, A'} + C_1' \overline{\sigma(:x)}^2 \tag{46}$$

When ordinary sampling is used the product of the cost and the variance is

$$CV \approx (C_o + C_1') \left[A' + \overline{\sigma^2(:x)} \right] \tag{47}$$

$$= C_o A' + C_o \overline{\sigma^2(:x)} + C_1' \, A' + C_1' \overline{\sigma^2(:x)}$$

Subtracting equation (46) from equation (47) and collecting terms

$$CV - CV_2 = (C_o + C_1') \; \overline{\left[\sigma(:x) - \overline{\sigma(:x)} \right]^2} + \left[\sqrt{C_1' A'} - \overline{\sigma(:x)}\sqrt{C_o} \right]^2 \tag{48}$$

The first term on the right side of equation (48) can be easily interpreted. $(C_o + C_1')$ is the average cost of a sample when doing straightforward sampling so the improvement is measured by comparing $\overline{\left[\sigma(:x) - \overline{\sigma(:x)} \right]^2}$ with V (i.e. the variance of $\sigma(:x)$ as compared with the variance of $z(x,y)$). There is an additional improvement given by the second term which is related to the fact that even if $\sigma(:x)$ didn't vary at all it might still pay to sample many y values for every x picked.

It should be clear to the reader that most of the examples mentioned in Importance Sampling could also be used to illustrate the use of Russian Roulette and Splitting. It is instructive to contrast the two techniques. In Importance Sampling we bias the sampling in favor of "interesting" regions and try to avoid "uninteresting" regions. Sometimes, though, $f(x)$ is not given explicitly, but a complicated process for getting x values is given instead. In these circumstances we may have very good estimates of the relative "importance" of different regions and still not be able to do this biasing. We can then use Russian Roulette and Splitting which, in effect, does the same thing but ad hoc; that is, we wait to see what region is entered and then decide what the size of the sample should be.

Two examples special to the Russian Roulette and Splitting technique will be given.

Application to Particle Diffusion

A special case of some interest involving three random variables (X, W, M) arises in particle diffusion problems. X is a generalized position variable which represents the position and momentum of the particle. W is a pseudo weight that is assigned to the particle, and which changes as the particle jumps from point to point. M is the final weight of the particle divided by the current weight. It is convenient to think of it the other way, as a factor which multiplies the current weight when the random walk is terminated. The function whose expected value is desired is the final weight of the particle; so

$$z(x,w,m) = wm \qquad\qquad (49)$$

where if ordinary sampling were being done the m would be independent of w. However if the w happened to be very small one would be willing to sample m rather inaccurately if it saved some cost; if it were large one would want to sample m quite accurately even if it were expensive. This is thus a natural problem on which to use Russian Roulette and Splitting.

The regions R_1 and R_2 will be defined in the (x,w) space and the decisions of Russian Roulette or Splitting concern the number of m values that are to be picked for an (x,w) value.

In discussing particles it is convenient to change the language slightly. Instead of speaking of picking n independent values of m for each (x,w) in region R_2, the particle is said to split into n independent particles each of weight w/n. Similarly in region R_1 if the particle loses the Russian Roulette it is said to have died (or disappeared); if it wins it is assigned a new weight, $w/q(x,w)$ and its random walk continued.

In the case of most interest the p.d.f. for (X, W, M) (after the Russian Roulette and Splitting has been done)

173

has the special form, $g(m:x)f(x,w)$; that is the conditional p.d.f. of m is not dependent on w. (The plausibility of the assumption is discussed below.) With this assumption,

$$\overline{z^2}(:x,w) = w^2\overline{m^2}(:x) \tag{50}$$

$$\sigma^2(:x,w) = w^2\left[\overline{m^2}(:x) - \overline{m}^2(:x)\right] \tag{51}$$

Since the cost of picking an m value is independent of w, the optimum choice of $q(x,w)$ and $n(x,w)$ is given by

$$q(x,w) = \lambda\, w\, \sqrt{\frac{\overline{m^2}(:x)}{C_1(x)}}$$

$$n(x,w) = \lambda\, w\, \sqrt{\frac{\overline{m^2}(:x) - \overline{m}^2(:x)}{C_1(x)}} \tag{52}$$

and regions R_1 and R_2 are determined as before by the appropriate inequalities. If the particle is in R_1 and happens to survive the Russian Roulette it is assigned a new weight

$$w' = \frac{w}{q(x,w)} = \frac{1}{\lambda}\sqrt{\frac{C_1(x)}{\overline{m^2}(:x)}} \tag{53}$$

If the particle is in R_2 then each of the n independent particles is given a weight.

$$w' = \frac{w}{n(x,w)}$$

$$= \frac{1}{\lambda}\sqrt{\frac{C_1(x)}{\overline{m^2}(:x) - \overline{m}^2(:x)}} \tag{54}$$

In both cases, the final weight of the particle is independent of the original weight and is a function of x only. (This seems to be, in general, one of the criteria for a good sampling scheme for particle diffusion problems.) It is because the weight of the particle after collision is independent of the weight before collision that m can be taken to be independent of w.

Truncating Sample Series

Sometimes in doing a Monte Carlo problem instead of getting a single number for the estimate from a single sample, one obtains an infinite series; more precisely each sample generates a process for calculating an infinite series term by term, and it is the sums of these series which are to be averaged in obtaining the final estimate. This occurs most often when the sampling technique in the next section, Use of Expected Values, is used.

The computer is then faced with the problem of terminating each of the sample series. This can be done by summing each series to a fixed number of terms or it can be done by summing until a term gets smaller than some previously assigned amount. Both of these methods are inefficient as one is then faced with either calculating a number of very small terms or truncating too soon and introducing an unknown bias into the estimate.

A much more effective method of terminating such sample series is made possible by the use of Russian Roulette. One can simply play the supplementary game of chance as soon as the terms in the series begin to get small. If a term fails to survive the supplementary game the series is terminated right then and there; if it survives, the weights of all subsequent terms are multiplied by the proper factor and the term by term summation continued until a new term becomes small. In this way the series can be terminated in a completely unbiased fashion and yet very little effort is spent computing small and insignificant numbers.

3.   Use of Expected Values

Sometimes it is a simple matter to evaluate $\bar{z}(:x)$.   In this case the problem of evaluating

$$\bar{z} = \iint z(x,y)f(x,y) \ dxdy \qquad (55)$$

can profitably be replaced by the problem of evaluating

$$\bar{z} = \int \bar{z}(:x)f(x) \ dx \qquad (56)$$

In many cases this simple integral cannot be evaluated either because x is multi-dimensional or because f(x) is not actually known and the sampling of x has to be done in some complicated manner. In either case there is no point in using Monte Carlo to do that part of the problem which can

175

be done analytically. Only the x's should be sampled--the sampling of the y space is bypassed by using the estimate

$$\hat{z}_3 = \frac{1}{N} \sum_{i=1}^{N} \bar{z}(:x_i) \tag{57}$$

The variance is easily calculated to be

$$V_3 = \frac{1}{N} \int \left[\bar{z}(:x) - \bar{z} \right]^2 f(x)dx \tag{58}$$

$$= \frac{1}{N} \overline{\left[\bar{z}(:x) - \bar{z} \right]^2}$$

This is less than the original variance by

$$V - V_3 = \frac{1}{N} \int \sigma^2(:x)f(x)dx \tag{59}$$

$$= \frac{1}{N} \overline{\sigma^2(:x)}$$

As is intuitively clear, the variance associated with the y space has been eliminated.

The reader should not conclude from the trivial nature of the explanation that the idea is not valuable. In many cases most of the variance of a problem can be eliminated by using only a little bit of analysis. The author knows of a surprisingly large number of Monte Carlo problems where people have either not done, or failed to use, the results of a very significant but trivial piece of analysis. As a result they used sampling for all of the probabilistic parts of the problem, and had to use much larger samples than were really necessary.

Examples

Expected values can be used in all the problems mentioned under Importance Sampling. In the shielding problem, for example, instead of counting the particles which succeed in piercing the shield, we can calculate the probability after each collision that the particle would go through the shield. An unbiased estimate of the penetration is obtained by summing these probabilities. This is one way, in fact, in which the infinite series of estimates mentioned in the Russian Roulette section arises.

Another application of the same idea is in the calculation of multiple scattering effects in nuclear cross section measurements. In this calculation one simulates a scattering experiment in which the main interest is in the number of particles which enter a detector. Now the probability of a particle's entering the detector may be very small, say of the order of 10^{-4} or 10^{-6}, so that if one wished to sample in a straightforward fashion, one would practically never get any counts. It is, however, very simple to calculate the probability that the particle will enter the detector from any point in the system. If these probabilities are recorded, rather than the number of particles counted, one usually finds that the per cent variance is enormously reduced, 10^3 being typical. The factor is larger in this case than in the previous (shielding) example because in this problem many samples tend to get into a region where the particle has a relatively high (though absolutely low) probability of getting into the detector; in the previous problem this is not true unless Importance Sampling or Russian Roulette and Splitting is also used.

This idea can be applied to more general problems than particle diffusion. For example, in vulnerability type studies, it is often true that the sampling is done in many stages and in the final stage there is given a probability p of achieving or not achieving a kill. It should be obvious to the reader at this point that it would be wrong to sample from this binomial distribution, but rather, the p's themselves should be recorded and their average used for the estimate.

A similar situation occurs in the particle diffusion problems mentioned previously. Usually there is a non zero probability that particles will be absorbed after they have had a collision. This binomial process could be sampled, but it is generally more accurate not to sample, but simply to weight the particle with the probability of survival, multiplying all the probabilities together after it has had all its collisions. This increases the average length (number of collisions) of a history and therefore its cost, but this effect is usually dwarfed by the decrease in variance.

Another way to use expected values is to integrate a sample over the initial conditions. For example, in particle diffusion problems, it is not much work to translate, rotate, or reflect histories (thus getting new ones) and then average these translated, rotated, or reflected histories over their a priori probabilities.

In our integral example this would correspond to picking a function $y_i(x)$ out of $g(y:x)$ for the ith sample and then never picking x at all but using

$$z_{3i} = \int \Big[z \; x, y_i(x) \Big] \; f(x)dx \tag{60}$$

as the estimate. There is a surprisingly large number of problems in which the above process can be carried through. If the pick on y is made by the standard method of solving the equation

$$\int_{-\infty}^{y_i(x)} g(y:x)dy = R_i \tag{61}$$

the above estimate corresponds to using $\bar{z}(:R_i)$. This kind of integration can be used for more than just the first stage. For instance, in plane geometry particle diffusion problems, it is possible to do the energy and angular part of the history by random sampling and then for this fixed energy-angular history, the spatial part can be done by an exact integration.

4. Correlation and Regression

There are many ways and many reasons for sampling two or more problems in a correlated fashion. We will discuss only a few of them here. As always we consider the evaluation of

$$\bar{z} = \iint z(x,y) f(x,y) dxdy \tag{62}$$

Let us assume that we know an integral

$$\bar{v} = \iint v(r,s) g(r,s) drds \tag{63}$$

where the function $v(r,s)$ and the p.d.f. $g(r,s)$ are in some unspecified way related to $z(x,y)$ and $f(x,y)$. (In most applications they will be approximations which are easy to integrate.) Assume also that sampling on (x,y) is such that it is easy or very cheap to do sampling on (r,s) also, and that in some or all parts of the calculation the same random numbers used in obtaining a value of (x,y) are also used in obtaining a value of (r,s), so that the two samples are not independent.

178

Instead of calculating the average value of $z(x,y)$ one can calculate the average value of

$$u(x,y,r,s) = z(x,y) - \alpha \left[v(r,s) - \bar{v} \right]. \qquad (64)$$

It will be noticed that the expected value of $u(x,y,r,s)$ is equal to the expected value of $z(x,y)$ since the extra term $\alpha \left[v(r,s) - \bar{v} \right]$ has zero expected value. The variance of $u(x,y,r,s)$, however, is quite different from the variance of $z(x,y)$.

$$V_4 = \frac{1}{N} \overline{\left[u(x,y,r,s) - \bar{u} \right]^2} \qquad (65)$$

$$= \frac{1}{N} \overline{\left\{ \left[z(x,y) - \bar{z} \right] - \alpha \left[v(r,s) - \bar{v} \right] \right\}^2}$$

$$= \frac{1}{N} \left\{ \overline{\left[z(x,y) - \bar{z} \right]^2} - 2\alpha \overline{\left[z(x,y) - \bar{z} \right] \left[v(r,s) - \bar{v} \right]} + \right.$$

$$\left. \alpha^2 \overline{\left[v(r,s) - \bar{v} \right]^2} \right\}$$

$$= \frac{1}{N} \left[\sigma_1^2 - 2\alpha\rho\sigma_1\sigma_2 + \alpha^2\sigma_2^2 \right]$$

where σ_1^2, $\rho\,\sigma_1\sigma_2$, and σ_2^2 have the obvious definitions. ρ is called the correlation coefficient and, in some sense, measures the stochastic similarity of the two processes.

In many practical cases α is chosen in advance, usually to be one. If then, in some sense, the (r,s) problem is similar to the (x,y) problem, then σ_1 may be close to σ_2 amd ρ close to 1. Under these circumstances the variance V_4 can be much less than σ_1^2. How much less depends on how "close" the (r,s) problem is to the (x,y) problem.

In some cases, we can try to improve the situation by trying to choose that value of α which minimizes the variance of $u(x,y,r,s)$. Differentiating equation (65), one finds that this best value of α is

$$\alpha = \rho \frac{\sigma_1}{\sigma_2} \qquad (66)$$

179

If this value of α is used, V_4 becomes

$$V_4 = \frac{1}{N} \ \sigma_1^2 (1 - \rho^2) \qquad\qquad (67)$$

It is clear from the above expression that the more highly the problems are correlated, the smaller one can make the variance of the difference. Of course, one does not ordinarily know $\rho \sigma_1 / \sigma_2$, so it must be estimated. If the estimate is made directly from the sample being analyzed it will then turn out that equation (64) may not give an unbiased estimate of the average value of $z(x,y)$, since the expected value of $\alpha \left[v(r,s) - \bar{v} \right]$ is not necessarily zero if α is a function of (r,s).

The bias can be avoided by the following technique:

The sample can be divided into two parts and the best estimate of $\rho \sigma_1 / \sigma_2$ determined for each part separately. Each of these estimated values of α can be used with the other half of the sample to form two estimates of $\bar{z}$. Under these circumstances the α's are independent of the terms they multiply. The two estimates are then averaged, to obtain a single unbiased estimate.

This causes a slight decrease in efficiency because two values of α are estimated and only one half of the sample is used for each estimate. The α's will therefore be a little more inaccurate than is necessary. It is not, however, usually important to estimate α very accurately and in some cases it is important to have unbiased answers, so it may be worthwhile to go to this scheme.

Elimination of the Variance Associated with $\bar{z}(:x)$

A special application of the above technique occurs when one can explicitly and easily evaluate integrals of the form

$$\bar{v} = \int v(x) f(x) dx \qquad\qquad (68)$$

In this case, one replaces $v(r,s)$ by $v(x)$ and $g(r,s)$ by $f(x)$. Equation (65) then becomes

$$V_{41} = \frac{1}{N} \ \overline{\left[z(x,y) - \bar{z} \right]^2} - 2 \overline{\left[z(x,y) - \bar{z} \right] \left[v(x) - \bar{v} \right]} \ +$$

$$\overline{\left[v(x) - \bar{v} \right]^2} \qquad\qquad (69)$$

180

It is easily shown that V_{41} is minimized when

$$v(x) = \overline{z}(:x) \qquad (70)$$

If this $v(x)$ is used, then the variance becomes

$$V_{41} = \frac{1}{N} \, \overline{\sigma^2(:x)} \qquad (71)$$

and the variance is reduced by

$$V - V_{41} = \frac{1}{N} \, \overline{\left[\overline{z}(:x) - \overline{z} \right]^2} \qquad (72)$$

As will be shown in the next section on Systematic Sampling, this same reduction can be achieved in what might seem to be a much simpler fashion and by a method that does not require one to know $\overline{z}(:x)$. However, it turns out that there are complicated situations where Systematic Sampling cannot be used, so it may be convenient to have this alternative technique available.

It is worth pointing out that one doesn't need to know $\overline{z}(:x)$ exactly. Any rough approximation $v(x)$ will do so long as one knows how to compute $\overline{v}$ reasonably accurately.

Three examples illustrating the three usual reasons for doing correlations follow:

Parametric Studies

It is sometimes necessary to calculate a series of expected values where each member of the series involves a slightly different p.d.f. In this case one wishes to calculate a series of expected values of the form

$$\overline{z}_n = \iint z(x,y) f_n(x,y) \, dx \, dy \qquad n = 1, 2, \ldots, N$$

$$(73)$$

A simple way to do this is to pick the (x,y) once and for all out of an approximate p.d.f., $f^+(x,y)$, and then estimate the z_n by weighting with $f_n(x,y)/f^+(x,y)$. In problems where the picking is costly, but calculating the weighting factor is cheap, this process reduces the work roughly by a factor of N.

Comparing Different Bombing Strategies[+]

If a strategic or tactical bombing campaign is studied by Monte Carlo, it is customary to introduce random events of the following types:

1. Number of aircraft that abort

2. Number of aircraft shot down by area defense on the way in to the target

3. Number of aircraft that stray through navigational errors

4. Number of aircraft shot down by local defense at the target

5. Weather conditions over target (affects reconnaissance and CEP)

6. Place where bombs land

7. Damage done

8. Number of aircraft shot down by area defense on the way out of target area

9. Number of aircraft that don't get back for a miscellany of minor reasons.

Because some of the probabilities involved depend on the number of aircraft surviving to a particular stage of the strike, the above problem is non-linear. This does not prevent one from using any of the techniques suggested.

If the computer wishes to compare different bombing strategies it is often effective to use correlation to cut down the sample size required to get significant information. If the correlation is done by using the same random numbers the computer cannot use a single list of random numbers in sequence in the two problems, for they would soon get out of step. He can either throw away the excess random numbers or, what is sometimes better, save them for use on later strikes. For example, if a larger number of targets were attacked on the first strike of one of the strategies, the extra random numbers that were used to determine the weather on these excess targets can be saved. If in a later strike an excess number of targets is attacked under the other strategy, the previously saved random numbers can then be used on these targets. Correlation can thus be achieved by using the same random numbers

---

[+] This example is given in some detail because there seems to be a somewhat general misunderstanding in the operations analysis field of the applicability of the techniques in this paper.

182

whenever the two strategies give rise to the same type of contingencies--even if they are on different strikes with different planes and targets.

Because the point is sometimes misunderstood, I would like to emphasize that when we say we are correlating the results of the same type of contingencies, the contingencies don't have to have the same detailed character. If for example in Strategy A, n_1 aircraft come up to the area defenses and in Strategy B, n_2 aircraft are used, the problems can still be correlated by using the same uniform random numbers in computing the number that survive. This is true as long as the picking is so arranged that the degree of success is a monotonic function of the uniform random numbers, so that fluctuations in the values of the uniform random numbers affect the two situations in the same qualitative way.

If the different strategies are such that a definite type of event is all-important to the comparison, then correlation by weighting may be better than by using the same random numbers. For example, if the effect of different types of defensive armament is being studied, the same kill probabilities could be used for the enemy fighters in the sampling, and weighting factors carried along to account for the differences being studied. The correlation may be higher if this is done, because exactly the same number of bombers is shot down each time, so all of the subsequent history is the same. If the correlating were done by using the same random numbers, different numbers of aircraft would be shot down and the actual progress of the two strategic campaigns might be quite different. It would still be possible to obtain correlation by using the same random numbers for the same contingencies, but it is unlikely that the correlation would be as high. Weighting will, of course not work well if by its use one is forced to use an f^+ which itself introduces a lot of variance because it is not good Importance Sampling for all the cases being considered (see next example).

Another case where weighting might be preferable to using the same random numbers would be when two different reconnaissance devices were being compared. The possible weather situations can then be classified according to the following criteria:

1. Both devices work
2. One works and the other does not
3. Neither works

Only situation 2 makes a difference between the two
devices so that in the sampling only it should be allowed
to occur. If 1 and 3 occur, the sample would give zero for
the estimate, so they need not be calculated; only the fraction r of time they occur is needed. Account of this is
automatically taken by the weighting factors. If instead
of weighting factors the same random numbers were used to
do the correlating then (1-r) of the time the sample would be
calculating zero and be wasted. If instead of being an all
or nothing situation the devices have different probabilities of working as the weather changes, then the appropriate modification must be made in the sampling. This last
is as much an example of Importance Sampling as of Correlation.

Polarization (comparing an exact and approximate theory)

In tracing γ rays through a medium it simplifies the
problem greatly to assume that the γ rays are unpolarized.
This assumption can be checked by doing two correlated
problems, one using the exact laws and the other the approximate ones that are obtained when it is assumed that
the particles are unpolarized. If weighting factors are used
to do the correlating they would fluctuate wildly because the
differential scattering laws are quite different in the two
cases. The actual effect of polarization turns out to be
quite small in most problems of interest. This is shown
very effectively if the correlating is done by using the
same random numbers. It then turns out, in most situations,
that every time the γ ray scatters, quite different azimuthal angles are picked in the two problems but the net
effect is small and is not affected very sharply.

5. Systematic Sampling

A common method of picking a sample point (x,y) out of
a population described by the p.d.f. f(x,y) is to solve the
equations[+]

$$\int_{-\infty}^{x_i} f(x)dx = R_1 \qquad\qquad (74)$$

$$\int_{-\infty}^{y_i} f(y:x_i)dy = R_2 \qquad\qquad (75)$$

[+]See Butler's paper.

184

where R_1 and R_2 are independent random numbers uniformly distributed between zero and one. The expected value of any function of (x_i, y_i) will not be changed appreciably if instead of using N independent R_1's to get the samples, the N numbers $(i - 1/2)/N$, $i = 1, 2, \ldots, N$ are used.[+]

If this is done, the estimate is

$$\hat{z}_5 = \frac{1}{N} \sum_{i=1}^{N} z(x_i, y_i) \tag{76}$$

where the x_i are deterministic. The expected value of $\hat{z}_5$ is given by

$$\overline{\hat{z}}_5 = \frac{1}{N} \sum_{i=1}^{N} \overline{z}(:x_i) \tag{77}$$

The $\overline{z}(:x_i)$ are not averaged because the x_i are systematically determined. However, from equation (74) and the use of $(i - 1/2)/N$ instead of R_1,

$$\frac{1}{N} = \int_{x_i}^{x_{i+1}} f(x)\, dx \tag{78}$$
$$\approx f(x_i)\, \Delta x_i$$

[+]The purpose of using $(i - 1/2)/N$ is to pick systematically the midpoints of the N intervals defined by

$$\int_{x_i}^{x_{i+1}} f(x)\, dx = \frac{1}{N}$$

Always picking the midpoint may introduce biases. These are eliminated if Systematic Sampling and random sampling are conbined by using $(i - R_1)/N$ instead of $(i - 1/2)/N$. A different R_1 is used with every i.

Therefore

$$\tilde{\hat{z}}_5 \approx \sum_{i=1}^{N} \bar{z}(:x_i) f(x_i) \Delta x_i \tag{79}$$

$$\approx \int \bar{z}(:x) f(x) dx$$

$$= \bar{z}$$

The variance is easily calculated.

$$V_5 = \overline{(\hat{z}_5 - \tilde{\hat{z}}_5)^2} \tag{80}$$

$$= \overline{\left\{ \frac{1}{N} \sum_{i=1}^{N} \left[z(x_i, y_i) - \bar{z}(:x_i) \right] \right\}^2}$$

$$= \frac{1}{N^2} \sum_{i=1}^{N} \overline{\left[z(x_i, y_i) - \bar{z}(:x_i)\cdot \right]^2}$$

$$= \frac{1}{N^2} \sum_{i=1}^{N} \sigma^2(:x_i)$$

$$\approx \frac{1}{N} \sum_{i=1}^{N} \sigma^2(:x_i) f(x_i) \Delta x_i$$

$$\approx \frac{1}{N} \overline{\sigma^2(:x)}$$

It follows that (see equation (36))

$$V - V_5 = \frac{1}{N} \overline{\left[\bar{z}(:x) - \bar{z} \right]^2} \tag{81}$$

The variance due to the variation of $\bar{z}(:x)$ has been eliminated.

186

If it was convenient, in addition to using the numbers $(i - 1/2)/N$ instead of R_1 in equation (74), we could randomly sort a second set of these numbers and use this second set in place of R_2 in equation (75), thereby doing Systematic Sampling in both the x and y spaces. If this is done, the variance is still further reduced and the improvement due to the use of Systematic Sampling becomes

$$V - V_5 = \frac{1}{N} \left\{ \overline{\left[\bar{z}(:x) - \bar{z} \right]^2} + \overline{\left[\bar{z}(:i) - \bar{z} \right]^2} \right\} \quad (82)$$

where $\bar{z}(:i)$ is defined by

$$\int_{-\infty}^{y_i(x)} g(y:x)\,dy = \frac{i - \frac{1}{2}}{N} \quad (83)$$

$$\bar{z}(:i) = \int_{-\infty}^{\infty} z\left[x, y_i(x) \right] f(x)\,dx$$

$\bar{z}(:i)$ is a sort of analogue in the y space to $\bar{z}(:x)$. Equation (82) indicates that the variance V associated with the ordinary Monte Carlo calculation of an n-dimensional integral must be larger than the sum of n terms of the type

$\overline{\left[\bar{z}(:i) - \bar{z} \right]^2}$, one for each dimension. If all the terms are of the same order of magnitude, then doing Systematic Sampling on any one variable will reduce the variance by less than V/n. While this implies that there will be no spectacular gains by doing Systematic Sampling, as already mentioned it is usually costless to use it.

The main application of Systematic Sampling is in those multi-stage problems where it is trivial to calculate the distribution of events at the first stage. In that case, the sampling should be done systematically.

6. Stratified Sampling

Stratified Sampling is a sort of combination of Systematic Sampling and Importance Sampling. One uses an $f^+(x)$ instead of $f(x)$, but does the sampling systematically.

187

That is, the x_i are picked by solving the equation,

$$\int_{-\infty}^{x_i} f^+(x)dx = \frac{i - \frac{1}{2}}{N} \qquad i = 1, 2, \ldots, N \qquad (84)$$

and the y_i are picked at random from $g(y:x_i)$. As one would expect the sample estimates are weighted with the factor $f(x_i)/f^+(x_i)$. i. e.,

$$\hat{z}_6 = \frac{1}{N} \sum_{i=1}^{N} z(x_i, y_i) \frac{f(x_i)}{f^+(x_i)} \qquad (85)$$

While equation (85) above is formally identical with the corresponding equation (16) in the section on Importance Sampling, the variance of $\hat{z}_6$ is quite different from that of $\hat{z}_{11}$. It is

$$V_6 = \frac{1}{N} \int \frac{\sigma^2(:x) f^2(x)}{f^+(x)} dx \qquad (86)$$

As a result the optimum $f^+(x)$ is not proportional to $f(x)\sqrt{\overline{z^2}(:x)}$ but is

$$f^+(x) = \frac{\sigma(:x) f(x)}{\int \sigma(;x) f(x) dx} \qquad (87)$$

and, $\sigma(:x)$ can be and in general is quite different from $\sqrt{\overline{z^2}(:x)}$. It is easy to find problems in which optimum Importance Sampling and Stratified Sampling are widely different. The reason for this is that in Importance Sampling one is simultaneously estimating the probability of getting into a certain x region and the expected value of $z(x,y)$ given x, while in Stratified Sampling the first quantity has, in effect, been calculated by numerical integration and only the last quantity is being estimated.

188

If the optimum Stratified Sampling is used then the variance becomes

$$V_6 = \frac{1}{N} \; \overline{\sigma(:x)}^2 \tag{88}$$

and the reduction in variance is given by

$$V - V_6 = \frac{1}{N} \left\{ \overline{\left[\sigma(:x) - \overline{\sigma(:x)} \right]^2} + \overline{\left[\overline{z}(:x) - \overline{z} \right]^2} \right\} \tag{89}$$

In many cases it is convenient to take f^+ as close as possible to

$$f^+(x) = \frac{\overline{z}(:x) f(x)}{\overline{z}} \tag{90}$$

The variance then becomes

$$V_{61} = \frac{1}{N} \; \overline{z} \left[\frac{\sigma^2(:x)}{\overline{z}(:x)} \right] \tag{91}$$

As can be seen from equation (24), V_{61} is the same as would have been obtained if the sampling on $f^+(x)$ had been done randomly rather than systematically. However, it is usually better to do the sampling systematically because for a general $f^+(x)$ the difference in variance between the two techniques is

$$V_1 - V_6 = \frac{1}{N} \left[\int \frac{\overline{z^2}(:x) f^2(x)}{f^+(x)} \, dx - \overline{z}^2 - \int \frac{\sigma^2(:x) f^2(x)}{f^+(x)} \, dx \right] \tag{92}$$

$$= \frac{1}{N} \left[\int \frac{\overline{z}^2(:x) f^2(x)}{f^+(x)} \, dx - \overline{z}^2 \right]$$

$$\geq 0$$

189

since $V_1 - V_6$ is the variance associated with doing Importance Sampling on the integral $\int \overline{z}(:x)f(x)dx$. Therefore, where it is easy to use Stratified Sampling, it is preferable to use Importance Sampling. In practice, though, the places where it can be used are essentially the same as Systematic Sampling and, as already mentioned, not too plentiful.

The single remark on the applications of Systematic Sampling also applies to Stratified Sampling; it is usually useful when it is trivial to calculate the distribution of events at the first stage. There is only the additional fact that one must have some idea of the relative importance of the various regions where importance in this case is measured by $\sigma(:x)f(x)$.

. . . . . .

It is probably clear to the reader that the problems faced by the Monte Carlo experimenter in trying to cut down his statistical fluctuations are quite similar to those that are faced in almost any application of sampling. Therefore, much of the literature of statistics is relevant to the problems we have been considering. In fact, a fairly complete discussion of the last two techniques, and to a slightly lesser extent, the preceding two, can be found in many statistics textbooks; only the first two do not seem to have been discussed. For this reason, it is very valuable to have professional statistical help in designing these calculations. However, if one has to choose between a person who is mainly interested in statistics and one who is mainly interested in the problem itself, experience has shown that, in this field at least, the latter is preferable. This last remark is not intended as a slur on statisticians, but simply to amplify a comment made earlier, that, "the greatest gains in variance reduction are often made by exploiting specific details of the problem, rather than by routine application of general principles."

A THEORETICAL COMPARISON OF THE EFFICIENCIES OF TWO CLASSICAL METHODS AND A MONTE CARLO METHOD FOR COMPUTING ONE COMPONENT OF THE SOLUTION OF A SET OF LINEAR ALGEBRAIC EQUATIONS

J. H. Curtiss

Institute of Mathematical Sciences
New York University

SUMMARY

In this paper a basis is established for a theoretical comparison of the amount of work required by three widely different methods of calculating (to a given accuracy) one component of the solution of a set of simultaneous linear algebraic equations. The equations are assumed to be in the form $\xi = H\xi + \gamma$, where γ is a given n-dimensional vector and H is a given n x n real matrix. The amount of work is measured by the number of multiplications required under the most unfavorable conditions. The three methods are (a) the Gauss elimination method, (b) the particular stationary linear iterative method defined by the recursion formula $\xi_{N+1} = H\xi_N + \gamma$, N = 0,1,2,..., and (c) a Monte Carlo method which consists essentially of a statistical process for estimating the iterates of H. The amount of work required by the first method is proportional to n^3, where n is the order of the matrix H. The amount of work required by the second method to achieve a predetermined accuracy is given by an expression of the form $kn^2 + n$, where k is ordinarily fairly large. The amount of work required by the Monte Carlo method is given by an expression of the form $n^2 + n + b$, where b is ordinarily a very large number. If no preliminary preparations aimed at reducing b are made, then the amount of work for the Monte Carlo method is given by an expression of the form $n + b$.

+This report represents results obtained at the Institute of Mathematical Sciences, New York University, under the sponsorship of the Army Office of Ordnance Research, Contract No. DA-30-069-ORD-1257, RAD Project No. TB2-0001 (1089), Research in the field of Probability, Statistics, and Numerical Analysis (Monte Carlo Method).

191

The result of this varying dependence on the dimensionality of the problem is that <u>the Monte Carlo method is theoretically more efficient than the other two methods for sufficiently large values of n</u>. The value of n at which one method becomes more efficient than the other depends on the accuracy with which the solution is to be computed.

Upper bounds, which are actually attained in special cases, are derived in this paper for the amount of work required by the iterative and the stochastic methods. From these, break-even points on the range of the dimensionality n are calculated which serve at least as indications of the intervals of values of n which are favorable for each of the three methods. A table in Section 5 gives the favorable numerical intervals of n for various typical specifications of the problem.

A feature of the presentation is the development of a new minimum-variance arrangement of the Monte Carlo method for solving linear equations, which exploits in a simple way an initial estimate of the solution to reduce variance. The construction of the Monte Carlo method will be found in Section 3. In section 6, this Monte Carlo arrangement is adapted to the problem of inverting a matrix. Section 6 also contains derivations and comparisons of certain general linear and polynomial iterative methods for matrix inversion.

I. INTRODUCTION

Many of the problems of numerical analysis to which Monte Carlo methods have been applied belong to the following general type: A rule is given whereby each one of a set of real or complex numbers a_1, a_2, ... can be computed. It is required to compute the sum of the series $a_1 + a_2 + \ldots$. (The series may be finite or infinite.)

The standard method of stochastic estimation ("Monte Carlo" method) for this type of problem consists in selecting numbers z_k and p_k, $k = 1,2,\ldots$, such that $z_k p_k = a_k$, $p_k \geq 0$, $\sum_k p_k = 1$. Then a random variable J is set up with the probability distribution given by $\Pr(J = k) = p_k$, $k = 1,2,\ldots$.

The random variable z_J will obviously have a theoretical
mean value equal to the sum of the series $a_1 + a_2 + \ldots$.
The statistic

$$\overline{Z}_\nu = \frac{z_{J_1} + z_{J_2} + \ldots + z_{J_\nu}}{\nu}$$

where J_1, J_2, ... are independent replicas of J, furnishes
an estimator of the mean value of z_J (that is, of the solution of the problem) which has various well-known optimum
statistical properties.

It is hard for some classically trained numerical
analysts to see how Monte Carlo methods can ever be advantageous in such a problem. A somewhat over-simplified
version of their reasoning might go as follows. Let s be
chosen so that $\sum_1^s a_k$ gives a satisfactory approximation to
the sum of the series. (If the series is finite, let s be
the number of terms.) Since each observed value of z_J
conditionally estimates just one of the numbers a_k, there
will have to be at least as many terms in the summation
for $\overline{Z}_\nu$ as in $\sum_1^s a_k$. Indeed, because of statistical fluctuations it will probably be necessary to make very many
more observations on z_J than there are terms in the finite
approximation $\sum_1^s a_k$, and even then, $\overline{Z}_\nu$ will probably not be
as good as $\sum_1^s a_k$. This means that the count of additions
alone will be very much greater for the stochastic approximation than for the straightforward method of solution;
and then too, there is the trouble of setting up the z_k's
and p_k's in advance, and of determining stochastically,
over and over again, the value of J to use in the observations.

The case against this argument can very conveniently be stated in terms of a specific problem which is fundamental to this paper. It is the problem of calculating the i-th component of the vector $K^{N+1}\Theta$, where K denotes the 2n x 2n matrix $[k_{ij}]$ and Θ is the 2n-dimensional vector $(t_1,\ldots,t_{2n})$. The i-th element of $K^{N+1}\Theta$, which we write as $[K^{N+1}\Theta]_i$, is the sum of $(2n)^{N+1}$ terms of the type $k_{i i_1} k_{i_1 i_2} \cdots k_{i_N i_{N+1}} t_{i_{N+1}}$. The stochastic estimation [3][+] is accomplished by selecting numbers z_{ij} and p_{ij}, $i,j = 1,\ldots,2n$, such that $z_{ij}p_{ij} = k_{ij}$, with $p_{ij} \geq 0$, $\sum_j p_{ij} = 1$ for all i. Then a family of random variables $J_o, J_1, J_2, \ldots, J_{N+1}$ is set up in such a way that it represents a Markov process (or "random walk") with states (resting places) designated by $1,2,\ldots,2n$ and with stationary transition probabilities. The specification of the joint probability distribution is accomplished by assigning an arbitrary distribution to J_o (but with $Pr(J_o=i) \neq 0$), and thereafter using the equations[++] $Pr(J_{k+1}=j|J_k=i) = p_{ij}$, $i,j = 1,\ldots, 2n$. Finally, a random variable

$$Z = z_{J_o J_1 \ldots J_{N+1}} = z_{J_o J_1} z_{J_1 J_2} \cdots z_{J_N J_{N+1}} t_{J_{N+1}}$$

is set up. It is now easily seen from the definition of mean value in probability theory, that[+++] $E(Z|J_o=i) = K^{N+1}\Theta]_i$. We use $(Z_1+\ldots+Z_\nu)/\nu$ as the estimator of

---

[+]The square brackets refer to the references at the end of the paper.

[++]By $Pr(z|b)$ we mean the conditional probability of the event a, given that the event b has occurred.

[+++]By $E(x|a)$, we mean the mean value of the conditional distribution of the random variable X, given that the event a has occurred.

$K^{N+1} \theta]_i$, where $Z_1, \ldots, Z_\nu$ denote ν independent determinations of Z.

The various possible values of $k_{ii_1} k_{i_1 i_2} \cdots k_{i_N i_{N+1}} t_{i_{N+1}}$ correspond to the values of a_k in the previous more general formulation. Let us think of these possible values as renumbered in a linear and serial order, using a single index k. There will be $s = (2n)^{N+1}$ such numbers. (They may not be all distinct.) Then the $(2n)^{N+1}$ correspondingly renumbered products $p_{ii_1} \cdots p_{i_N i_{N+1}}$ play the role of $p_1, p_2, \ldots, p_s$ in the previous formulation, and the various possible values of the vector random variable $\underline{J} = (J_0, J_1, \ldots, J_{N+1})$ correspond to the values of J in the previous formulation.

It now begins to be evident that our formulation of the general summation problem at the beginning of the section was deceptively over-simplified. In a multi-dimensional summation problem, the following two factors may come into play on the side of a Monte Carlo method of solution:

(a) If the calculation of each a_k is a complicated one, it may be possible to arrange things so that the calculation of each observation on z_J is very much simpler than the calculation of the corresponding term a_J. This will in particular be the case if the calculation of each a_k involves the formation of a continued product, because then part of the work of calculating the product can be sidestepped in the stochastic process by using the multiplicative law of probabilities.

(b) Some of the numbers a_k in the finite approximation to Σa_k may be very unimportant and need not be represented in the statistical estimator at all. The stochastic estimation process, if properly set up, will automatically take care of this by making the appearance of the representative of a non-essential term a very rare event.

We add here, more or less as an aside, the remark that when the calculation of each particular z_J is much simpler than that of the corresponding a_J, then the problem of the accumulation of round-off errors may not be nearly as serious for the stochastic method as it is in the direct computation.

All of these factors favoring the Monte Carlo method are present in the case of the problem $K^{N+1}\Theta]_i$ and in the related problem of solving systems of linear algebraic equations. The factor (a) is usually particularly in evidence in numerical problems of stochastic origin, and indeed it is in such problems that the Monte Carlo method has had its chief successes. Matrix problems can always be thrown into a form in which they are numerically equivalent to problems with a stochastic pedigree. We shall exploit that fact in the present paper to obtain a favorable environment for the comparisons to be made.

But we cannot conclude this introduction without making a remark which is on the negative side as far as Monte Carlo methods are concerned. It certainly would seem that whenever Monte Carlo methods appear to advantage in summation problems, factor (b) above must be playing an important role, because otherwise the criticisms regarding the necessary number of addition operations required for any reasonable degree of accuracy in the Monte Carlo approach would be valid. But if that is so, why cannot a deterministic method be devised which will ignore the unimportant terms and be even more efficient? The author suspects that what we now need is a more highly developed deterministic theory of quadrature and of linear computation in many dimensions. When this becomes available, the Monte Carlo method may, at least for matrix problems, lose the very modest advantages which will be claimed for it in this paper.

II. THE NUMERICAL PROBLEM AND ITS NON-STOCHASTIC SOLUTION

Throughout the paper we shall continue to denote matrices by capital letters, and their elements by the corresponding lower case letters; thus, for example, $H = [h_{ij}]$. We represent vectors by lower case Greek letters and their components by the corresponding Roman letters; thus for example, $\xi = (x_1, x_2, \ldots, x_n)$. We shall also find it convenient occasionally to designate the elements of a matrix by double subscripts affixed to the symbol for the matrix (thus, H_{ij} or $[(I-H)^{-1} H^2]_{ij}$). Furthermore we shall frequently designate the components of a vector by a similar subscript notation (thus $\xi = (\xi]_1, \xi]_2, \ldots, \xi]_n)$. All vectors will be real and n-dimensional and all matrices will have only real elements.

By $\| H \|$ we shall mean $\max_i \sum_j |h_{ij}|$, and by $\| \xi \|$, we shall mean $\max_i |x_i|$. It is obvious that $\| H\xi \| \leq \| H \| \, \| \xi \|$ and that $\| A+B \| \leq \| A \| + \| B \|$. It is well-known[+] that $\| AB \| \leq \| A \| \, \| B \|$; therefore, by induction $\| H^N \| \leq \| H \|^N$.

The numerical problem with which we shall be mainly concerned is that of solving the linear system

$$(2.1) \qquad\qquad A\xi = \eta,$$

for ξ, where A is a given non-singular n x n matrix and η is a given vector. We assume that this system has been thrown into the form

$$(2.2) \qquad\qquad \xi = H\xi + \gamma,$$

where $H = [h_{ij}]$ is an n x n matrix with the property that

$$(2.3) \qquad\qquad \| H \| = \max_i \sum_j |h_{ij}| < 1 .$$

[+]See for example Courant and Hilbert [1]; p. 16, footnote.

It is beyond the scope of this paper to give an extended discussion of the methods of passing from (2.1) to (2.2), but a few general remarks on the subject are in order at this point. In the first place, it is always theoretically possible to transform the problem represented by (2.1) in this manner. Indeed, let H be any matrix whatsoever with the property (2.3). (For instance, let H = dI, where I is the unit matrix and d is a scalar lying between 0 and 1.) It is known that if H satisfies (2.3), then I-H cannot be singular[+]. Let M be defined by the equation I - MA = H. This says that M = (I-H)A^{-1}. Therefore M cannot be singular. The system

$$\xi = H\xi + M\eta = (I-MA)\xi + M\eta,$$

is just the same as the system

$$MA\xi = M\eta,$$

and since M is non-singular, this system is precisely equivalent (2.1).

But in practice it is not feasible to set up an arbitrary H satisfying (2.3), and then to determine M as above. The reason is that the formula M = (I-H)A^{-1} presupposes a knowledge of A^{-1}, and in the presence of this the original problem becomes trivial. Thus it is natural to think of M as being chosen first, the choice being made in such a way that I - MA = H has suitable properties. There are a number of different procedures in the literature of linear computation for arriving at an appropriate choice of M. For example, if A has dominant diagonal--that is, if

$$|a_{ii}| > \sum_{j \neq i}^{n} |a_{ij}|, \quad i = 1,\ldots,n,\text{--then M can be chosen}$$

as the inverse of the principal diagonal matrix whose principal diagonal is that of A. This will obviously insure that $\| H \| < 1$[++].

[+]O. Taussky-Todd, [9].

[++]Further discussion will be found in any good treatise on numerical analysis which deals with iterative methods of solving linear equations. See for example Householder [7] and Milne [8]. See Forsythe [6] for further references.

There are numerous non-stochastic methods of solving (2.1)+. We shall here restrict our considerations mainly to a class of methods known as linear iterative processes. An effective Monte Carlo method for the problem (2.1) can be based on this type of process, as we presently shall see.

The general stationary linear iterative process for solving (2.1) is arrived at by throwing (2.1) into an equivalent form which has the appearance of (2.2), but with H restricted only by the requirement that its eigenvalues all lie in the unit circle. An initial estimate ξ_o of the solution is made, and successive approximations $\xi_1, \xi_2, \ldots$, are then defined by

$$(2.4) \qquad \xi_{N+1} = H\xi_N + \gamma, \quad N = 0,1,2,\ldots \quad .$$

If ξ_∞ denotes the solution of the equations (2.2), then clearly, since $\xi_\infty = H\xi_\infty + \gamma$,

$$(2.5) \qquad \xi_\infty - \xi_N = H(\xi_\infty - \xi_{N-1})$$
$$= H^2(\xi_\infty - \xi_{N-1})$$
$$= H^N(\xi_\infty - \xi_o)$$

Thus the condition for convergence for any starting vector ξ_o is that $\lim_{N \to \infty} H^N = 0$. The well-known necessary and sufficient condition [7] for $\lim_{N \to \infty} H^N = 0$ is that all the eigenvalues of H should lie in the unit circle, which explains the requirement on H imposed earlier in this paragraph.

But in the present discussion, we go one step beyond this requirement and insist that $\| H \| < 1$. Since $\| H^N \| \leq \| H \|^N$, this condition will certainly insure that $H^N \to 0$.

+See previous footnote for references.

For purposes of error analysis[+] it is advantageous now to introduce the residual vectors

(2.6)
$$\rho_N = \gamma - (I-H)\xi_N ,$$

$$= H\xi_N + \gamma - \xi_N = \xi_{N+1} - \xi_N, \quad N = 0,1,2,\dots$$

The vectors ρ_N are of course always computable at any stage in the iterative solution. If $\xi_N \to \xi_\infty = (I-H)^{-1}\gamma$, then obviously $\rho_N \to 0$. The converse is also true, because $(I-H)^{-1}\rho_N = \xi_\infty - \xi_N$. Thus ρ_N, or $\|\rho_N\|$, are logical measures of the error in the N-th approximation to the solution. It is to be noted from (2.4) and (2.6) that

(2.7)
$$\rho_N = \xi_{N+1} - \xi_N = (H\xi_N + \gamma) - (H\xi_{N-1} + \gamma)$$

$$= H(\xi_N - \xi_{N-1}) = H\rho_{N-1}$$

$$= \dots \qquad = H^N \rho_o .$$

From (2.6) and (2.7) it follows that the successive approximations ξ_N generated by (2.4) can theoretically also be generated in the following manner: Select ξ_o as before and compute ρ_o from the definition of residual vector, $\rho_o = \gamma - (I-H)\xi_o$. Then conduct the iterations by means of the pair of formulas

(2.8)
$$\xi_{N+1} = \xi_N + \rho_N , \quad N = 0,1,\dots ,$$

(2.9)
$$\rho_{N+1} = H\rho_N , \quad N = 0,1,\dots .$$

We note that by back substitution, we find that

[+]By error in this paper, we shall mean truncation error or statistical error or both at once. There will be no study of round-off error, nor of the effect of miscellaneous arithmetical mistakes.

(2.10) $\xi_{N+1} = \xi_0 + \rho_0 + \rho_1 + \ldots + \rho_N = \xi_0 + (I + H + \ldots$
$$+ H^N) \rho_0 .$$

In actual practice, the customary running check on the accuracy of the solution consists in computing $\|\rho_N\|$ from time to time to see how small it is. The iterations are stopped when $\|\rho_N\|$ reaches a predetermined order of smallness. If (2.4) were used for the iterations, the computation of ρ_N would be done by using the formula $\rho_N = \xi_{N+1} - \xi_N$. If (2.8) and (2.9) were to be used, it would be advisable to compute test values of $\|\rho_N\|$ from the definition of ρ_N (that is, from the formula $\rho_N = \gamma - (I-H)\xi_N$), rather than to accept the values of $\|\rho_N\|$ given by (2.9). We shall come back to this point in a moment.

An <u>a priori</u> truncation error analysis, made with the purpose of estimating the number of iterations which will be required to achieve a given accuracy, can be conducted either in terms of ρ_N or in terms of the error vector $\xi_\infty - \xi_N$. If the size of $\|\rho_N\|$ is to be the criterion, then we use (2.7) to obtain the very simple estimate

(2.11) $$\|\rho_N\| \leq \|H\|^N \|\rho_0\| .$$

But if the deviation of ξ_N from ξ_∞ seems to be a more appropriate or convenient measure of the truncation error, then we use the fact that $(I-H)^{-1}\rho_0 = \xi_\infty - \xi_0$. Substituting this into (2.5), we find that

(2.12) $$\xi_\infty - \xi_N = H^N(I-H)^{-1}\rho_0 .$$

Since $(I-H)^{-1} = I + H + H^2 + \ldots$, it follows that
$$\|(I-H)^{-1}\| \leq \|I\| + \|H\| + \|H\|^2 + \ldots = (1 - \|F\|)^{-1}.$$
Therefore

(2.13) $$\|\xi_\infty - \xi_N\| \leq \frac{\|H\|^N}{1 - \|H\|} \|\rho_0\| .$$

It is perhaps worthwhile to point out here, by way of
an aside, that the inequalities (2.11) and (2.13) hold for
any one of the various matrix and vector norms in common
use[+] , and not just for the norm $\|H\| = \max_i \sum_j |h_{ij}|$. We are
using this particular norm here because of a special application it has to the Monte Carlo method, which will be
brought out in the next section.

The iterative formulas (2.8) and (2.9) are (so to
speak) homogeneous, and therefore look easier to use than
(2.4). But (2.8) and (2.9) have the great disadvantage of
being not self-correcting in case a mistake is made at one
stage, whereas (2.4) does have this property. Suppose for
example that for some N, ρ_{N+1} is mistakenly computed as a
zero vector in using (2.9). Then since all subsequent vectors ρ_N will equal zero, it is obvious from (2.10) that ξ_N
will be irretrievably wrong. But if a mistake is made in
computing ξ_{N+1} by (2.4), the subsequent effect is like
starting over again with another ξ_o.

Therefore we are not proposing (2.8) and (2.9) as a
practical substitute for (2.4) for a non-stochastic numerical solution of the problem $\xi = H\xi + \gamma$. Our real purpose
in introducing the alternative iteration formulas was to
develop the representation of ξ_N given by formula (2.10).
This representation seems to be an advantageous one upon
which to construct a Monte Carlo solution, as we shall see
in the next section.

It is not without interest, however, to point out that
if the amount of work involved in a computing job is measured
in any sensible way, it theoretically requires no more work
to use (2.8) and (2.9) up to a predetermined value of N than
to use (2.4). This assumes that check values of ρ_N will not
have to be computed from the definition of residual vector
from time to time in the use of (2.8) and (2.9). In this
paper, we shall measure amount of work by merely counting up
the number of multiplications required under the worst conditions, assuming no zero or unit elements. Additions and
subtractions will be ignored. A division or reciprocation
will count as a single multiplication. To arrive at ξ_N by

[+]See Householder [7], pp. 38-44.

(2.4), starting with ξ_o, requires n^2 multiplications per
iteration, or Nn^2 in all. To arrive at ξ_N by (2.8) and
(2.9) without computing any intermediate or final check
values of ρ_N takes n^2 multiplications for ρ_o, and thereafter $(N-1)n^2$ multiplications for each iterative determination of ρ_N. So once again the count is Nn^2.

Actually, in later sections we are going to set up an
error analysis which implies that ρ_o will always have to
be computed. The use of (2.4) will be tacitly assumed, so
n^2 extra multiplications will have to be added to the total
count.

III. STOCHASTIC SOLUTION OF THE PROBLEMS

It should be apparent from the foregoing section that
even if one restricts oneself to the class of stationary
linear iterative processes, there is literally an uncount-
ably infinite number of methods for solving the problem
$A\xi = \eta$, because of the different possible choices of H
or M. An even more disconcerting fact than this was impli-
cit in the discussion in the foregoing section. It can be
expressed in the form of a theorem: "Given any one way of
solving $A\xi = \eta$, there is always a much better way." For
given any one H, a happier choice of H from the standpoint
of the error analyses given by (2.11) and (2.12) always
exists.

Under such circumstances it is evident that some strict
ground rules are required if meaningful comparisons are to
be made between methods. This statement applies even to
comparisons within very special classes of classical methods,
and it is especially relevant when an utterly unorthodox
method such as the Monte Carlo Method is to be brought into
the picture.

We propose then to adhere to the following set of rules:

(1) It will be assumed that the problem is given in
the form $\xi = H\xi + \gamma$, with $\|H\| < 1$.

(2) The primary comparison will be between a Monte

Carlo Method for solving $\xi = H\xi + \gamma$ and a stationary linear iterative method of the type described in the preceding section. Both methods will be based on the particular H given in (1). The linear iterative method will be defined by the recursion relations $\xi_{N+1} = H\xi_N + \gamma$, $N = 0,1,\ldots$, or alternatively, by the formula

$$(3.1) \qquad \xi_N = \xi_0 + (I + H + \ldots + H^{N-1})\rho_0,$$

where ξ_0 is the initial estimate and ρ_0 is the initial residual vector (see equation 2.10). The Monte Carlo Method will consist in effect of a statistical estimation of

$$(3.2) \qquad \xi_\infty = \xi_0 + (I + H + H^2 + \ldots)\rho_0,$$

using the same H, the same ξ_0, and same ρ_0 as in (3.1).

(3) No speculation will be permited as to the existence of a better H on which to base either the stochastic or the non-stochastic method.

(4) The measure of approximation used in the case of the iterative method will be $\|\xi_\infty - \xi_N\|$. The measure of approximation used in the stochastic method will be $|\xi_\infty]_i - \bar{Z}_\nu|$, where $\xi_\infty]_i$ denotes the i-th component of the solution vector ξ_∞, and $\bar{Z}_\nu$ is its statistical estimator, based on a sample of size ν.

(5) To furnish some contact with the large family of alternative methods of solving $\xi = H\xi + \eta$, a simple direct method of solution will be brought into the comparison. For simplicity, it will be assumed that this direct method gives the exact solution. Round-off error will be ignored. The direct method which we select is the Gauss Elimination Method, because for present purposes it seems to be as good as any other and better than most.

(6) As previously stated in Section II, the amount of work required for a computation will be measured only by the

number of multiplications required in the worst cases, counting a reciprocation or division as one multiplication. In counting multiplications, the possibility of unit or zero factors is not taken into account.

(7) **It will be assumed that the problem is to find only one component of the solution of** $\xi = H\xi + \gamma$.

It is recognized freely that the last restriction on the comparison is a strange one. It is made because the question of efficient Monte Carlo estimation of all components of the solution simultaneously has not yet been adequately investigated. Of course, separate statistically independent estimations can be made for each of the n components of the solution. This would multiply the measure of work which we shall derive for the Monte Carlo method[+] by a factor of n. At the same time, for a given sample size ν, the probability that all estimations fall within preassigned limits of error, will be smaller than it is for the estimation of a single component[++]. Therefore ν should be correspondingly increased. But it is almost surely inefficient to use separate independent estimators for each component of the solution. It seems intuitively clear that data obtained in the course of estimating one component should be used again for other components[+++].

With these preliminary comments out of the way, we proceed to set up the Monte Carlo estimation of $\xi_\infty]_i$.

The standard method of estimating $K^{N+1}\theta]_i$, where $K = [k_{ij}]$ is a given 2n x 2n matrix and $\theta = (t_1,\ldots,t_{2n})$ is a 2n-dimensional vector, has already been described in Section I. Here we recapitulate it briefly. Numbers z_{ij}

_____

[+]That is, the measure of the work for the purely stochastic part of the solution. This is represented by the third quantity in the sum on the right side of (4.5), or of (4.6), in Section IV, below.

[++]The question involved here is that of the distribution of the extreme absolute value of n normally distributed independent random variables with zero means and differing variances.

[+++]The re-use of samples to estimate various components simultaneously is discussed briefly in [4].

and p_{ij}, $i, j = 1, \ldots, 2n$, are chosen such that $z_{ij} p_{ij} = k_{ij}$, with $p_{ij} \geq 0$, $\sum_j p_{ij} = 1$. A Markov process with states $1, 2, \ldots, 2n$, and with the matrix $[p_{ij}]$ as its matrix of transition probabilities is set up. Let J_o, J_1, $\ldots$, J be a family of random variables which represent the process, in the sense that $\Pr(J_{k+1} = j \mid J_k = i) = p_{ij}$, $i, j = 1, \ldots, 2n$. The random variable $Z = z_{J_o J_1} z_{J_1 J_2} \cdots z_{J_N J_{N+1}} t_{J_{N+1}}$ has the property that $E(Z \mid J_o = i) = K^{N+1} \Theta]_i$.

Consider now the $2n \times 2n$ matrix

$$(3.3) \qquad K = \left[\begin{array}{c|c} H & I \\ \hline O & I \end{array} \right] \quad ,$$

and the vector

$$(3.4) \qquad \Theta = \left[\begin{array}{c} O \\ \hline \rho_o \end{array} \right] \quad ,$$

where H is the matrix of the equation $\xi = H\xi + \nu$, I is the $n \times n$ matrix and ρ_o is the residual vector corresponding to the initial estimate ξ_o of the solution of these equations. (That is, $\rho_o = \gamma - (I-H)\xi_o$.) Then it is easily shown that

$$K^{N+1} = \left[\begin{array}{c|c} H^{N+1} & I+H+\ldots+H^N \\ \hline O & I \end{array} \right] \quad .$$

Therefore

$$K^{N+1}\Theta = \left[\begin{array}{c} (I+H+\ldots+H^N)\rho_o \\ \hline \rho_o \end{array} \right] \quad .$$

Our Monte Carlo solution of the equations $\xi = H\xi + \gamma$ consists of statistically estimating the i-th component of this vector $K^{N+1}\theta$, adding this statistical estimate to $\xi_0]_i$, and with reference to (2.10) or (3.1), using this sum to approximate thereby the i-th component of the solution vector ξ_∞. More specifically, we set up the numbers z_{ij} and p_{ij} for the special matrix K appearing in (3.3). For each sample random walk, represented by a determination of the vector random variable $J_0, J_1, \ldots, J_{N+1}$, made with $J_0 = i$, we compute the statistic

$$\xi_0]_i + Z = \xi_0]_i + z_{J_0 J_1} z_{J_1 J_2} \cdots z_{J_N J_{N+1}} t_{J_{N+1}} ,$$

in which $t_{J_{N+1}}$ is the J_{N+1}-th component of the vector θ given by (3.4). The conditional mean value of this statistic, given that $J_0 = i$, is $\xi_0]_i + (I+H+\ldots+H^N)\rho_0]_i$, or $\xi_{N+1}]_i$.

The statistical estimation of ξ_{N+1} is accomplished by taking the average of ν independent determinations of the random variable $\xi_0]_i + Z$, which we denote by $\xi_0]_i + Z_1$, $\xi_0]_i + Z_2, \ldots, \xi_0]_i + Z_\nu$. This average takes the form

$$\overline{Z}_\nu = \xi_0]_i + \frac{Z_1 + Z_2 + \ldots Z_\nu}{\nu} .$$

Of course, $\overline{Z}_\nu$ directly estimates or approximates $\xi_{N+1}]_i$ and not the solution component $\xi_\infty]_i$. But we now eliminate the truncation error completely from consideration in the Monte Carlo solution by assuming that N, although finite, is so large that $\| \xi_\infty - \xi_{N+1} \|$ is completely negligible. From (2.12) it is obvious that this can always be done. For all practical purposes then, $\overline{Z}_\nu$ will be an estimator directly of

$$\xi_\infty]_i = \lim_{N \to \infty} K^N \theta]_i = \xi_0]_i + (I+H+H^2+\ldots) \rho_0]_i .$$

This is the i-th component of the vector which appears in (3.2).

We shall now discuss the choice of the numbers z_{ij} and p_{ij} with reference to the special matrix K now under consideration. Obviously it is necessary to choose z_{ij} and p_{ij} so that $z_{ij}p_{ij} = h_{ij}$, $i,j = 1,\ldots,n$, and $z_{i,i+n}p_{i,i+n} = 1$. Moreover, for $i > n$, $z_{ij}p_{ij} = 1$ if $i = j$ and otherwise $z_{ij}p_{ij} = 0$.

Within these limitations, there are of course an infinite number of possible choices of the numbers z_{ij} and p_{ij}. It seems likely from evidence of various types that an optimum choice, or at least a near-optimum choice, in the present instance consists in letting $p_{ij} = |h_{ij}|$, $i,j = 1,\ldots,n$, $p_{ij} = 0$, $i = 1,\ldots,n$, $j = n+1, n+2, \ldots, n+i-1, n+i+1, \ldots,2n$, $p_{ij} = 0$, $i > n$, $j \neq i$ and $p_{i,i+n} = 1 - \sum_{j=1}^{n} p_{ij}$, $i = 1,\ldots,n$, $p_{ij} = 1$, $i > n$. We must defer a complete discussion of this choice of the numbers p_{ij} to another paper which is now under preparation.

It is to be noticed that $\sum_{j=1}^{n} p_{ij} \leq \|H\| < 1$, $i = 1,\ldots,n$. With this choice of the numbers p_{ij} it follows that $z_{ij} = \pm 1$ $i,j = 1, \ldots, n$, and $z_{i,i+n} = 1/p_{i,i+n}$ for $i = 1,\ldots,n$. We henceforth shall usually drop the subscript on ρ_o and write $\rho = (r_1,\ldots,r_n)$. Then

$$Z = z_{J_o J_1} z_{J_1 J_2} \cdots z_{J_N J_{N+1}} t_{J_{N+1}}$$

$$(3.3) \quad = \begin{cases} 0 \quad, \quad J_{N+1} = 1,2,\ldots,n \\[2em] \pm \dfrac{r_{J_{N+-1}}}{p_{J_{N+-1}, n+J_{N+-1}}} \quad, \quad J_{N+1} = n+1,\ldots,2n \ , \end{cases}$$

where N^+ is the "duration" of the random walk represented by J_o, J_1, ... ; that is, N^+ is the number of times a state in the first n states is visited before any state in the last n states is visited.[+] (The present set-up of the Markov process makes the last n states play the role of absorbing states.)

It is to be noted at this point that

(3.4)
$$|Z| \leq \frac{\|\rho\|}{\min_i p_{i,i+n}} = \frac{\|\rho\|}{1 - \max_i \sum_{j=1}^{n} p_{ij}}$$

$$= \frac{\|\rho\|}{1 - \|H\|} \quad .$$

This means that $E(Z^2 | J_o = i)$ exists and is uniformly bounded for all values of N.

Let v denote the conditional variance of the random variable Z, relative to the hypothesis that $H_o = i$. This is a measure of dispersion of Z defined by $v = E\left\{[Z-E(Z)]^2 | J_o = i\right\} = E(Z^2 | J_o = i) - (\xi_o]_i)^2$. It is necessary for later developments to obtain an appraisal of v. The explicit formula for v is known[++], but in the present situation a rough method of appraisal which bypasses the formula will give just as good a bound for v as can be obtained from the explicit formula for v.

[+]We shall here count in the first state--the state from which the random walk starts--in computing N^+. Thus if 4 non-absorbing states are visited including the starting point and then absorption takes place, then $N^+ = 4$, and J_3 is the last one of the J's taking on one of the values 1, 2, ..., n, and J_4 is equal to $n + J_3$. This convention concerning N^+ is adopted so as to conform with the definition given in Curtiss [3], and so as to simplify later formulas slightly.

[++]See [3], p. 223.

The rough method is this. Given any random variable X distributed on the interval $(-a,a)$, it obviously follows from the mean-value definition that $E(X^2) \leq E(a^2) = a^2$ and $E[X-E(X)]^2 \leq a^2 - [E(X)]^2$. Thus the highest value that the variance of such a random variable can have is a^2. But if the random variable has a uniform distribution on this interval, direct computation reveals that the variance is only $a^2/3$. If the distribution is somewhat bell-shaped, the variance may be much less, with zero as the greatest lower bound. Therefore, as a rough approximation, we shall in the present instance take the variance to be not greater than $a^2/2$. That is, our appraisal of v will be

$$(3.5) \qquad v \leq \frac{1}{2} \frac{\|P\|^2}{(1 - \|H\|)^2} \quad ,$$

where the right side is obtained by referring to $(3.4)^+$.

Another appraisal which will be needed relates to the mean value of the duration of N^+. It is known[++] that

$$E(N^+|J_o=i) = \sum_{j=1}^{n} (I+P+P^2+\ldots+P^N)_{ij} \, ,$$

where $P = [|h_{ij}|]$.

Therefore,

$$E(N^+|J_o=i) \leq \max_{i} \sum_{j=1}^{n} (I+P+P^2+\ldots \quad)_{ij},$$

$$\leq \|I\| + \|P\| + \|P\|^2 + \ldots$$

$$= \frac{1}{1 - \|P\|} \, .$$

[+]If the reader prefers to work with a bound which is one hundred per cent certain not to be exceeded, he will have to comb through the remaining calculations in this paper and replace the factor 1/2 by unity wherever (3.5) is used. There are enough safety factors in our estimates, insofar as avoiding the favoring of the Monte Carlo method is concerned, so that this ought to be unnecessary.

[++]See Curtiss [3], p. 226.

This formula holds good for any Markov process with absorbing states and with stationary transition probabilities given by a matrix such as P. In the present case, $P = [|h_{ij}|]$, so our upper bound for the mean deviation is

$$(3.6) \qquad E(N^+|J_o = i) \leq \frac{1}{1 - \|H\|} \quad .$$

It should be noted that (3.6) becomes an equality if the sum of the elements of the i-th row of $P = [|h_{ij}|]$ is constant for $i = 1, \ldots, n$.

Incidentally, the reason for using the matrix norm $\max\limits_{i} \Sigma\limits_{j} |h_{ij}|$ instead of one of the other norms should now be apparent. The natural appraisals for both v and the mean duration seem to involve this particular norm.

The conditional variance of N^+, given that $J_o = i$, has the following bound[+] in the case $N = \infty$:

$$(3.7) \qquad Var(N^+|J_o=i) \leq \frac{2}{1-\|P\|} - \left\{1+E(N^+|J_o=i)\right\} E(N^+ J_o=i)$$

$$< \frac{2}{1-\|P\|} - \left\{E(N^+|J_o=i)\right\}^2 .$$

In view of certain safety factors in this formula, we shall accept the following simpler heuristic appraisal of the variance, obtained by discarding the second term in the third member of (3.7) and halving the first term:

$$(3.8) \qquad Var(N^+|J_o=i) \leq \frac{1}{1 - \|H\|} \quad .$$

___

[+]See Curtiss [3], p. 226.

Thus our appraisal of the conditional variance of the duration is identical with our appraisal of the conditional mean value of the duration.

In concluding this section, we shall make two general remarks about the Monte Carlo method for solving $\xi = H\xi + \gamma$ developed above.

In the first place, one of the desirable features of any Monte Carlo solution is to achieve an arrangement whereby the more that is known about the solution of the problem in advance, the smaller the variance of the statistical estimator is, with zero variance attained in the presence of full knowledge of the solution. Such an arrangement has been achieved in the present case. If the solution is known in advance, then $\rho_0 = \rho = 0$, and consequently $v = 0$. The inequality (3.5) gives a bound for v which depends on the square of the norm of the zero-th residual vector, and thus the better the initial estimate or guess is, the smaller the variance is[+].

In the second place, our Monte Carlo solution has an automatic self-correction feature similar to that of the iterative method based on (2.4). If an error is made in computing the Z for any one sample walk, this erroneous Z merely is incorporated into the average of a great many other realizations of the same random variable, and its effect will ordinarily be negligible.

IV. THE A PRIORI ESTIMATION OF THE REQUIRED AMOUNT OF WORK

In the fourth of the ground rules stated at the beginning of Section III, we announced that the measure of approximation to be used in the case of the iterative method would be $\|\xi_{\infty} - \xi_N\|$, and in the case of the stochastic method it would be $|[\xi_{\infty}]_i - \bar{Z}_\nu|$. We shall now state more explicitly just how we are going to use these measures of approximation.

The general idea is that in each case, the computation is to proceed until the approximate solution is suitably close to the exact solution, and the definition of "suitably

---

+ Another minimum variance Monte Carlo solution of the problem $A\xi = \eta$ is presented in Curtiss [3], pp. 227-231. The present arrangement seems to be simpler and somewhat easier to use in practice.

close" used in each case will be comparable. Specifically, given a small number d > 0, we propose that the iterations in the non-stochastic method shall be carried on until finally $\|\xi_\infty - \xi_N\| < d$, and we propose that the sampling of the Markov process shall be continued until finally $|\xi_\infty|_i - Z_\nu| < d$.

But the vector ξ_∞ is unknown. We must therefore translate our measures of error into terms of the data of the problem and the initial estimate ξ_0. To achieve a theoretical rather than empirical comparison, we shall restrict ourselves entirely to an a priori error analysis.

The error analysis and consequent appraisal of the amount of work required to achieve a given accuracy, is of necessity carried out very differently in the case of the two methods. In the case of the non-stochastic method, we base the analysis on the inequality (2.13). With an eye on this inequality, we seek the lowest value of N such that

$$\frac{\|H\|^N}{1 - \|H\|} \|\rho\| < d \quad .$$

Taking logarithms of both sides, we find that the required value of N is

$$(4.1) \qquad N_0 = 1 + \left[\frac{\log \dfrac{d}{\|\rho\|} + \log (1 - \|H\|)}{\log \|H\|} \right]$$

where the square bracket here means "largest integer in." (The logarithms can be taken to any convenient base, as for example, 10.)

We must therefore carry out N_0 iterations of the recursion formula $\xi_{N+1} = H\xi_N + \gamma$. As pointed out at the end of Section II, each iteration counts as n^2 multiplications. However, since we have set ourselves the peculiar

213

problem of finding only one component of the solution vector, the last iteration (in which ξ_{N_o} is computed from ξ_{N_o-1}) can be abbreviated to just n multiplications. The formula for N_o involves $\|\rho\|$, and it seems reasonable to suppose therefore that in using this error analysis in practice, $\rho = \rho_o$ would always be computed at the outset. This would take n^2 more multiplications. Thus the grand total of the number of multiplications required a priori to achieve the inequality $\|\xi_\infty - \xi_N\| < d$ is

$$(4.2) \qquad m = (N_o-1)n^2 + n + n^2$$

$$= n^2 + n + n^2 \left[\frac{\log \dfrac{d}{\|\rho\|} + \log(1-\|H\|)}{\log \|H\|} \right]$$

We now attack the analogous problem for the stochastic method.

The statistical estimator $\overline{Z}_\nu$ is given by the formula

$$\overline{Z}_\nu = \xi_o]_i + \frac{Z_1+Z_2+\ldots+Z_\nu}{\nu} \quad ,$$

where Z_1, Z_2, $\ldots$, Z_ν are ν mutually independent determinations of the random variable which appears in the right member of (3.3). The mean value of $\overline{Z}_\nu$ is $\xi_\infty]_i$ for all practical purposes. It will not be possible to adjust ν so as to assure ourselves a priori, given any $d > 0$ however small, that $\overline{Z}_\nu$ will deviate from its mean value by less than d. We must therefore have recourse to the theory of statistical estimation.

Probably the easiest way to approach the question is to demand that a priori, the probability of a deviation of less than d shall be at or above some predetermined rather high level. Specifically, we choose a small number p, and require that ν shall be taken as the lowest value for which, a priori, the following inequality holds:

$$\Pr(|[\xi_\infty]_i - \overline{Z}_\nu| < d) > 1 - 2p \quad .$$

Now $\overline{Z}_\nu$ is a constant plus the average of ν independent, identically distributed random variables, each with a finite variance v. It therefore follows from a well-known result in probability theory called the Central Limit Theorem[+] that $(\overline{Z}_\nu - E(\overline{Z}_\nu))/v_\nu^{1/2}$ is approximately distributed according to the normal or Gaussian distribution, where v_ν denotes the conditional variance of $\overline{Z}_\nu$, given that $J_0 = i$. The approximation is ordinarily very good for $\nu > 100$, and in all of our subsequent applications of this theorem we shall be dealing with values of ν much greater than this. At worst, the effect of a poor approximation would be merely to deceive us by a few one hundredths as to the value of the probability level p which is really in effect.

The variance of a constant plus a random variable is the same as the variance of the random variable alone. Therefore the variance v_ν of $\overline{Z}_\nu$ is equal to that of the average of ν independent determinations of the random variable Z. A familiar formula of statistical theory[++] then states that $v_\nu = v/\nu$, where as in Section III, v is the conditional variance of Z, given that $J_0 = i$.

Putting the above facts together, we have:

$$\Pr(|[\xi_\infty]_i - \overline{Z}_\nu| < d)$$

$$= \Pr\left(\frac{|E(\overline{Z}_\nu) - \overline{Z}_\nu|}{v_\nu^{1/2}} < \frac{d}{v_\nu^{1/2}}\right)$$

$$= \Pr\left(\frac{|E(\overline{Z}_\nu) - \overline{Z}_\nu|}{v_\nu^{1/2}} < \frac{d\nu^{1/2}}{v^{1/2}}\right)$$

$$\doteq \int_{-d\nu^{1/2}/v^{1/2}}^{d\nu^{1/2}/v^{1/2}} \frac{1}{\sqrt{2\pi}} e^{-t^2/2} dt$$

$$= 1 - 2\int_{d\nu^{1/2}/v^{1/2}}^{\infty} \frac{1}{\sqrt{2\pi}} e^{-t^2/2} dt \quad .$$

+See e.g. [2], Chap. 17.   ++See e.g. [2] p. 345.

At this point we shall make an arbitrary decision about the level of certainty $1 - 2p$ which is to be demanded. If $x = 2$, then

$$2 \int_x^\infty \frac{1}{\sqrt{2\pi}} \, e^{-t^2/2} \, dt = .0455 \; .$$

A level of certainty equal to $1 - 0.0455 = .9545$ seems more than adequate for present purposes, in view of various other safety factors which are embodied in our appraisals.

Thus we are seeking the smallest value of ν such that

$$\frac{d\,\nu^{1/2}}{\nu^{1/2}} > 2 \; .$$

This value of ν is

(4.3)
$$\nu_o = \left[\frac{4v}{d^2} \right] + 1 \; ,$$

where again $[\;]$ means "largest integer in."

This is the number of independent sample realizations of the Markov process needed to achieve the demanded order of accuracy with a probability of at least 95.45%.

To estimate the amount of work required to attain this level of accuracy, we must make some further assumptions as to how the Monte Carlo computations will be carried out. From (3.3), we see that each sample will (almost surely) involve computing some one of the numbers $r_i/p_{i,i+n}$, $i = 1,\ldots,n$. It seems logical therefore to assume that these quantities will all be calculated in advance. It will require n^2 multiplications to compute ρ_o, given ξ_o, and thereafter it will require n multiplications to get the quotients $r_i/p_{i,i+n}$.

We must now come to an agreement as to how much work is involved in following each random walk $J_0, J_1, \ldots$ to absorption. It seems to be not unreasonable to assume that each step before absorption, and the step in which absorption takes place, <u>always requires the equivalent of one multiplication</u>. Of course, after absorption takes place in one of the states numbered n+1, n+2, ..., 2n, no more computations are required for the particular realization of the Markov process at hand, and a new independent sample is started. In other words, each complete random walk, represented by $J_0 \to J_1 \to J_2 \to \ldots \to J_{N^+-1} \to J_{N^+} = J_{N^+-1} + n$, will require N^+ multiplications.

In ascribing to each step the equivalent of one multiplication, we have in mind the fact that to select the value of J_{k+1}, given J_k, a pseudo-random number will presumably be generated and certain comparison operations will have to be performed.

Putting these assumptions together, we find that the total amount of work required, measured in multiplications, is

$$(4.4) \qquad n^2 + n + N_1^+ + N_2^+ + \ldots + N_{\nu_0}^+ \quad ,$$

where $N_1^+, \ldots, N_{\nu_0}^+$ are ν_0 independent determinations of the random variable N^+ introduced in Section III. This is a random variable whose (conditional) mean value is $n^2 + n + \nu_0 E(N^+|J_0=i)$ and whose (conditional) variance is $\nu_0 \text{Var}(N^+|J_0=i)$.

In Section III (e.g. 3.7) we arrived at an appraisal of the magnitude of $\text{Var}(N^+|J_0=i)$ which was just the same as our appraisal of the magnitude of $E(N^+|J_0=i)$. Interpreted very broadly, and giving our appraisals more credit for sharpness than they probably deserve, this means that if the same problem $\xi = H\xi + \gamma$, were solved over and

217

over by the Monte Carlo method, the amount of work could be expected to exhibit statistical fluctuations around its mean, of a magnitude as great as something like 2 or 3 times the square root of $\vee_0 E(N^+|J_0=i)$. Qualitatively speaking, we can state with some assurance that the amount of work required to achieve a given accuracy would vary greatly from trial to trial if the solution by Monte Carlo methods were to be carried out over and over. Due to the effect of the Central Limit Theorem as applied to (4.4) if the Monte Carlo solution were to be carried out over and over again, about half of the time the total amount of work (excluding preliminary preparations) would be less than $\vee_0 E(N^+|J_0=i)$, and about half the time it would be more than this quantity. It would practically never be more than $\vee_0 E(N^+|J_0=i) +$

$$3\left\{\vee_0 E(N^+|J_0=i)\right\}^{1/2} .$$

These statistical fluctuations of the amount of work constitute just one more obstacle to a comparison between stochastic and non-stochastic methods of solution of linear equations. It seems logical, however, to settle on the mean value of the random variable in (4.4) as the most suitable representative of the amount of work in the stochastic method to use for comparison purposes, and this we shall do.

Our formula for the mean number of multiplications required a priori to assure that $|\zeta_{\infty\ i} - \overline{Z}_\vee| < d$ is thus

$$(4.5) \qquad n^2 + n + \left\{\left[\frac{4v}{d^2}\right] + 1\right\} E(N^+|J_0=i).$$

Into this, we substitute the bounds given by (3.5) and (3.6), which are in terms of the data of the problem. We finally arrived at the formula

$$(4.6) \qquad \overline{m} = n^2 + n + \frac{1}{1 - \|H\|}\left\{1 + \left[\frac{2\|\rho\|^2}{d^2(1-\|H\|)^2}\right]\right\} ,$$

which is our basic estimate of the (mean) amount of work required in the Monte Carlo method.

V. NUMERICAL COMPARISONS

It will now be convenient to express the number d (which measures the desired closeness of approximation) as a percentage or fraction of the norm of the initial residual vector $\rho = \rho_0$. That is because $\|\rho\|$ and d appear in our formulas for amount of work only in a ratio. Thus we let

$$ d = r \, \|\rho\| \, , \qquad r > 0. $$

The goal of the non-stochastic iterative method can now be phrased as being to reduce $\|\xi_\infty - \xi_N\|$ until it becomes less than some suitably small multiple r of the largest element (in absolute value) of the initial residual vector. The goal of the stochastic method will be to reduce $|\,[\xi_\infty]_i - \bar{Z}_\nu\,|$ by repeated sampling until it too becomes less than the same small multiple r of the largest element of $\rho = \rho_0$.

With this agreement, we recapitulate our basic formulas for measuring the amount of work. The upper bound for the amount of work required in the non-stochastic iterative method is

$$ (5.1) \qquad m = n^2 + n + n^2 \left[\frac{\log r + \log(1-h)}{\log h} \right] \, , $$

where $h = \|H\|$.

The upper bound for the mean amount of work required in the stochastic method is

$$ (5.2) \qquad \bar{m} = n^2 + n + \frac{1}{1-h} \left\{ 1 + \left[\frac{2}{r^2(1-h)^2} \right] \right\} \, , $$

In each formula, the square brackets mean "largest integer in."

The quantity in braces in (5.2) represents ν_0, the total number of times the Markov process must be sampled.

Perhaps a more natural formulation of the goals of the iterative method and the Monte Carlo method from the purely theoretical point of view would be obtained if instead of requiring that the inequalities $\|\xi_\infty - \xi_N\| < r\|\rho_0\|$ and $|\xi_{\infty}]_i - \bar{z}_\nu| < r\|\rho_0\|$ shall hold (the latter with high probability), we required that the inequalities $\|\xi_\infty - \xi_N\| < r'\|\xi_\infty - \xi_0\|$ and $|\xi_{\infty}]_i - \bar{z}_\nu| < r'\|\xi_\infty - \xi_0\|$ shall hold for some specified $r' > 0$. These modified requirements lead to simpler estimates for the total amount of work. Proceeding in the spirit of our previous analysis, we use the relation

$$\|\xi_\infty - \xi_0\| = \|(I-H)^{-1}\rho_0\| \leq \frac{\|\rho_0\|}{1-h} ,$$

and rephrase the new requirements as follows:

$$\|\xi_{\infty} - \xi_N\| < r' \frac{\|\rho_0\|}{1-h} ,$$

$$|\xi_{\infty}]_i - \bar{z}_\nu| < r' \frac{\|\rho_0\|}{1-h} .$$

Substituting the right-hand members of these inequalities for d in (4.2) and (4.6) respectively, we get

$$m' = n^2 + n + n^2 \left[\frac{\log r'}{\log h} \right] ,$$

and

$$\bar{m} = n^2 + n + \frac{1}{1-h} \left\{ 1 + \left[\frac{2}{r'^2} \right] \right\} .$$

Of course in practice, $\|\xi_\infty - \xi_0\|$ is itself not computable before the solution is known, so the new requirements will always have to be translated into terms of $\|\rho_0\|$ and h, just as they were in the above theoretical error analysis. This essentially reduces the new set of requirements to the old ones, with an intermediate appraisal thrown into the picture. Therefore at the expense of a slight complication in our formulas, we choose to assume that the required degree of approximation is expressed in terms of a multiple of the computable quantity $\|\rho_0\|$ rather than in terms of a multiple of the non-computable quantity $\|\xi_\infty - \xi_0\|$.

In addition to the iterative and Monte Carlo methods of solving $\xi = H\xi + \gamma$, we promised in the ground rules in Section III that a non-iterative direct method will be brought into the comparison as a sort of standard of reference. The method we propose to consider is the Gauss Elimination Method[+]. It seems to be the particular direct method best adapted to the peculiar problem to which we have addressed ourselves; namely, that of computing just one component of the solution vector.

To apply it, we might proceed as follows: We are seeking $\xi_\infty]_i$, for some fixed $i = i_0$. Permute the columns of I-H and the components of ξ, so that the i_0-th column of I-H becomes the n-th one and the i_0-th component of ξ becomes the n-th one. Triangularize the (new) matrix I-H as in the first part of the Gauss elimination method, always using leading row elements as pivots. At the end of the triangularization procedure, which requires approximately $n^3/3 + n^2$ multiplications[++], the coefficient of the desired component is sitting out in the open, so to speak, at a vertex of a triangular array, with nothing but zeros for the other terms in its row. Of course at the same time γ must be suitably transformed.

It would require only about $(1/2)n^2$ more multiplications now to get the rest of the components of the solution, but for present purposes we ignore the fact that a complete solution would lie so near at hand at this point.

[+]See for example Dwyer [5], Section 6.4.

[++]The exact count depends on the order in which the arithmetic operations are carried out.

The elimination solution, as we said in Section 3, is assumed to be exact. No questions of approximation (which for large matrices in practice will indeed arise because of round-off error) will be considered here.

As indicated above, our formula for the amount of work in the direct solution is, then

$$(5.3) \qquad\qquad m_g = \frac{n^3}{3} + n^2 \quad .$$

It follows from formulas (5.1), (5.2), and (5.3) that with reasonable values of h and r, the direct method will be more economical for small values of n, the non-stochastic iterative method for intermediate values of n, and the Monte Carlo method for large values of n. The formulas for the break-even points, obtained by equating our estimates for the amount of work, are as follows:

The amount of work for the Gauss elimination method, as estimated by (5.3), is less than that for the stationary linear iterative method, as estimated by (5.1), for values of n in the interval

$$1 \leqq n < \frac{3a + (9a^2 + 12)^{1/2}}{2} \quad ,$$

where

$$a = \left[\frac{\log r + \log (1-h)}{\log h} \right] \quad .$$

It is greater than that for either the linear iterative method or the Monte Carlo method for values of n exceeding the right member of (5.4).

The amount of work, as estimated by (5.1), for the stationary linear iterative method is less than the mean amount of work for the Monte Carlo method, as estimated by (5.2), for values of n in the interval

$$(5.5) \qquad\qquad 1 \leqq n < \left(\frac{b}{a}\right)^{1/2} \quad ,$$

where

$$b = \frac{1}{1-h} \left\{ 1 + \left[\frac{2}{r^2(1-h)^2} \right] \right\} .$$

It is greater than the mean amount of work for the Monte Carlo method for values of n exceeding the right menber of (5.5).

In the accompanying table, we list numerical values of these limits, together with some related quantities, for various typical values of r and h. In one case--that in which h = 9/10, r = 1/10--the linear iterative method always requires (by our a priori estimates) more multiplications than some one or both of the other two methods. (We are referring to the mean amount as usual in the case of the Monte Carlo method). The break-even dimensionality for the Monte Carlo method was computed in this case by equating (5.1) and (5.3).

It is important to notice that the measure of work for the Monte Carlo method will increase only as n^2, and not as an^2, a>1. The term n^2 in (5.2) represents the work required to prepare the vector ρ_o before the stochastic estimation procedure is begun. If one is willing to content oneself with $\xi_o = 0$ as the initial estimate, then no multiplications whatever are needed to find $\rho = \rho_o$, and the term n^2 in (5.2) drops out. Under the circumstances, the total mean amount of work required by the Monte Carlo method increases only as the first power of n. If we also decide not to calculate the numbers $r_i/p_{i,i+n}$ in advance, but only as needed in the sampling, then all direct formal dependence of the mean amount of work in the Monte Carlo method on n disappears.

The reader should be warned not to try to check the table for consistency by assuming that two stages of a reduction in the magnitude of $\|\xi_\infty - \xi_N\|$ by an amount $r\|\rho_o\|$, using the approximate solution of $\xi = H\xi + \gamma$ obtained in the first stage as the ξ_o for the second stage, should theoretically require just the same amount of work as a one-stage reduction in $\|\xi_\infty - \xi_N\|$ by an amount of $r^2\|\rho_o\|$. Let N_o be the number of iterations required by the first stage. The methods

Table 1.

Favorable ranges of dimensionality for the Gauss elimination method, a linear iterative method, and the corresponding Monte Carlo method, as determined by a priori analysis.

Note: The problem is to compute only one component of the solution of $\xi = H\xi + \gamma$.

Norm of H and measure of accuracy required.	$h=\frac{5}{10}, r=\frac{1}{10}$	$h=\frac{5}{10}, r=\frac{1}{100}$	$h=\frac{5}{10}, r=\frac{1}{1000}$	$h=\frac{9}{10}, r=\frac{1}{10}$	$h=\frac{9}{10}, r=\frac{1}{100}$	$h=\frac{9}{10}, r=\frac{1}{1000}$	$h=\frac{9}{10}, r=10^{-10}$
Favorable range of dimensionality for Gauss elimination method.	$n \le 12$	$n \le 21$	$n \le 33$	$n \le 84$	$n \le 195$	$n \le 261$	$n \le 720$
Favorable range of dimensionality for linear iterative method.	$13 \le n \le 20$	$22 \le n \le 151$	$34 \le n \le 1206$	(b)	$196 \le n \le 554$	$262 \le n \le 4794$	$n \ge 721$
Favorable range of dimensionality for Monte Carlo method.	$n \ge 21$	$n \ge 152$	$n \ge 1207$	$n \ge 85$	$n \ge 555$	$n \ge 4795$	(c)
Mean number of multiplications required by Monte Carlo method at beginning of favorable range.	2064	183,258	17,458,058	207,320	20,308,590	2,022,996,830	(c)
Approximate time to perform multiplication in row above. (a)	3 sec.	4 min.	5 hrs.	4 min.	6 hrs.	563 hrs.	(c)

Notes: (a) Calculated at the rate of one millisecond per multiplication and rounded off to the next higher unit of time.

(b) The linear iterative method is never more favorable than both of the other two methods simultaneously in this case. For $n \le 68$, it is more favorable than the Monte Carlo method. For $n \ge 130$ it is more favorable than the elimination method.

(c) The Monte Carlo method does not become more favorable than the iterative method in this case until a ridiculously high dimensionality, of the order of 10^{+10}, is reached. At this dimensionality, it would take 10^{13} years to perform the Monte Carlo calculations.

224

used to compute the table would place N_o at the smallest
value compatible with

$$(5.6) \qquad \frac{h^{N_o}}{1-h} < r \quad .$$

If N_o' is the number of iterations required to effect a one-
stage reduction in $\|\xi_\infty - \xi_N\|$ by an amount $r^2\|\rho_o\|$, the
methods used to compute the table would place N_o' at the
smallest value compatible with

$$\frac{h^{N_o'}}{1-h} < r^2 \quad .$$

This inequality is the same as the following one:

$$\frac{h^{N_o'/2}}{1-h} < \frac{r}{(1-h)^{1/2}} \quad .$$

Since $(1-h)^{1/2} < 1$, it follows by comparison with (5.6) that
$N_o'/2 < N_o$.

It should also be pointed out that to perform a Monte
Carlo approximation in two stages would require that all components of the solution vector must be estimated in the first
stage, and not just one component. The reason is that to set
up the random variable Z (see (3.3)) for the second stage of
estimation, all the components of the initial residual vector
for this stage must be available.

VI. AN ANALOGOUS COMPARISON
FOR MATRIX INVERSION

If the problem is to solve AX = I, where A is a given
n x n matrix, a suitable modification of (3.2) on which to
construct a Monte Carlo solution is as follows:

(6.1) $\qquad X_\infty = A^{-1} = X_0 + (I+H_0+H_0^2+\ldots)H_0X_0 ,$

where X_0 is an initial estimate of A^{-1} and $H_0 = I - X_0A$.
If X_0 is a reasonably good estimate of A^{-1}, then $\| H_0 \| < 1$,
and the infinite series in (6.1) converges. We assume that
$\| H_0 \| < 1$ throughout the remainder of this section.

We set up the numbers z_{ij} and p_{ij} in terms of the elements of H_0 exactly as in Section III. Assuming that we are trying to approximate the (i,k)-th element of X_∞, we take as the $\wp$ of formula (3.3), the k-th column of H_0X_0. The statistical estimator will now be

$$ \overline{z}_\nu = \xi_0]_i + \frac{z_1+z_2+\ldots+z_\nu}{\nu} , $$

where ξ_0 is the k-th column of X_0.

The stationary linear iterative process which corresponds to (6.1) is given by the recursion formula

(6.2) $\qquad X_{N+1} = H_0X_N + X_0, \quad N = 0,1,\ldots,$

where X_N is the N-th approximation to A^{-1}. Obviously $A^{-1} = H_0A^{-1} + X_0$, so

$$ A^{-1} - X_N = H_0(A^{-1} - X_{N-1}) = \ldots = H_0^N(A^{-1} - X_0) . $$

This is the analogue of (2.5). Since $A^{-1} - X_0 = (I-H)^{-1}HX_0$, we find that

(6.3) $\qquad A^{-1} - X_N = H_0^N(I-H_0)^{-1}H_0X_0 .$

This equation is the analogue of (2.12).

226

If we let ξ_N denote the k-th column of X_N, $N = 0, 1, \ldots,$ then the iterations defined by (6.2) give the following sequence of approximations to ξ_∞, the k-th column of A^{-1}.

$$(6.4) \qquad \xi_{N+1} = H_o \xi_N + \xi_o, \quad N = 0, 1, \ldots \quad .$$

Also, from (6.3),

$$\xi_\infty - \xi_N = H_o^N (I - H)^{-1} \rho \, ,$$

where ρ is the k-th column of $H_o X_o$. This equation is formally identical with (2.12). Moreover, from it we find that

$$(6.5) \qquad \| \xi_\infty - \xi_N \| \leq \frac{\| H_o \|^N}{1 - \| H_o \|} \| \rho \| \, ,$$

which is the same as (2.13).

If we now define our problem as that of insuring that $\| \xi_\infty - \xi_N \| < d$ in the non-stochastic method, and $| [\xi_\infty]_i - \overline{z}_\nu | < d$ in the stochastic method, where $d > 0$ is preassigned, then the <u>a priori</u> error analyses become precisely the same as those given in Section IV. It requires n^3 multiplications to set up H_o, given X_o, and then n^2 more to find $\rho = H \xi_o$. However, $H \xi_o$ will be used again in the non-stochastic method to pass from ξ_o to ξ_1. The resulting formula for the total amount of work, including the preparatory work becomes in the non-stochastic case,

$$(6.6) \qquad m = n^3 + n + n^2 \left[\frac{\log r + \log (1-h)}{\log h} \right] \, ,$$

where $h = \| H_o \|$ and $r = d / \| \rho \|$. In the stochastic case it becomes

$$(6.7) \qquad \overline{m} = n^3 + n^2 + n + \frac{1}{1-h} \left\{ 1 + \left[\frac{2}{r^2 (1-h)^2} \right] \right\} \quad .$$

227

The break-even point for the two methods is given by the formula $\{b/(a-1)\}^{1/2}$, where a and b have the same meaning as in Section V. For values of n less than this quantity, the non-stochastic method requires less work than the stochastic method, and for values of n greater than this quantity, the stochastic method requires less work than the non-stochastic method.

In comparing these formulas with (5.1), (5.2) and (5.5) it should be remembered that in arriving at the earlier work-estimates (5.1) and (5.2) for the problem $A\xi = \eta$, we assumed that the H and the γ in the equivalent form $\xi = H\xi + \gamma$ were given, and so we did not count in work required to find them. Here we did count in the work required to find our H (denoted here by H_o). (The vector γ is here ξ_o, and it comes free, so to speak.) The methods have therefore become nominally unfavorable as compared to the Gauss elimination method, which for the present problem (finding one component of the solution of $A\xi = \varepsilon_k$ where ε_k is the k-th column of I) would require rather less than $n^3/3 + n^2$ multiplications.

We can sidestep the n^3 multiplications required to get H_o, by taking X_o as a very simple matrix (maybe even $X_o = I$ if $\| I-A \| < 1$). But we should state here that the real motivation for using a linear iterative method, or one of the many orthogonalization and gradient methods, for the problem $A\xi = \eta$, or the problem $AX = I$, in place of a straightforward elimination method, usually does not lie in a theoretical count of the number of operations required in the worst cases. It lies in the fact that A may have special properties (e.g., symmetry, or many zeros) which are not suitably exploited by the elimination methods. We are completely ignoring such considerations throughout this study. Another motivation sometimes is presented by the necessity of controlling round-off error. (The Monte Carlo method looks very good from this standpoint.)

It would also be possible to construct a Monte Carlo solution on the following rearrangement of (6.1):

$$X_\infty = A^{-1} = (I + H_o + H_o^2 + \ldots) X_o .$$

The vector form of this equation is

228

$$\xi_\infty = (I + H_0 + H_0^2 + \ldots)\xi_0,$$

where ξ_∞ and ξ_0 have the same meaning as before. This procedure would avoid the necessity of calculating $H\xi_0$ in advance, and so the n^2 term would drop out of (6.7). The numbers z_{ij} and p_{ij}, and the random variables $J_0, J_1, \ldots$ would be set up as in Section III, but in the random variable Z, the components of ρ would be replaced by those of ξ_0, and the estimator $\bar{Z}_v, [\xi_0]_i$ would be replaced by zero. With these changes, the estimate (3.5) of the variance of Z becomes

$$v \leq \frac{1}{2} \frac{\|\xi_0\|^2}{(1 - \|H_0\|)^2},$$

and formula (4.6) for the mean amount of work (now augmented by the calculation of H_0 but decreased by the amount of work previously necessary to calculate ρ) becomes

$$\bar{m} = n^3 + n + \frac{1}{1 - \|H_0\|} \left\{ 1 + \left[\frac{2\|\xi_0\|^2}{d^2(1 - \|H_0\|)^2} \right] \right\}.$$

The disadvantage of this arrangement is that it does not exploit the fact that v varies with the square of the norm of whatever vector is playing the role of the vector Θ of Section III. Therefore the goodness of the initial estimate is here made use of to reduce the statistical fluctuations and consequent mean amount of work only through the effect it has on the value of $1/(1 - \|H_0\|)$.

These remarks suggest a more general comment which is perhaps the key to all the developments in this paper. The statistical part of the amount of work required by the Monte Carlo method to achieve a given accuracy in computing one element of a solution, is independent of the dimensionality of the problem. Other known methods vary as the square and cube of the dimensionality, and those which vary as the square do so with a proportionality constant much larger than unity. Therefore if one uses the Monte Carlo method, one can afford to make substantial preliminary preparations, involving an amount of work which varies even with the square of the dimensionality, if these preparations will substantially cut down the error in the subsequent statistical estimation procedure.

For the sake of completeness, we shall bring into the comparison a certain class of non-linear iterative processes for computing A^{-1} which theoretically converge much faster than the linear iterative process (6.2) for a given initial estimate X_o. A typical member of the class is defined by the recursion formula[+]

$$(6.8) \qquad X_{N+1} = (I+H_N+H_N^2+\ldots+H_N^{s-1})X_N, \qquad N = 0,1,2,\ldots,$$

where $H_N = I-X_N A$, and s is some integer not less than 2. If s = 2, the formula becomes $S_{N+1} = (2I-X_N A)X_N$, which is mentioned in most textbooks on numerical analysis as an analogue of the Newton-Raphson method for finding the roots of non-linear single equations in scalars[++].

The clue to an a priori error analysis for (6.8) lies in observing that

$$H_N = I - X_N A = I - (I+H_{N-1}+H_{N-1}^2+\ldots+H_{N-1}^s)X_{N-1}A$$

$$= I - (I+H_{N-1}+\ldots+H_{N-1}^s)(I-H_{N-1})$$

$$= H_{N-1}^s \quad .$$

[+]Our presentation of these polynomial iteration procedures will be slightly different from that usually encountered in the literature, so as to line them up with (6.1) and (6.2). The usual presentation replaces our $H_N = I-X_N A$ by $I - AX_N$. A number of references relating to these methods, as well as to all other methods discussed in this paper will be found in Forsythe [6].

[++]See e.g., Householder [7], pp. 56-57.

Therefore by back substitution,

$$H_N = H_O S^N \; .$$

Now $A^{-1} - X_N = (I - X_N A) A^{-1} = H_N A^{-1}$; and $X_O A = I - H_O$, so $A^{-1} = (I - H_O)^{-1} X_O$. From all this we obtain:

$$A^{-1} - X_N = H_O^{S^N} (I-H_O)^{-1} X_O = H_O^{S^N-1} (I-H_O)^{-1} H_O X_O \; .$$

This equation is the analogue of (6.3). From it we get in place of (6.5),

$$(6.9) \qquad \| \xi_\infty - \xi_N \| \leq \frac{\| H_O \|^{S^N - 1}}{1 - \| H_O \|} \| \rho \| \; ,$$

and this clearly represents a much faster rate of convergence than (6.5).

The difficulty is that each iteration of (6.8) requires sn^3 multiplications. Moreover in the special problem at hand--that of finding only one element of A^{-1}--the method does not appear to good advantage, because there seems to be no way to avoid computing all the elements of the matrix X_N each time, and not just the k-th column, as we did in the linear iterative method. In other words, there seems to be no direct analogue of the vector recursion formula (6.4) in the method given by (6.8).

The formula for the total amount of work required to make the right hand member of (6.9) less than $r \| \rho \|$, where $r > 0$ is preassigned, is as follows:

$$(6.10) \qquad sn^3 + sn^3 \left[\frac{\log \left(1 + \dfrac{\log r + \log (1-h)}{\log h} \right)}{\log s} \right]$$

where, as usual, the square brackets means "largest integer in" and $h = \| H_O \|$. A study of the maximum and minimum of this expression, considered as a function of s, reveals that s = 2 or s = 3 usually are the most advantageous values of s to use. For example, if $r = 10^{-3}$ and $h = 9/10$, then the formula (6.10) becomes

$$sn^3 \left(1 + \left[\frac{1.9465}{\log s} \right] \right) .$$

If s = 2, this equals $14n^3$. If s = 3, it equals $15n^3$. If s = 4, it equals $16n^3$. For higher values of s, the disadvantage becomes more pronounced.

With $r = 10^{-3}$, $h = 9/10$, s = 2, the amount of work required by the non-linear iterative method given by (6.4), as estimated from (6.10), is less than required by the linear method given by (6.4), as estimated from (6.6), for $n \leq 6$. It is greater for $n \geq 7$.

REFERENCES

[1] Courant, R., and Hilbert, D., Methoden der Mathematischen Physik, Berlin, 1931.

[2] Cramér, H., Mathematical Methods of Statistics, Princeton, 1951.

[3] Curtiss, J. H., "Monte Carlo" methods for the iteration of linear operators, Journal of Mathematics and Physics, vol. 32 (1954), pp. 209-232.

[4] Curtiss, J. H., Sampling methods applied to differential and difference equations; Proceedings of a Seminar on Scientific Computation, held by the International Business Machines Corporation, Endicott, New York, November, 1949; pp. 87-109.

[5] Dwyer, P. S., Linear Computations, New York, 1951.

[6] Forsythe, G. E., Tentative Classification of Methods and Bibliography on Solving Systems of Linear Equations. In "Simultaneous Linear Equations and the Determination of Eigenvalues," National Bureau of Standards Applied Mathematics Series 29, Washington, 1953.

[7] Householder, A. S., Principles of Numerical Analysis, New York, 1953.

[8] Milne, W. E., <u>Numerical Solution of Differential Equations</u>, New York, 1953.

[9] Taussky-Todd, O., <u>A recurring theorem on determinants</u>, American Mathematical Monthly, vol. 56 (1949), pp. 672-676.

A DESCRIPTION OF THE GENERATION AND TESTING OF A
SET OF RANDOM NORMAL DEVIATES[+]

Ernest J. Lytle, Jr.

University of Florida

A set of 25,000 random normal deviates, with mean zero, variance one, was generated and tested rather exhaustively. Since the deviates were generated to five decimal places, they were so listed, as unneeded places may easily be dropped.[++] The generation process was, in effect, accomplished by numerically transforming variates (drawn at random) from the rectangular distribution to their associated values in the normal distribution. For example, if we let

$$Y = \frac{1}{\sqrt{2\pi}} \int_{-\infty}^{x} e^{-t^2/2} \, dt, \qquad (1)$$

and obtain random values of Y from a suitable table of random numbers, then for each particular one of these Y values the associated value from the normal distribution may be obtained by determining a value of x, the upper limit of the integral, such that (1) is satisfied.

The RAND table of random numbers [6] was used as a source of values of Y; the associated values of x which satisfy (1) were obtained with the aid of a table of the normal distribution [5] which also contained pairs of values of the necessary constants for linear interpolation. Linear interpolation with the aid of this table yields values which are correct to five decimal places in the range $-4.51500 \leq x \leq 4.51500$.

The table of random normal deviates is listed on 100 pages with ten columns of twenty-five six-digit variates on each page. The table is available on a deck of 2,500 IBM cards with negative values indicated by the usual x overpunch.

[+]Prepared in connection with research sponsored by WADC.

[++]The first quarter of the odd-numbered columns of the 100,000 RAND normal deviates [7] correspond to the first five columns of this table, rounded to three decimals. The remaining five columns are independent of and in addition to those of the RAND table.

At the bottom of each page, the totals, Σx and Σx^2, and range W for each of the ten columns of 25 deviates are listed. Also included is the quantity Σxy and the correlation coefficient R between x and y, where x is an element of an odd-numbered column and y is the element adjacent to x in the succeeding even-numbered column. Each deviate consists of one whole number and five decimals, together with an indication of sign.

The overall mean value of the variate is -0.00412 and the standard deviation is .99591. The average range for the samples of size 25 as listed by columns on all the pages is 3.97736. Extreme deviates in the table are +3.56375 and -4.37000, although the method of generation would have permitted extreme values as large as $\pm$4.51500. The correlation coefficient between adjacent values as described above for the entire table is -.01554.

TESTS OF NORMALITY AND RANDOMNESS

Assuming that the table of random numbers used has been thoroughly tested, then the table of normal deviates derived from this set should also be random and further testing could be considered as redundant. However, the conversion to normal deviates is of necessity an approximate one and tests are required to determine whether or not the approximations are close enough for practical use. The following tests are designed to answer this question. Except for the incidence of duplicate values in the tails, the table would seem to be quite satisfactory.

Actual sampling distributions of means, variances, ranges and correlations of samples drawn from this normal population were compared with the corresponding theoretical distributions. Of the multitudinous possible arrangements which could be used in drawing samples from such a distribution, the plan of drawing samples in order by columns over the entire table and drawing by columns within pages is the plan adopted and presented in the tables which follow. The sign run tests in which sequences of runs above and below the median are enumerated and compared with the theoretical values are presented as partial evidence of randomness in arrangements within columns.

1. <u>Means or Sums</u>. The means or sums should be distributed normally. So if

$$t = \left| \frac{\Sigma x}{n} \right| \;, \quad P = 1 - 2 \int_0^t \phi(t) dt.$$

Listed below in Table 1 are the sums, means and the P-value in percent, based on sums of columns as they appear on the pages; Column 1, for example, includes 100 pages of the 25 items in Column 1 of each page.

TABLE 1

SUMS, MEANS AND TEST RESULTS BASED ON SUMS BY COLUMNS

Column	Σx or Sums	x̄ or Means	Sum Test P-value in Percent
1	19.60142	.00784	69.5
2	57.68699	.02307	24.8
3	-58.17223	-.02327	24.5
4	-32.80429	-.01312	51.2
5	-46.59499	-.01864	35.1
6	-66.21621	-.02649	18.6
7	57.70210	.02308	24.9
8	16.81443	.00673	73.7
9	-62.83288	-.02513	20.9
10	11.77807	.00471	81.3

The values of the sums, means and P for the entire 25,000 items are -103.03759, -.00412 and 51.4 percent, respectively.

The same test was applied using each of the 100 pages of 250 values as the sampling unit, with the result that two of the 100 pages, page 44 and page 63, failed at the 2% probability level. When tested by columns as the 25 values would appear on the pages there were 17 columns out of 1000 which could be rejected at the 2% level. These tests seem to show that the table as a whole, used by columns and pages as printed, varies according to expectation with respect to means and sums.

2. <u>Square Sums or Variances</u>. The variances, as well as the related Σx^2 should be distributed as Chi-square. This test can be used for the individual samples of 25. When testing by pages, columns or the table in its entirety, that is for large n, the distribution of $\sqrt{2\Sigma x^2}$ can be taken as normally distributed with mean $\sqrt{2n-1}$ and standard deviation one. So if $\qquad t = \left| \sqrt{2\Sigma x^2} - \sqrt{2n-1} \right|$,

$P = 1 - 2 \int_0^t \phi(t)dt$. In applying this test the same rejection level of 2% was used.

Table 2 contains the sums of squares, standard deviations and P-values based on tests of sums of squares of columns detailed in somewhat the same manner as in Table 1.

TABLE 2

SUMS OF SQUARES, STANDARD DEVIATION, AND TEST RESULTS
BASED ON SUMS OF SQUARES BY COLUMNS

Column	Σx^2 or Sum of Squares	σ or Standard Deviation	Square Sum Test P-value in Percent
1	2372.74397	.97419	6.9
2	2624.25437	1.02440	8.0
3	2449.97045	.98968	48.2
4	2468.76024	.99365	66.3
5	2402.52129	.98015	16.6
6	2564.23776	1.01242	36.3
7	2478.15631	.99536	76.2
8	2518.18174	1.00360	79.2
9	2545.91227	1.00882	51.4
10	2370.89554	.97383	6.5

The sum of squares, standard deviation and the P-value for the whole table are 24796.23394, .99591 and 36.8 percent, respectively.

When the square sum test was applied to each page, page 69 failed to pass at the 2% level. The test, when applied to each sample of 25 values, found 18 failures as against 20 failures expected. Again the tests seem favorable even to including the predicted number of failures.

3. The Range. Before examining the formal tests for normality and randomness using ranges, somewhat indirect tests may be inferred from tables of frequency distributions of ranges of sample size 10 (Table 4) and size 25 (Table 5). By use of tables computed by Pearson and Hartley [3], the percentage levels for sample size 10 on the lower and upper ends of the distribution were determined. These levels and the frequencies within these levels are indicated in Table 3. Using a Chi-square test on these values, a P = 75% was indicated. Table 5 is given only as a descriptive table, since computed probabilities for sample size 25 are not available.

TABLE 3

FREQUENCY DISTRIBUTION OF EXTREME VALUES OF RANGE

Percent	Ranges Under	Cumulative Frequencies	
		Observed	Expected
1	1.47	24	25
2	1.61	44	50
2.5	1.67	58	62.5
5	1.86	115	125
Percent	Ranges Over		
95	4.47	112	125
97.5	4.79	49	62.5
98	4.88	41	50
99	5.16	18	25

A more formal range test is based on samples of size 10, with samples taken consecutively from each column. Sets of 250 samples, 1000 samples and 2,500 samples were tested. The intervals of ranges for 6 classes and 10 classes were determined by interpolation from the theoretical distribution mentioned above. The frequencies tabulated were compared with the expected frequencies of n/20 and n/100 (n equal to the total number of observations in a set). The degrees of freedom used for the Chi-square test were 5 and 9, respectively.

TABLE 4

RANGE FOR SAMPLE SIZES OF 10 (RANDOM NORMAL DEVIATES)

Range	I	II	III	IV	V	VI	VII	VIII	IX	X	Total
1.1										1	1
1.2	1				1	1	1				4
1.3						2		1	1	2	6
1.4	1	2		1	3		1	1	1	1	11
1.5	4	2		1	2	1		2	1	1	14
1.6	2	2	1	2	2	1	1	2	1		14
1.7	3	1	1	2	3	1	1	7	5	2	26
1.8	6	1	4	3	7	5	3	1	5	3	38
1.9	2	1	4	7	1	4	6	2	6	8	41
2.0	5	4	5	7	4	8	4	6	9	4	56
2.1	5	6	9	6	8	1		3	9	8	55
2.2	9	4	9	9	10	6	8	10	8	5	78
2.3	12	7	12	14	10	7	12	9	15	8	106
2.4	9	6	8	11	7	10	12	9	7	12	91
2.5	14	15	7	13	11	11	14	12	7	15	119
2.6	12	9	14	11	12	11	12	14	6	16	117
2.7	18	16	15	4	14	12	12	7	5	15	118
2.8	15	10	16	11	20	7	10	6	11	10	116
2.9	12	13	8	21	6	13	13	16	18	15	135
3.0	12	14	18	12	9	19	18	17	13	17	149
3.1	11	18	15	7	11	13	16	17	14	15	137
3.2	12	14	9	9	11	9	15	9	11	9	108
3.3	7	12	13	16	8	12	15	21	13	11	128
3.4	14	8	8	8	13	12	12	10	9	12	106
3.5	7	14	13	10	9	14	12	7	10	7	103
3.6	8	7	11	9	10	12	3	9	10	11	90
3.7	8	6	12	9	6	9	8	11	7	6	82
3.8	6	6	8	4	8	11	8	3	4	5	63
3.9	4	13	5	6	6	4	6	6	2	4	56
4.0	4	6	5	4	10	3	6	7	8	8	61
4.1	8	7	4	5	7	6	5	5	5		52
4.2	4	6	3	5	3	4	7	3	8	5	48
4.3	2	3	3	2	2	4	2	3	7	3	31
4.4	5	6	1	4		2	2	1		3	24
4.5	1	4	2	2	4	3		2	3	3	24
4.6	5		2	5	1	2	1	4	3	4	27
4.7	1			2	4	1		3	1		12
4.8			1	3	2	2			1		9
4.9	1	1	1	1	1		2	1	1		9
5.0		3		1	1	3	1		1		10
5.1		1		1	1			2	1	1	7
5.2		1	1	1	1	2		1			7
5.3			1			1			1		3
5.4		1	1		1		1		1		5
5.5									1		1
5.6											
5.7											
5.8						1					1
5.9				1							1
Total	250	250	250	250	250	250	250	250	250	250	2500

239

TABLE 5

RANGE FOR SAMPLE SIZES OF 25 (RANDOM NORMAL DEVIATES)

Range	I	II	III	IV	V	VI	VII	VIII	IX	X	Total
2.2								1	1		2
2.3											
2.4	1										1
2.5			1	1	1				1	1	5
2.6	2	1			1	1		2		2	9
2.7	1		1	2	1	1	2	1	1	1	11
2.8	1	1	2	1		3	3	1	2	1	15
2.9	3		3	4	4	2	1		5	1	23
3.0	4	4	3	2	2	4	2	5	1	6	33
3.1	3	4	3	5	4	3	3	8	1	4	38
3.2	4	2	3	3	6	3	1	2	2	4	30
3.3	3	2	5	6	3	1	9	7	3	4	43
3.4	7	1	6	2	5	1	8	5	4	5	44
3.5	3	2	3	1	5	7	8	6	11	7	53
3.6	4	4	3	11	6	5	5	5	4	7	54
3.7	8	8	6	2	7	2	5	4	1	7	50
3.8	9	9	3	6	5	8	7	4	4	6	61
3.9	5	9	9	10	3	9	6	5	7	4	67
4.0	6	6	6	3	7	6	5	6	4	6	55
4.1	4	6	6	8	4	6	7	4	9	7	61
4.2	3	6	5	1	6	3	6	5	7	3	45
4.3	7	2	8	5	2	3	5	2	10	5	49
4.4	5	12	6	5	3	6	2	4		7	50
4.5	2	1	5	2	7	4		6	3	2	32
4.6	6	2	2	4	1	5	2	6	7	1	36
4.7	1	4	2	3	3	4	5	3	1	2	28
4.8	2	2	4	1	3				4	2	18
4.9	4	1	1	1	1	1	1		1		11
5.0		6		4	3	2	2	1	1		19
5.1		1		1	3	1		2		3	11
5.2	1	2	1	2	2	3		2		1	14
5.3			1			1	1	1	1		5
5.4		1	1	1	1		3		1		8
5.5			1				1		1		3
5.6		1				1					2
5.7				1	1				1	1	4
5.8	1					2					3
5.9			1	1				1			3
6.0						1		1			2
6.1						1					1
6.2											
6.3											
6.4									1		1
Total	100	100	100	100	100	100	100	100	100	100	1000

240

Table 6 shows the distribution of ranges by columns of 250 samples of size 10 with 6 class intervals, together with corresponding Chi-square values.

Table 6

RESULTS OF RANGE TEST FOR 6 CLASSES AND SAMPLE SIZE 10

%	Range of W	Frequencies of W (Range) by Columns										Total
		1	2	3	4	5	6	7	8	9	10	
0 to 16.7	0.000 to 2.306	43	25	39	43	48	31	29	38	54	38	388
16.7 to 33.3	2.307 to 2.692	51	42	40	44	38	39	50	43	29	54	430
33.3 to 50.0	2.693 to 3.024	45	43	47	45	40	45	44	40	39	47	433
50.0 to 66.7	3.025 to 3.376	38	48	44	36	37	44	56	53	46	41	443
66.7 to 83.3	3.377 to 3.842	38	40	49	39	43	53	35	38	37	39	411
83.3 to 100.0	3.843 to	35	52	31	43	44	40	36	38	45	31	395
χ^2 =		4.13	10.32	5.09	1.44	2.06	6.24	12.43	4.18	8.93	7.58	5.95
P =		53%	7%	41%	92%	84%	29%	3%	53%	12%	19%	31%

Columns 2, 4 and 7 seem a little unusual with respect to ranges.

The same test was repeated except that ten classes were used instead of six. The corresponding P-values differed considerably from those for which but six classes were used. The Chi-squares by columns for the ten class intervals were 4.40, 10.64, 12.88, 11.28, 9.84, 7.76, 10.00, 8.48, 16.00 and 10.72, with corresponding P-values of 88, 30, 17, 26, 37, 56, 36, 49, 7 and 30, respectively. For the table as a whole, when ten classes were used, a Chi-square of 7.12 and a P-value of 63 were obtained.

4. <u>Sign Runs</u>. The sequence of plus and minus signs (above and below the median) should be purely random. The sign run test is based on the expected number of sign runs of both signs of length i from n values. This expected value is $n/2^{i+1}$ [1] for i = 1,2,3,4,5 and $n/2^6 + 1/2^{n-1}$ for all values of length six and above. For n = 2500, and i = 1,2,3,4,5 and 6, these expected values are 625, 312, 156, 78, 39 and 39, respectively. The test was applied to each of the columns of 2500 items each, and to the entire table.

TABLE 7

SIGN RUN LENGTHS AND CHI-SQUARE TEST BY COLUMNS AND TOTALS

Length of run (i)	of	Runs of Length i by Column									
	1	2	3	4	5	6	7	8	9	10	
1	609	644	656	593	659	599	659	604	610	590	6221
2	312	342	315	328	312	295	288	317	298	336	3144
3	150	161	146	146	148	157	160	171	160	156	1556
4	83	79	88	86	87	82	83	73	80	74	814
5	42	31	34	41	40	37	45	41	35	37	383
6	41	30	37	38	33	45	32	34	45	41	377
x^2 =	1.294	7.353	4.233	4.049	4.247	3.245	6.298	3.292	2.476	4.217	2.316
P =	97	29	65	67	64	78	46	77	87	65	89

The results in Table 7 appear to be quite satisfactory. Using the formula $k_{.05} \simeq 3.3 (\log n + 1)$, the length of the longest run for which we would expect to get at least one with probability of 5% can be found [1]. This value is 14. There were two runs of 14 and none any longer.

5. <u>Coefficient of Correlation</u>. Correlation coefficients were calculated between the 25 elements of an odd-numbered column and the adjacent elements of the next even-numbered column. Table 8 shows frequency distributions by hundreds and for the total 500 samples.

242

TABLE 8

DISTRIBUTION OF COEFFICIENTS OF CORRELATION R FOR SAMPLE SIZE 25

R	Frequency of R between Columns					
	1 and 2	3 and 4	5 and 6	7 and 8	9 and 10	Total
-.6 and under					1	1
-.6 to -.5		1			.	1
-.5 to -.4	2	1	3	4	2	12
-.4 to -.3	2	7	2	4	6	21
-.3 to -.2	16	4	9	12	15	56
-.2 to -.1	15	23	14	17	12	81
-.1 to 0	21	26	27	23	15	112
0 to .1	18	15	13	9	17	72
.1 to .2	13	9	14	13	15	64
.2 to .3	8	12	11	12	9	52
.3 to .4	3	1	5	4	5	18
.4 to .5	1	1	2	2	3	9
.5 to .6	1					1

The null hypothesis, $\rho = 0$, was tested by use of student's t, where $t = R\sqrt{(n-2)/(1-R^2)}$ with (n-2) degrees of freedom [4]. From this we find that we can expect that in 1% of the samples $|R|$ will be greater than .5, or in 5 out of 500. It is noted that in the table above there are three such values.

By setting probabilities of deviations greater than t at 10%, 20%, ..., 90%, corresponding values of t were found to be -1.319, -.858, -.532, -.256, .000, .256, ..., 1.319.

Using these values of t and n = 25, the range of values for R for 0% to 10%, 10% to 20%, ..., 90% to 100% were calculated. Of course the expected values would be 10 for sets of 100 and 50 for sets of 500. Chi-square values were calculated, together with corresponding values of P, and both listed in Table 9 below.

TABLE 9

RESULTS OF TEST OF COEFFICIENTS OF CORRELATION

%	Range of R	Frequencies of R between Columns					
		1 and 2	3 and 4	5 and 6	7 and 8	9 and 10	Total
0- 10	-.26518 to -1.00000	8	12	8	13	17	58
10- 20	-.17251 to -.26518	16	5	9	12	12	54
20- 30	-.11025 to -.17251	9	15	9	9	6	48
30- 40	-.05330 to -.11025	15	15	11	15	10	66
40- 50	.00000 to -.05330	8	15	18	11	6	58
50- 60	.00000 to .05330	11	7	7	4	11	40
60- 70	.05330 to .11025	8	9	6	6	8	37
70- 80	.11025 to .17251	10	4	8	9	8	39
80- 90	.17251 to .26518	6	13	10	8	12	49
90-100	.26518 to 1.00000	9	5	14	13	10	51
	$\chi^2 =$	9.2	18.4	11.6	10.6	9.8	15.9
	P =	40%	3.4%	24%	31%	37%	7%

5. **Distribution of values.** After ordering on columns, a goodness of fit test was made using Chi-square and twenty equal classes (19 degrees of freedom). The same test was also made with the upper and lower five percent, each broken into one-percent classes (27 d.f.). Results were also obtained for the lower 5% alone, lower 50% alone, the upper 5% alone, and the upper 50% alone. For P = 5% with 5 d.f., $\chi^2 = 11.07$; with 14 d.f., $\chi^2 = 23.69$. In the lower 5%, Columns 3 and 10 failed to pass the test; while Column 2 failed in the upper 5%. In the lower and upper 50%, none of the columns failed; and there were no failures in any of the tests at the 2% level. The remainder of the P-values are given in Table 10. The same type tests were made after combining classes in Table 10, so that 0-1 percent is combined with 99-100 percent, 1-2 percent is combined with 98-99 percent, ..., 45-50 percent is combined with 50-55 percent. In no case were P-values below the 5% level.

244

TABLE 10

DISTRIBUTION OF VALUES BY COLUMNS

Percent	Columns										Total
	1	2	3	4	5	6	7	8	9	10	
0 - 1	13	29	17	27	35	36	18	17	31	14	237
1 - 2	17	22	16	20	19	31	36	25	19	20	225
2 - 3	30	22	34	19	30	23	16	27	34	19	254
3 - 4	23	32	31	27	16	25	23	27	29	18	251
4 - 5	27	33	30	34	28	21	23	26	25	33	280
χ^2(5 d.f.) =	9.64	5.88	11.48	6.00	10.04	7.08	10.36	2.92	6.76	11.80	6.84
5 - 10	130	112	136	134	109	128	121	112	120	140	1242
10 - 15	122	119	120	125	130	106	135	141	126	111	1235
15 - 20	133	126	136	118	125	128	118	146	133	133	1296
20 - 25	113	121	107	138	116	130	126	133	124	134	1242
25 - 30	122	132	135	111	120	140	115	117	125	107	1224
30 - 35	133	115	128	131	128	124	118	117	127	127	1248
35 - 40	140	134	144	122	138	126	109	104	126	133	1276
40 - 45	128	116	137	121	130	132	126	129	119	104	1242
45 - 50	126	129	119	125	137	112	130	106	131	131	1246
χ^2(14 d.f.) =	14.04	10.27	21.41	10.45	15.91	13.80	15.14	17.93	8.10	23.28	9.96

Expected frequencies are based on the total number of deviates in the overall sampling distribution; thus there is no constraint on the total frequency for any one particular portion of the sampling distribution. Tests of these individual parts are not independent.

245

TABLE 10 (Continued)

Percent	Column										Total
	1	2	3	4	5	6	7	8	9	10	
99 -100	24	28	27	24	18	22	23	22	20	18	226
98 - 99	31	23	28	26	18	29	20	27	27	23	252
97 - 98	21	40	18	18	16	29	33	29	25	27	256
96 - 97	25	25	27	25	33	30	23	24	26	27	265
95 - 96	16	32	17	24	20	26	34	29	24	28	250
χ^2 (5 d.f.) =	5.36	11.48	5.20	2.08	10.72	2.68	7.12	1.84	1.24	2.80	3.36
90 - 95	125	146	125	119	127	105	132	143	136	127	1285
85 - 90	120	120	121	130	117	124	126	123	135	115	1231
80 - 85	133	122	112	103	117	112	133	120	107	128	1187
75 - 80	119	120	121	133	114	144	112	135	117	127	1242
70 - 75	116	124	126	140	130	126	143	114	125	125	1269
65 - 70	134	116	116	116	156	112	125	119	130	141	1265
60 - 65	130	109	119	116	124	119	134	137	131	124	1243
55 - 60	118	134	141	131	128	139	125	130	105	144	1295
50 - 55	131	119	112	143	121	121	123	121	123	122	1236
χ^2 (14 d.f.) =	8.54	19.12	11.15	12.93	20.84	13.47	12.66	8.20	9.83	8.75	10.24
χ^2 (27 d.f.) =	22.58	29.39	32.56	23.38	36.75	27.27	27.80	26.13	17.93	32.03	20.10
P =	71	34	21	66	10	40	43	51	90	23	84
χ^2 (19 d.f.) =	9.89	17.62	16.46	15.88	19.26	19.45	11.47	21.73	13.60	20.99	9.91
P =	95	55	63	66	44	43	91	30	81	34	95

As might be expected, there are duplicates in the values
of the table due to the method of generation. To determine
the extent of this duplication, the tails of the distribution
were ordered and listed completely. The listing showed that,
of the values for which x is greater than 2, in 62 instances
there were values occurring in duplicate and 4 in triplicate
out of 542 values. For x less than -2, duplicates occurred
in 57 instances and triplicates 5 times out of a total of
543. It may be noted that the expected number of values in
each of the above tails was 569.

SUMMARY

For the table as a whole, the value of the mean is
-.00412, the variance is .99184, and the mean range for
samples of size 25 drawn in order by columns is 3.97736.
For the table as a whole, the arrangement appears to be
reasonably random, and the distribution of values seems
to be about what could be expected.

It may be noted that pages 44 and 63 failed the mean
test and page 69 failed to pass tests on the square sum.
From the point of view of the table as a whole, such depar-
tures are expected. What would not be expected in such a
table, however, is the occurrence of duplicate rare values.
With this exception, the table would appear to be satisfactory.

BIBLIOGRAPHY

[1]. Hald, A., "Statistical Theory with Engineering Applications," John Wiley and Sons, New York, 1952,
pp. 342-353.

[2]. Hoel, Paul G., "Introduction to Mathematical Statistics,"
John Wiley and Sons, New York, 1947. (Tables
of Normal Area, Chi-square Distribution and
Student's t Distribution.)

[3]. Pearson, E. S. and Hartley, H. O., "The Probability
Integral of the Range in Samples of n Observations from a Normal Population," Biometrica 32:
301-308, 1942.

[4]. Snedecor, George W., "Statistical Methods," Iowa State
College Press, p. 149, 1948.

[5]. RAND's 5D Gaussian Error Function Table, RAND Cor-
         poration, Santa Monica, California. (Fixed
         Interval, prepared for linear interpolation,
         886 cards.)

[6]. RAND's Derived Number Table of One Million Digits,
         RAND Corporation, Santa Monica, California.
         (Digits 0(1) 9 drawn at random with equal
         probability; 50 random digits per card;
         20,000 cards.)

[7]. RAND Corporation, "A Million Random Digits with
         100,000 Normal Deviates," The Free Press,
         Glencoe, Illinois, 1955.

MACHINE SAMPLING FROM GIVEN PROBABILITY DISTRIBUTIONS

James W. Butler

Argonne National Laboratory
Lemont, Illinois

I. INTRODUCTION

During the course of the calculations associated with
any Monte Carlo problem, it is necessary to produce random
variables according to a variety of different probability
distributions. A common method of doing this is to incor-
porate into the computing machine or program being used a
mechanism for producing uniformly distributed random numbers. The desired random variables are then obtained by
transformations based on the laws of probability theory,
employing such operations as the machine is capable of
performing.

Satisfactory "random" numbers can be produced by a
number of arithmetical schemes; a summary of most of those
used to date is presented by John Todd in another paper in
this symposium. What I should like to present here is a
discussion of some simple methods for utilizing these numbers effectively so as to produce variates distributed
according to given probability distributions, with most
attention to procedures which are readily "understood" by
computing machines and so require a minimum of programming
and coding.

Some techniques of this kind were presented by von
Neumann[1] at the previous Monte Carlo symposium in 1949,
and in fact, the present investigation arose from attempts
to arrive at certain of his results in a non-tentative
manner. Essentially these same recipes and some others
were published by Votaw and Rafferty [2] in 1951, and a
forthcoming report by H. Kahn will contain a general discussion of the subject accompanied by some thirty examples.

In what follows it will be assumed that there is
available an indefinite supply of random real numbers,
uniformly distributed on the interval (0, 1). The problem
then consists in the determination of sampling schemes

which will consume these numbers and produce others having assigned probability distributions. The task is approached, so to speak, in reverse; known ways of operating on available distributions to produce new ones are surveyed to see what results can be obtained by applying them to uniform distributions. The term "sampling efficiency" will mean merely the reciprocal of the average number of uniform random numbers used up to produce one acceptable variate value.

There are three methods of operating with probability distributions which can be adapted to serve the present purpose. These are based on direct functional transformation, the principle of compound probabilities, and the procedure of rejecting part of the sampled values according to an appropriate test or rule. The first will be termed the "direct method," the second the "composition method" and the third the "rejection technique."

II. THE DIRECT METHOD

This is well known [3] and ought not to require too much discussion. If one desires to sample from the population with density $f(\cdot)$, the procedure is to select a uniform random number r and solve the equation

$$\int_{-\infty}^{s} f(y)dy = r \tag{1}$$

for the sample value s or, what is the same thing, to compute

$$s = \phi(r), \tag{2}$$

where $\phi(\cdot)$ is the inverse function of the cumulative distribution on the left side of equation (1). The existence of the inverse is, of course, guaranteed by the positivity of $f(\cdot)$.

Conversely, if a random number r be selected and the number $s = g(r)$ computed, the probability that s will lie in the interval $(x, x + dx)$ will be:

$$f(x)dx = \int_{C_1} dy, \qquad (3a)$$

Where C_1 is the intersection of the interval $(0, 1)$ with the set determined by the inequality $x < g(y) < x + dx$. If the function $g(\cdot)$ has a unique, differentiable, inverse g^{-1}, an equivalent expression is:

$$f(x)dx = |dg^{-1}(x)|. \qquad (3b)$$

Example (a). "Random Cosines": $g(y) = \cos \pi y$. In this case, the inverse function has one branch which intersects the unit interval and the result is the familiar expression:

$$f(x) = \frac{1}{\pi} \frac{1}{\sqrt{1 - x^2}} \quad (-1 < x < +1). \qquad (4)$$

The direct generalization of this procedure to two dimensions is the scheme in which two random numbers r_1 and r_2 are selected and two sample values s and t are computed from:

$$s = g(r_1, r_2), \qquad (5a)$$

and
$$t = h(r_1, r_2). \qquad (5b)$$

The joint density function of s and t is now given by:

$$f(x,y)dxdy = \int_{C_2} dzdw, \qquad (6)$$

where C_2 is the region common to the unit square $(0 < z < 1, 0 < w < 1)$ and the set determined by the inequalities $x < g(z,w) < x + dx$ and $y < h(z,w) < y + dy$. This formula is in complete analogy to the expression (3a), and similar expressions may be written immediately for higher dimensional transformations.

The density function of s alone is likewise found from:

$$f(x)dx = \int_{-\infty}^{\infty} f(x, y)dydx = \int_{D_2} dzdw, \qquad (7)$$

where D_2 is the intersection of the unit square with the strip $x < g(z, w) < x + dx$.

As explained in Wilk's book [3], if the transformation (5) possesses a unique, differentiable inverse;

$$r_1 = u(s, t),$$

$$r_2 = v(s, t),$$

then the joint frequency function (6) may be expressed in terms of the Jacobian of u and v. Thus,

$$f(s, t) = |u_s v_t - u_t v_s|, \qquad (8)$$

and the marginal distribution (7) are therefore expressible in the form

$$f(s) = \int_{-\infty}^{\infty} |u_s v_t - u_t v_s| dt. \qquad (9)$$

Formulas (5) are analogous to (2) in the one-dimensional case, but the deduction of these relations from knowledge of the joint density $f(\cdot, \cdot)$ is somewhat more difficult. Thus, assuming momentarily that the Jacobian is positive in the order written, in order to find the functions g and h the differential equation

$$u_s v_t - u_t v_s = f(s, t)$$

must be solved for u and v and the transformation then inverted. The precise degree of latitude in the solution is not clear, but if v, for example, is assumed known, the method of characteristics easily produces the general integral, a form of which is:

$$u(s, t) = \int_0^s \frac{f(x, t)}{v_t(x, t)} dx + F(v), \qquad (10)$$

where, in the integrand, t is defined as a function of x
by $v(t, x) = a$, a being an arbitrary constant. $F(\cdot)$ is an
arbitrary differentiable function. If v depends only on
t, say, there is the simpler form:

$$u(s, t) = \frac{1}{v'(t)} \int_0^s f(x, t)dx + F(t). \qquad (11)$$

$F(\cdot)$ and $v(\cdot, \cdot)$ must, of course, be chosen so that the
image of the unit square under the mapping g, h contains
the desired range of s and t. Similar manipulations are
possible in more dimensions, but the situation rapidly
increases in complexity.

Example (b). The Law of Cosines for the Scattering
of Neutrons by Hydrogen. The law of cosines is used con-
tinually in one-dimensional attenuation problems to calculate the direction cosine of the particle after
scattering. For the particular case of neutron scattering
by hydrogen, the direction cosine after scattering, μ, and
the energy ratio ν may be calculated by

$$\mu = g(r_1, r_2) = u\sqrt{r_1} + \sqrt{(1 - r_1)(1 - u^2)} \cos \pi r_2 \qquad (12a)$$

and $\quad \nu = h(r_1) = \sqrt{r_1} . \qquad (12b)$

Here $u(-1 < u < +1)$ is the direction cosine of the neutron
before scattering.

This transformation maps the unit square $(0 < r_1 < 1,
0 < r_2 < 1)$ onto the interior of the ellipse
$1 - \mu^2 - \nu^2 - u^2 + 2\mu\nu u = 0$ in the (μ, ν) plane, and, making use of (8), the joint frequency function of μ and ν is
found to be

$$f(\mu, \nu) = \frac{2}{\pi} \frac{\nu}{\sqrt{(1 - \nu^2)(1 - u^2) - (\mu - u\nu)^2}} . \qquad (13)$$

The marginal density of μ, given by (7) or (9), is

$$f(x) = \begin{cases} 2ux \left[\sqrt{1 - u^2} < x < 1, u \geq 0; -1 < x < -\sqrt{1 - u^2}, \right. \\ \left. \qquad\qquad\qquad\qquad\qquad\qquad u < 0 \right] \\ 2ux \left[\frac{1}{2} + \frac{1}{\pi} \frac{\sqrt{1 - x^2 - u^2}}{ux} + \frac{1}{\pi} \arcsin \frac{ux}{\sqrt{(1 - x^2)(1 - u^2)}} \right] \\ \qquad\qquad\qquad\qquad \left[-\sqrt{1 - u^2} < x < \sqrt{1 - u^2} \right]; \end{cases}$$

253

it vanishes outside the indicated x intervals. It is
instructive to draw figures and observe the geometrical
relations corresponding to the above analysis.

III. THE COMPOSITION METHOD

This procedure is based upon the elementary definition
of conditional probability or, in other words, upon the
identity variously known as the "multiplication law" or
the "law of compound probabilities."

Consider a one-parameter family of frequency functions $g_y(\cdot)$, in which y is the parameter identifying a
member of the collection. If values of y are now drawn
from a population with a cumulative distribution $H(\cdot)$,
and if s is then sampled from the corresponding $g_y(\cdot)$,
the density function of the random variable s will be

$$f(x) = \int_{-\infty}^{\infty} g_y(x)dH(y). \qquad (14)$$

By using this simple principle, it is possible to generate a wide variety of sampling distributions; evidently it
is most directly applied when the desired frequency functions are initially defined by certain types of definite
integrals or series. The composition principle will
ordinarily be used to generate functions of "higher" type
from simpler ones which can be sampled from effectively by
means of the direct or rejection methods.

It will undoubtedly occur to the reader that one can
deal similarly with functions defined by double and more
highly multiple integrals. These, however, do not seem to
occur too frequently in Monte Carlo problems.

Example (a). The Exponential Integrals. Take

$$dH(y) = ndy/y^{n+1} \quad (1 < y < \infty, n \geq 1) \qquad (15)$$

and

$$g_y(x) = ye^{-yx} \quad (0 < x < \infty); \qquad (16)$$

one then obtains, from formula (14),

$$f(x) = n \int_1^\infty y^{-n} e^{-xy} dy = n E_n(x) \quad (0 < x < \infty). \quad (17)$$

Proper samples from the distributions (15) and (16) may be obtained by selecting two uniform random numbers r_1 and r_2 and calculating successively $s_1 = r_1^{-1/n}$ and $s = (1/s_1) \log r_2$, in which case the process is seen to be identical to the application of (7), with $g(z, w) = z^{1/n} \log w$. Such distributions as (15) and (16) can, however, be generated in a more pleasant way by making use of rejection techniques, as will be explained in the next section.

Example (b). Power Series. Let $H(y)$ be a step function with jumps of $a_n/(n + 1)(a_n \geq 0)$ at the integral points $y = n \left[n = 0, 1, 2, \ldots; \Sigma a_n/(n + 1) = 1 \right]$ and take for $g_n(x)$ the frequency $(n + 1)x^n (0 < x < 1)$. On applying (14), these choices yield:

$$f(x) = \sum_{n=0}^\infty a_n x^n \quad (0 < x < 1). \quad (18)$$

This sampling operation may be actually carried out as follows: Select a random number r_1 and find the value of n which causes the inequality

$$\sum_{k=0}^{n-1} \frac{a_k}{k + 1} \leq r_1 < \sum_{k=0}^{n} \frac{a_k}{k + 1}$$

to be satisfied, defining the sum on the left to be zero in the case $n = 0$. Using this value of n, determine a sample value s from the density $(n + 1)x^n$ by drawing another random number r_2 and computing

$$s = r_2^{1/(n + 1)}$$

The random variable s will then be distributed according to the frequency function (18). The root extraction is unpleasant but may be bypassed by using a rejection method.

255

IV. THE REJECTION TECHNIQUE

As already stated in the introduction, this process consists in drawing a random value from an appropriate probability distribution and subjecting it to a test of some sort to determine whether or not it will be accepted for use. The method is attractive for automatic computing machines since rather complex distributions may be generated by performing quite simple calculations.

A formulation of sufficient generality for the present purpose is provided by the following scheme: Choose a set of n uniform random numbers r_1, r_2, ..., r_n, compute a function $g(r_1, r_2, ..., r_n)$ of these values, and accept or reject a subset r_1, r_2, ..., r_k according as the value of g does or does not lie in a certain set S. The probability of acceptance of the collection r_1, r_2, ..., r_k is then the conditional probability

$$P\left[g(x_1, x_2, ..., x_k, r_{k+1}, ... r_n) \in S \,|\, x_1 = r_1, x_2 = r_2, ..., x_k = r_k \right] \qquad (19a)$$

or, to put the matter in another way, the joint density function of the accepted values r_1', r_2', ..., r_k' is proportional to

$$f(x_1, x_2, ..., x_k) = P\left[g(x_1, x_2, ..., x_k, r_{k+1}, ..., r_n) \in S \right]. \qquad (19b)$$

The function g need not be numerically valued; it may, for instance, represent a point in a Euclidean space, in which case the set S must, of course, be taken large enough to contain a positive proportion of the function values.

If the numbers r_1, r_2, ..., r_k, instead of being drawn from a uniform distribution, are selected from a population with a joint density function $h(x_1, x_2, ..., x_k)$, formula (19b) is clearly to be replaced by

$$f(x_1, x_2, ..., x_k) = h(x_1, x_2, ..., x_k) P\left[g(x_1, x_2, ..., x_k, r_{k+1}, ..., r_n) \in S \right]. \qquad (20)$$

This relation may be interpreted in a way useful for the present purpose by noticing that it may be thought of as referring to a given density function which has been factorized in the form, say, f = hp. Judicious choice of the factors h and p may result in a worthwhile decrease in the number of arithmetical operations involved. The frequency h, for example, might easily be generated by direct transformation, with acceptance probabilities p obtained by a rejection process. Unbounded frequency functions can sometimes be treated effectively in such a way.

A particular case of the foregoing deserves special notice. Suppose that one wants to obtain samples from a population with density $f(x_1, x_2, \ldots, x_k)$ ($0 < x_1 < 1$, $0 < x_2 < 1$, $\ldots$, $0 < x_k < 1$), where f has a maximum value on the indicated region. Let m be this maximum value and take, in (19b), $g(x_1, x_2, \ldots, x_k, y) = (1/m)f(x_1, x_2, \ldots, x_k) - y$, letting S be the unit interval (0,1). According to (19b), then, the frequency of the accepted values r_1', r_2', $\ldots$, r_k' is proportional to $(1/m)f(x_1, x_2, \ldots, x_k)$

$$P\left[(1/m)f(x_1, x_2, \ldots, x_k) - r_{k+1} \in (0,1)\right] = \int dy = $$

$$(1/m)f(x_1, x_2, \ldots, x_k) \quad (21)$$

This is but a slight generalization of the ordinary rejection scheme as given by Kahn[4] and others. Its sampling efficiency, as defined in the introduction, is k/(k + 1)m.

Example (a). More About "Random Cosines". The ideas contained in the paragraph following equation (20) may be applied with profit to the problem of obtaining samples with the frequency distribution (4). To see this, consider the two factorizations

$$\frac{1}{\pi} \frac{1}{\sqrt{1 - x^2}} = \frac{1}{(1 + x)\sqrt{1 - x^2}} \cdot \frac{1}{\pi}(1 + x), \quad (22a)$$

and

$$\frac{1}{\pi} \frac{1}{\sqrt{1 - x^2}} = \frac{1}{4} \frac{1}{\sqrt{1 - |x|}} \cdot \frac{4}{\pi} \frac{1}{\sqrt{1 + |x|}} . \qquad \text{(22b)}$$

The method described by von Neumann in reference [1] is essentially based on the first decomposition; the second, however, leads to simpler results. If equation (2) is applied to the first factor in (22b) and an acceptance probability proportional to the second factor is generated by taking $g(x, y) = (1 + |x|)y^2$ in (19a), there is obtained the following sampling design:

Produce a random number r_1, compute

$$s = 1 - 4(1 - r_1)^2 \quad \text{if} \quad r_1 \geq 1/2, \qquad \text{(23a)}$$

and

$$s = 4r_1^2 - 1 \qquad \text{if} \quad r_1 < 1/2. \qquad \text{(23b)}$$

Draw another random number r_2 and accept s only if

$$(1 + |s|)r_2^2 \leq 1 ;$$

according to (20), then, the frequency of the sample values s is proportional to (4) on (-1, +1). If random numbers on (-1, +1) are available, as they are with most generating schemes, the factors "4" in equations (23) may be omitted and the discrimination level 1/2 replaced by zero. The sampling efficiency is $\pi/8$.

An alternative which may be preferable is simply to compute $s = 1 - r_1^2$, accept if $(1 + s)r_2^2 \leq 1$, and attach the sign of r_1 or r_2 to the result.

Example (b). "Random Square Roots." If a random number r_1 is selected and its square root, $s = \sqrt{r_1}$, is computed, the sample value s has the frequency function $f(x) = 2x$ $(0 < x < 1)$, as may be seen from formula (3b).

To produce such sample values in a more agreeable way, use formula (5a), with

$$g(r_1, r_2) = \begin{cases} r_1 & (r_1 \geq r_2) \\ r_2 & (r_1 < r_2) . \end{cases}$$

Application of the integral expression in (7) then shows that the values s are distributed in the required way, the demonstration being easily accomplished geometrically. The sampling efficiency is, of course, 1/2.

Example (c). The Power Function. It is often necessary to obtain sample numbers distributed according to the frequency function

$$f(x) = (n + 1)x^n \qquad (0 < x < 1) . \qquad (24)$$

As explained in example III(b), the direct method requires extraction of an (n + 1)-st root, which has to be done iteratively and may require excessive computing time. One way of proceeding is by direct application of (21), with $(1/m)f(x) = x^n$. This is, in general, preferable to the root extraction but still requires a number of multiplications to form the n-th power.[+] The sampling efficiency is $1/(2n + 2)$.

Another method, which eliminates all multiplications, is based on the well-known distribution of the largest value in a sample of size n + 1 [5]. One merely selects n + 1 random numbers $r_1, r_2, \ldots r_{n+1}$ and accepts the largest one for the sample value s, which then has the frequency distribution (24). Example (b), above, is obviously the special case of this for a sample of two (n = 1). The sampling efficiency is $1/(n + 1)$, which is about as good as can be expected.

Negative powers can be produced by taking reciprocals of numbers generated by the above means, since, if is is distributed according to (24), 1/s has the frequency $(n + 1)/x^{n+2}$ $(1 < x < \infty)$.

Since rational functions are easily evaluated by automatic computing machines, a problem of some interest is to

---

[+]The minimum number of multiplications to form x^n is $\log_2 n$ + (the number of ones in the binary representation of n) - 1.

see what kinds of acceptance frequencies can be produced
by employing rational rejection schemes, that is, by letting the function g in equations (19) be a polynomial or
other rational combination of its arguments. It is easy
to see, after some experimentation with Jacobians, that
the class of density functions capable of being generated
in this way is essentially the class of algebraic functions and their integrals, perhaps restricted by certain
conditions on roots, extreme values, etc. Such conditions
would not be easy to write down in the general case, since
the properties of algebraic functions are not, in themselves, very simple.

The next two examples, (d) and (e), will show, in a
general way, what one can expect from this approach.

Example (d). Logarithms, etc. Take, in (19b),
$g(x, r_1, r_2) = r_1(x + r_2)$, and think of S, as usual, as
being the unit interval (0,1). The acceptance probability
of x is then equal to the fraction of the area of the unit
square $(0 < z < 1, 0 < w < 1)$ which lies under the curve
$z(x + w) = 1$, this being equal to:

$$f(x) = (1 - x) + \log(1 + x) \qquad (0 < x < 1).$$

Other functions containing logarithms, arc tangents, etc.,
can be produced in a similar way.

More generally, suppose that $g(x, r_1, r_2) = r_1 h(x, r_2)$,
where h, for definiteness, is a non-negative function
having the properties $h(x, 0) \leq 0$ and $h(x, 1) > 1$, and
such that the equation $h(x, w) = 1$ has only one root w_0 in
the interval $(0 \leq w < 1)$. The frequency distribution of
the sample values obtained is then easily seen geometrically to be

$$f(x) = w_0(x) + \int_0^{w_0} \frac{1}{h(x, w)} dw .$$

Here h is not, of course, restricted to be a rational
function.

Example (e). Algebraic Functions. Again take S to
be the unit interval (0, 1), and let $g(x, y) = a_0 y^n +$

$a_1 y^{n-1} + \ldots, + a_n - x$, where $a_0 y^n + a_1 y^{n-1} + \ldots + a_n$
($a_n = 1$) is a polynomial such that, for $0 < x < 1$, the equation $g(x, y) = 0$ has one simple root in the interval $0 < y < 1$; the coefficients thus satisfying $\Sigma a_n < 0$. Sample numbers accepted according to this function will then have frequency

$$f(x) = y_0(x) \qquad (0 < x < 1),$$

where y_0 is defined as a function of x by $a_0 y_0^n + a_1 y_0^{n-1} + \ldots + a_n = x$ and $0 < y_0 < 1$.

Example (f). The Exponential Function. As might be suspected, the efficient selection of sample numbers according to the exponential frequency

$$f(x) = e^{-x} \qquad (0 < x < \infty) \tag{25}$$

is of fundamental importance in treatment of Monte Carlo problems. Free flights of particles in attenuation problems follow this law, and also, due to its basic position in analysis, the exponential function forms an essential starting point for construction of higher functions [See Example III(a)].

As far as I know, the only representation of the exponential function that is useful for the present purpose is its power series expansion. The sampling problem is treated by generating the power functions $g_n(x) = (n + 1)x^n$ and compounding them according to (14), the cumulative distribution $H(y)$ being a step function with steps of $1/n!$ at the integral points $y = n$ ($n = 0, 1, 2, \ldots$). Moreover, since this process only covers the limited range $0 < x < 1$, one must also provide a source of integers t with the probability distribution $P(t = n) = e^{-n}$. The numbers $t + s$ will then have the frequency (25), since

$$P(x < t + s < x + dx) = P(t = [x]) \, P(x - [x] < s < x + dx - [x])$$

$$= e^{-[x]} e^{-x+[x]} dx = e^{-x} dx.$$

The actual procedure which seems to be preferable is the one due to von Neumann [1] and Votaw and Rafferty [2];

the presentation will follow that of the latter authors, except for trifling changes in notation.

Select random numbers x_0, r_1, r_2, ..., r_i, x_1 ... and form the sequence of sums:

$$1 - x_0 + r_1 + r_2 + \ldots + r_i$$

$$1 - x_1 + r_{i+1} + r_{i+2} + \ldots + r_{i+j}$$

$$\cdot \quad \cdot \quad \cdot$$

$$\cdot \quad \cdot \quad \cdot$$

$$1 - x_t + r_{p+1} + r_{p+2} + \ldots + r_{p+q}.$$

The individual sums are terminated when they become ≥ 1 for the first time; the sequence is ended on the first trial involving an odd value of q. The quantity $x_t + t$ is then accepted as the required sample value s.

To see why this works, consider the last sum $s_q = 1 - x_t + r_{p+1} + r_{p+2} + \ldots + r_{p+q}$. Let u_q be the probability of the event $(s_q \geq 1 | x_t = x)$ and v_q represent the probability of the event $(s_q \geq 1$ for the first time $| x_t = x)$. Now

$$u_q = 1 - \int_0^x x^{q-1}/(q-1)! \, dx = 1 - x^q/q!, \quad (26)$$

and, since the numbers r_n are all positive, the events corresponding to v_q and u_{q-1} are mutually exclusive, which means that $u_q = v_q + u_{q-1}$. Consequently, the acceptance probability of the value x is

$$P(q \text{ odd } | x_t = x) = \sum_{\text{odd } j} v_j = e^{-x} \quad (0 < x < 1).$$

Finally, the distribution of the integer t is proportional to:

$$\left[\int_0^1 P(q \text{ even } |x_t = x)dx \right]^n = \left[\int_0^1 (1 - e^{-x})dx \right]^n = e^{-n},$$

since t trials are unsuccessful. The sampling efficiency seems to be $(e - 1)/e^2 = 1/4.3$.

Another method, which is perhaps more transparent, is based on the distribution of the sum of $n + 1$ uniform random numbers on $(0, 1)$ [5]. If the sum $s_j = r_0 + r_1 + \ldots r_j$ is formed, and its value rejected if it does not lie in the interval $(0, 1)$, then the frequency distribution of the remaining values of $1 - s_j$ will be $(1 - x)^j/j!$ $(0 < x < 1)$. Suppose further that j is given a distribution by terminating the sum on the first occasion when $r_j \geq 1/2$. The distribution of the sample numbers $s = 1 - s_j$ is thereby proportional to $e^{-x/2}$. Next produce integers t with distribution $P(t = n)$ proportional to $e^{-n/2}$ by taking for t the number of consecutive random numbers $r_p, r_{p+1}, \ldots, r_{p+q}$ that can be chosen less than $1/\sqrt{e}$. This appears to have a somewhat better sampling efficiency than the above procedure, presumably because of the extra information contained in the constant $1/\sqrt{e}$.

V. DISCUSSION

Some general points may be brought out in reference to the above material. The background idea in the entire study is an attempt to extend the usefulness of Monte Carlo calculations in a direction which has not, as yet, received a great deal of attention. This is in the direction of obtaining larger sample sizes within the same amount of computing time. The various procedures mentioned here were selected in an attempt to strive for great simplicity of individual operations and programming possibilities, even at the expense of sampling efficiency.

If rapid methods for generating random numbers are available, such as the additive method described earlier by John Todd, over-all savings in computing time can often be effected in this way. The gains are, of course, not as great as those resulting from such techniques as importance sampling, etc., but may be worthwhile nevertheless.

Some of the techniques presented here should be used on almost all occasions; for instance, one should never compute a square root or a cosine of a random number. Others are in a marginal category where their usefulness depends strongly on the type of problem at hand and on the type of computing machine available.

It should be stated, perhaps, that the operations studied here are exact. The burden of randomness is forced, so to speak, onto the random number generating process, and the results will be as reliable as is that device.

BIBLIOGRAPHY

[1]   John von Neumann, "Various Techniques Used in Connection with Random Digits," Paper No. 13 in "Monte Carlo Methods," NBS Applied Mathematics Series No. 12, U. S. Govt. Printing Office, (1951).

[2]   D. F. Votaw, Jr. and J. A. Rafferty, "High Speed Sampling," MTAC, Vol. 5 (1951), pp. 1-8.

[3]   S. S. Wilks, "Mathematical Statistics," Princeton University Press, 1947, pp. 23-29.

[4]   H. Kahn, "Random Sampling (Monte Carlo) Techniques in Neutron Attenuation Problems - I," Nucleonics, Vol. 6, No. 5 (1950), p. 29.

[5]   H. Cramér, "Mathematical Methods of Statistics," Princeton University Press, 1946, p. 370.

A MONTE CARLO TECHNIQUE FOR OBTAINING TESTS AND CONFIDENCE INTERVALS FOR INSURANCE MORTALITY RATES

John E. Walsh

U. S. Naval Ordnance Test Station

SUMMARY

Observed insurance mortality rates ordinarily are based on units which are not statistically independent (policies, amounts, etc.) and involve lives which are not completely homogeneous. Reasonably accurate determination of the probability properties of these observed rates requires some method of allowing for this dependence and heterogeneity. For most investigations, cost of the method used is a major consideration. Since the amount of data is nearly always large, a procedure involving the recording and processing of additional information can be very expensive. This paper presents a method whereby reasonably accurate tests and confidence intervals can be obtained for the expected value of an observed rate without additional information and with little extra cost. The procedure consists in introducing a supplementary probability process with known properties (a Monte Carlo technique). The price paid for using this method is a low efficiency for the resulting tests and confidence intervals (usually in the neighborhood of 5 to 25%). However, the amount of data ordinarily is large enough to yield useful results even for efficiencies this small. Also, the method is applicable to any situation where the observed mortality rate and the number of units exposed to risk are known (in particular, completed mortality studies where obtaining further information is either impossible or impracticable).

INTRODUCTION AND DESCRIPTIVE OUTLINE

An observed mortality rate consists of the number of units associated with lives who died while the units were under observation divided by the total number of units exposed to risk for the subdivision of data considered. Here the observation periods are specified quantities and each unit might possibly have a different observation period. Let the value of the observed mortality rate be denoted by q' while the number of units exposed to risk is E (a fixed

quantity not having a probability distribution). The problem is to derive reasonably accurate significance tests and
confidence intervals for the expected value of the random
variable q'; this is to be done without further information
and at little additional expense. The expected value of q'
is denoted by q and can be regarded as the "true" mortality
rate.

If the units were statistically independent and each
unit had the same probability of "death" while under observation, the variance of q' would be $q(1 - q)/E$. Then, for
E sufficiently large, reasonably accurate tests and confidence intervals for q could be obtained by assuming that
the statistic

$$(q' - q) \Big/ \sqrt{q(1 - q)/E}$$

has a standard normal probability distribution (zero mean
and unit variance). For practical applications, however,
this idealized situation may not be even roughly approximated. First, the units may be appreciably dependent.
This dependence is due to many lives having more than one
associated unit and to a possible lack of independence
among the lives. Second, the units may not have the same
mortality probabilities. This is due to heterogeneity
among the lives and to differences in observation periods.
Finally, the value of E may not be large enough to assure
even approximate normality for the distribution of q'. If
q is very small, an extremely large value of E may be required to yield approximate normality for q'.

For a practical type situation the variance of q' is
not necessarily $q(1 - q)/E$ but some value $Mq(1 - q)/E$,
where M is unknown. In many cases upper and lower bounds
can be specified for M on the basis of past experience and
perhaps other considerations. Let the lower bound be represented by L while the upper bound is denoted by U, so that
$L \lesseqgtr M \leqq U$. Ordinarily the values for L and U are so far
apart that probabilities obtained by assuming that $M = L$
are appreciably different from those obtained by assuming
that $M = U$. However, by the introduction of an auxiliary
probability process, a statistic is developed which has
controlled probability properties. Explicitly, this statistic has a probability distribution which does not differ
greatly from the standard normal distribution for all values
of M between L and U.

The statistic used to obtain tests and confidence
intervals for q is denoted by X and has the form

266

$$X = A\left[BY + (q' - q) \middle/ \sqrt{q(1 - q)/E} \right].$$

Here Y is an independent random value from a standard normal probability distribution while A and B are appropriately chosen constants. The values of A and B are selected so that, for M within its bounds, the variance of X lies between specified limits $1/V$ and $V(\sqrt{L/U} \leq V < 1)$. The value chosen for V determines the accuracy of the probability distribution assumed for X. A value of V near unity assures that the distribution of X is almost standard normal for all M between L and U. If V deviates appreciably from unity (say, $V \leq .5$), the probability distribution of X may be only very roughly standard normal. As V increases toward unity, however, the efficiency of the tests and confidence intervals for q decreases toward zero. Thus the value selected for V represents a compromise between low efficiency and accurate knowledge of the probabilities involved. For significance tests, the value of V determines the relative emphasis that is placed on Type I and Type II errors.

The procedure of using an independent probability process with known (and specified) properties to help in the solution of a problem is referred to as Monte Carlo. In this paper the Monte Carlo technique used consists of introducing the auxiliary random variable Y. This procedure serves a dual purpose. First, the variance properties of X are controlled to the extent that reasonably accurate probability results can be obtained. Second, use of Y tends to make the probability distribution of X more nearly normal. If B^2 is of the same order of magnitude or larger than M ($B^2 \geq U$ is a sufficient condition), the distribution of X should be almost normal even though the distribution of q' is only very roughly normal.

For the usual type mortality situation of a somewhat homogeneous nature, M should be roughly equal to the average number of units per life for the lives under investigation. The true value of M is this average number of units increased and decreased by factors which should be somewhere near unity. These factors depend on the variation in the number of units per life, the variation among mortality probabilities, any correlation (assumed small on the average) which may exist among the lives, etc. Thus, for situations which are at least roughly homogeneous, bounds for the average number of units per life are helpful in selecting values for L and U. Let L' and U' be upper and lower limits, respectively, for the average number of units per

life. Relations which should be useable for most practical
applications are

$$L = \frac{4}{5} L', \qquad U = \frac{5}{4} U'.$$

The factors 4/5 and 5/4 are introduced to compensate for
the additional effects involved. Here the goal is to present a procedure which will be accurate for nearly all
practical situations rather than one which holds for all
possible situations. A moderate mistake in the selection
of values for L and U is not serious. No large probability
errors should result even if the true value of M lies a
moderate distance outside the interval between the values
chosen for L and U.

The procedure of using L' and U' to determine L and U
is particularly useful for situations where a policy is the
unit. The average number of policies per life seldom exceeds three and is never less than unity. Thus L = .8 and
U = 3.75 should be safe selections of the limits for most
cases. If the investigation is simultaneously carried out
for policies and one or more other types of units (e.g.,
policies and amounts), the bounds for policies can be used
to obtain bounds for the other types of units. For the
subdivision of data being analyzed, let

R = (total no. of units of type considered)/(total no.
    of policies).

Then L = .8R and U = 3.75R should be safe selections of the
limits for the type of unit considered. If additional information is available, the values L = .8 and U = 3.75
mentioned for policies sometimes can be noticeably improved.

For the results of this paper to be accurate, it is
essential that, to a good approximation, the value used for
Y represent a random result of a standard normal probability
process. One possible way of evaluating Y would be to select a value from a table of random normal deviates. However, this procedure is open to several possible sources of
bias. As an example, bias can enter in deciding which of
several available tables is to be utilized. As another
example, the procedure of deciding which deviate of the table
is to be used can introduce a bias. Also the fact that any
deviate of the table is a possible selection can lead to
criticism of the results. Namely, that there was no strong
reason for selecting the deviate used rather than some other

deviate which would have yielded appreciably different
results. Thus the use of a random normal deviate table
to determine Y would seem to be of questionable desirabil-
ity. Development of a method which avoids biases and
furnishes a unique value for Y would appear to be of interest.

This paper outlines an experimental method for obtaining a highly accurate random normal deviate. The procedure
consists in flipping ordinary minted coins and performing
suitable operations on the results of these coin flips. If
two evidently acceptable assumptions hold, the resulting
deviate value can be rigorously shown to closely approximate a random result of a standard normal probability process. Since only one deviate is to be determined, the
amount of extra work involved is not great. An explicit
specification of the procedure and related assumptions is
given in the final section of this paper under the heading
"Experimental Determination of Y."

Only asymtotic ($E \rightarrow \infty$) efficiencies are evaluated
in this paper. Let q" be an observed mortality rate for
the case where the number of units exposed to risk is rE
(r fixed and ≤ 1). In deriving asymtotic efficiencies, it
is assumed that as $E \rightarrow \infty$.

1. The expected values of both q' and q" converge
    to the same value q.

2. The variances of $(q' - q) \sqrt{E}$ and $(q" - q) \sqrt{rE}$
    converge to the same value $Mq(1 - q)$.

3. The probability distributions of $(q' - q) \sqrt{E}$ and
    $(q" - q) \sqrt{rE}$ both tend to normality.

Then an efficiency of 100r% has the technical meaning that
the probability properties of the significance tests and
confidence intervals for q based on X are identical with
those of the corresponding tests and confidence intervals
(some significance level or confidence coefficient) based on

(1) $(q" - q) / \sqrt{q(1 - q)/rE}$.

For significant tests, this means that the limiting
power functions are identical. For one-sided confidence intervals, the endpoints have identical probability distributions; similarly for corresponding endpoints of two-sided

269

confidence intervals. Intuitively, an efficiency of 100r%
implies that the "best" results based on 100r% as much
data furnish the same probability information as the results
of this paper. Roughly interpreted, only about 100r% of
the "information" contained in the data is utilized by the
method of the paper.

The results for the asymptotic case should furnish
reasonably accurate estimates of the efficiencies for non-
asymptotic situations where the distribution of $(q" - q)\sqrt{rE}$
is at least roughly normal. Thus the asymptotic efficiencies should be applicable to most practical type situations
involving at least a moderately large amount of data.

The next section is titled "Results." This section
contains a statement of the basic conclusions of the paper.
The following section is titled "Derivations" and outlines
the mathematical verification for the results presented.

RESULTS

First let us consider the values obtained for A and B
along with some additional notation which is useful in pre-
senting the results of this section.

$$A = \sqrt{(1 - V^2)/[V(U - L)]}$$

$$B = \sqrt{(V^2U - L)/(1 - V^2)}$$

α = representative value for confidence coefficient

K_ξ = standardized normal deviate exceeded with
probability ξ

$$k_\alpha = k_\alpha(Y; L,U,V,E) = \left[K_\alpha\sqrt{V(U - L)} + Y\sqrt{V^2U - L}\right]/\sqrt{(1 - V^2)E}$$

α' = value defined by relation $K_{\alpha'} = K_\alpha\sqrt{V}$

$\alpha"$ = value defined by the relation $K_{\alpha"} = K_\alpha/\sqrt{V}$.

In applying the results of this paper, any two of the four
quantities α, V, α', $\alpha"$ can be specified. The other two
quantities are then determined by the relations defining α'
and $\alpha"$.

The principal probability results consist of one-sided confidence intervals for q. Two-sided confidence intervals can be obtained as non-overlapping combinations of one-sided confidence intervals. Significance tests can be obtained from these confidence intervals in the usual manner. To save space, results will be presented only for the case of one-sided confidence intervals.

The basic one-sided confidence interval result of this paper is furnished by the relation

$$(2) \quad \min(\alpha',\alpha'') \leq \Pr\left[q > \frac{q'+1/2k_\alpha^2+k_\alpha\sqrt{q'(1-q')+1/4k_\alpha^2}}{1+k_\alpha^2}\right] \leq$$

$$\max(\alpha',\alpha'').$$

This relation defines a one-sided confidence interval for q with a confidence coefficient which is bounded between min (α',α'') and max (α',α''). The value of α is a representative confidence coefficient for this one-sided confidence interval. One-sided confidence intervals in the other direction are obtained by considering the complement of this type of confidence interval. The properties stated in (2) should hold to a reasonable approximation if $B^2 \geq U$.

Now let us consider the asymtotic efficiency, 100r%, of the probability results based on (2). The value of r depends on the unknown quantity M and is given by

$$r = \frac{(1-V^2)M}{(M-L)+V^2(U-M)}.$$

In any case

$$\frac{(1-V^2)L}{V^2(U-L)} \leq r \leq \frac{(1-V^2)U}{U-L}.$$

A representative value for r can be obtained by setting M equal to $(1/2)(U+L)$.

Then

$$\text{representative } r = \frac{(1-V^2)(U+L)}{(1+V^2)(U-L)}.$$

271

The bounds and the representative value should furnish a satisfactory indication of the order of magnitude of the asymptotic efficiency.

Policy example. As a partial illustration of the scope and application of the results of this paper, let us consider the case where a policy is the unit and V = .9. Then U = 3.75 and L = .8.

Since B = 3.44 and U = 3.75, $B^2 \geq U$ and the results of the paper should be reasonably accurate. Examination of the relations defining $\alpha' \alpha''$ shows that these two values are always close together. For example, when $\alpha = .95$ one value is .941 and the other .958. The asymptotic efficiency lies between 6.4% and 24% with a representative value of 16%.

DERIVATIONS

This section is devoted to verification of the statements made in the "Results" section. Determination of A and B followed by development of relation (2) is presented first.

The expressions for A and B are determined from the requirement that the variance of X lies between V and 1/V for M within its bounds. That is

$$V \leq A^2(B^2 + M) \leq 1/V$$

for $L \leq M \leq U$. The values of A and B are required to be non-negative for the sake of definiteness. This requirement combined with simultaneous solution of the two equations

$$A^2(B^2 + L) = V, \qquad A^2(B^2 + U) = 1/V$$

for A^2 and B^2 yields the expressions stated for A and B.

By hypothesis, the probability distribution of X is normal with zero mean and a standard deviation lying between $\sqrt{V}$ and $1/\sqrt{V}$. Let σ be the true standard deviation of X. Then

$$Pr\ (X < -K_\alpha) = Pr\ (X/\sigma < -K_\alpha/\sigma).$$

From this it follows that

$$\min(\alpha',\alpha'') \leqq \Pr(X < -K_\alpha) \leqq \max(\alpha',\alpha'').$$

Also

$$\Pr(X < -K_\alpha) = \Pr\left[q > q' + k_\alpha \sqrt{q(1-q)}\right].$$

On the basis of this relation and solution of the quadratic equation

$$(q - q')^2 = k_\alpha^2 q(1-q)$$

for q, it is found that $X < -K_\alpha$ if and only if

$$q > \frac{q' + 1/2k_\alpha^2 + k_\alpha \sqrt{q'(1-q') + 1/4k_\alpha^2}}{1 + k_\alpha^2}.$$

Thus

$$\Pr(X < -K_\alpha) = \Pr\left[q > \frac{q'+1/2k_\alpha^2+k_\alpha \sqrt{q'(1-q')+1/4k_\alpha^2}}{1 + k_\alpha^2}\right].$$

This completes the verification of relation (2).

Consider the sum of two statistically independent random variables the first of which has a normal distribution and a variance of the same order of magnitude or greater than that of the second variable. Under rather general conditions, the distribution of this sum is approximately normal if the distribution of the second variable is at least roughly continuous, symmetrical, and unimodal. For example, the distribution of the sum is very nearly normal if the second variable has a rectangular distribution. Now the distribution of q' tends to normality as $E \longrightarrow \infty$ under very general conditions and should be at least roughly continuous, symmetrical, and unimodal if E is even moderately large. Thus for practical type situations the distribution of X should be approximately normal for cases where the variance of BY is of the same order of magnitude or greater than the variance of $(q' - q) \big/ \sqrt{q(1-q)/E}$; that is, B^2 of the same order of magnitude or greater than M. This should almost always be the case if B^2 is greater than or equal to the value chosen for U.

Finally let us consider derivation of the expression for the asymptotic efficiency. Let r have the value stated

273

in the "Results" section. Then the problem is to show that asymptotically (E $\rightarrow \infty$) the probability properties of tests and confidence intervals for q based on X are identical with those of the corresponding tests and confidence intervals (same significance level or confidence coefficient) based on (1). Here the three assumptions stated in the "Introduction and Descriptive Outline" section also are satisfied. To do this it is sufficient to show that asymptotically the endpoint of the one-sided confidence interval defined in (2) has the same probability distribution as the endpoint of the corresponding one-sided confidence interval (same confidence coefficient) based on (1). The endpoint of a confidence interval of this type is also the endpoint of the complementary one-sided confidence interval in the other direction. The two-sided confidence intervals considered are non-overlapping combinations of one-sided confidence intervals while the significance tests are based on these one-sided and two-sided confidence intervals. Thus the asymptotic probability properties of the other results are determined by those of the type of one-sided confidence interval defined in (2).

First let us determine the endpoint of the one-sided confidence interval based on (1) which corresponds to the endpoint of the one-sided confidence interval defined in (2). Here and in the remaining derivations,

$$r = \left[(1 - V^2)M \right] \Big/ \left[(M - L) + V^2(U - M) \right]$$

and the three asumptions stated in the "Introduction and Descriptive Outline" section are utilized. Since the confidence coefficients are required to be equal and asymptotically

$$\Pr(X < -K_\alpha) = \Pr\left[(q' - q) \Big/ \frac{\sqrt{V(U-L)q(1-q)}}{(1 - V^2)E} < -K_\alpha \right]$$

$$= \Pr\left[q > q'' + k'_\alpha \sqrt{q(1 - q)} \right] ,$$

where

$$k'_\alpha = K_\alpha \sqrt{V(U - L) \Big/ (1 - V^2)E} ,$$

the endpoint expression sought can be obtained by solving the quadratic equation (in q)

$$(q - q'')^2 = k'^2_\alpha \, q(1 - q)$$

for the appropriate root. The value of the endpoint is found to be

$$(3) \quad \left[q'' + 1/2k_\alpha'^2 + k_\alpha' \sqrt{q''(1-q'') + 1/4k_\alpha'^2} \right] \Big/ (1 + k_\alpha'^2).$$

That is, asymptotically

$$Pr \left[q > \frac{q' + 1/2k_\alpha^2 + k_\alpha \sqrt{q'(1 - q') + 1/4k_\alpha^2}}{1 + k_\alpha^2} \right]$$

$$= Pr \left[q > \frac{q'' + 1/2k_\alpha'^2 + k_\alpha' \sqrt{q''(1 - q'') + 1/4k_\alpha'^2}}{1 + k_\alpha'^2} \right] .$$

Now let us show that asymptotically the probability distribution of the statistic

$$(4) \quad \left[q' + 1/2k_\alpha^2 + k_\alpha \sqrt{q'(1 - q') + 1/4k_\alpha^2} \right] \Big/ (1 + k_\alpha^2)$$

is the same as the probability distribution of (3). By noting the orders (as a function of E) of the quantities involved and using Cramér's convergence theorem (see reference [1]), it can be shown that asymptotically the probability distribution of (3) is the same as that of

$$q'' + k_\alpha' \sqrt{q(1 - q)}$$

while the probability distribution of (4) is the same as that of

$$q' + k_\alpha \sqrt{q(1 - q)} .$$

Thus asymptotically both endpoints are normally distributed with

$$\text{expected value} = q + k_\alpha \sqrt{\frac{V(U - L)q(1 - q)}{(1 - V^2)E}} ,$$

$$\text{variance} = \frac{\left[(M - L) + V^2(U - M) \right] q(1 - q)}{(1 - V^2)E} ,$$

and consequently have the same probability distribution. This completes the derivations.

EXPERIMENTAL DETERMINATION OF Y

An experimental method for obtaining a value which is very nearly the random result of a standard normal probability process is outlined in this section. The first step consists of performing 168 coin flips. The results of these coin flips are combined to yield 20 very nearly random binary digits. These binary digits are used to form a number which closely approximates a random value from a rectangular population. The resulting value represents some percentage point of the rectangular population. The deviate which represents this same percentage point for the standard normal population is the value used for Y. If two intuitively plausible assumptions hold, the random process involved in this procedure can be proved to approximate the standard normal probability process closely enough for almost any practical application.

The value of the normal deviate can be obtained to six significant figures and is in reality from a truncated distribution with limits at the $100 \, (1/2)^{21}$% and $100[1-(1/2)^{21}]$% points of the standard normal distribution. The two assumptions used in determining the accuracy of the experimental method are

(a) For each coin flip the probability of obtaining a "head" lies somewhere between 1/4 and 3/4/

(b) The coin flips are statistically independent.

If these assumptions are satisfied, little probability error arises from assuming that the 20 binary digits used in obtaining Y are truly random. Direct application of the results of reference [2] shows that the probability of any relation based on these 20 approximately random binary digits never differs from the value for a truly random set by more than .62%. Moreover the percentage difference is this large only for situations where the probability of "heads" is near 1/4 or near 3/4 for all flips.

It is not necessary to use the same coin for each flip nor is it necessary to use a different coin for each flip. In fact, the choice of coins for the flips is optional except that no coin should be so malformed that the validity of assumption (a) is doubtful. Each coin should be flipped separately. The coin should be tossed high into the air, preferably revolving, and should land on a hard, smooth surface. If these rules are followed in selecting and flipping the coins, assumptions (a) and (b) should be acceptable beyond any reasonable doubt.

The method is designed to produce 20 binary digits. The procedure consists in obtaining 21 sets of eight flips per set. The first eight flips represent the first set, the second eight flips the second set, etc. For the first set of eight flips, consider whether the number of "heads" obtained is even or odd. Next consider the remaining 20 sets of eight flips. If the number of "heads" for the first set is even, for each of the remaining sets an even number of "heads" will be denoted by 0 and an odd number by 1. If the number of "heads" for the first set is odd, in each of the other sets an even number of "heads" will be denoted by 1 and an odd number by 0. For the second, third, ..., 21st sets record either a 0 or 1 according to this rule.

Let ϵ_1 represent the value recorded for the second set, ϵ_2 the value for the third set, ..., ϵ_{20} the value for the 21st set. The rectangular population considered ranges from 0 to 1 and the percentage point determined by the values for the 20 binary digits has the value

$$(5) \qquad \left(\frac{1}{2}\right)\epsilon_1 + \left(\frac{1}{2}\right)^2\epsilon_2 + \cdots + \left(\frac{1}{2}\right)^{20}\epsilon_{20} + \left(\frac{1}{2}\right)^{21} .$$

The deviate which represents this percentage point for the standard normal probability distribution is the value for Y. The process of determining Y given the value of (5) is easily carried out by use of a table of areas and ordinates for the standard normal probability distribution.

REFERENCES

1. Cramér, Harald: Mathematical Methods of Statistics, Princeton University Press, 1946, p.254.

2. Walsh, John E.: Concerning compound randomization in the binary system, Annals of Mathematical Statistics, Vol. 20 (1949), pp. 580-589.

EXPERIMENTS AND MODELS FOR THE MONTE CARLO METHOD

Alwin Walther

Institut fur Praktische Mathematik (IPM)
Technische Hochschule Darmstadt

The education work in my Institute for Practical Mathematics (IPM) at the Darmstadt Institute of Technology is characterized by four principles:

1. Synthesis of pure and applied mathematics.

2. Bringing into relief and exhausting the basic ideas. That means: The student shall understand the simple fundamentals, and he shall work as much as possible by them.

3. Intuitive obviousness.

4. Exercises are more important than lectures.

According to (2) and (3), mathematics is appearing as concentrated common sense. It is learned not only by logical reasoning but also by eyes and hands. Therefore we demonstrate frequently the mathematical notions and methods by experiments and models.

Under this point of view, the 450 students of Mathematics Part I (which comprehends especially Calculus) in the winter of 1953/54 received an introduction to the Monte Carlo method. They had learned the usual evaluation of a definite integral either as the limit of a sum or as the difference of two values of the indefinite integral, e.g.

$$\int_0^1 x^2 dx = \frac{1}{3} \quad \text{(Fig. 1)}.$$

For the Monte Carlo evaluation, two girl students are called up as goddesses of fortune. Each of them gets a box containing 99 counters (Fig. 2). The counters in the first box (the x-box) are marked by 01, 02, 03, ..., 97, 98, 99 corresponding to a partition of the x-interval from 0 to 1 into 100 subintervals. They show moreover the squares 0001, 0004, 0009, ..., 9409, 9604, 9801. The counters in the

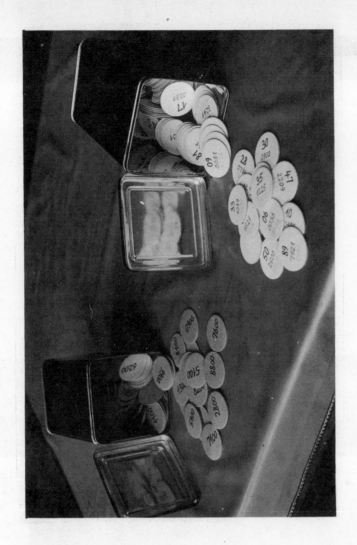

Fig.2

Boxes with counters for a Monte Carlo experiment

Right: x-box   Left: y-box

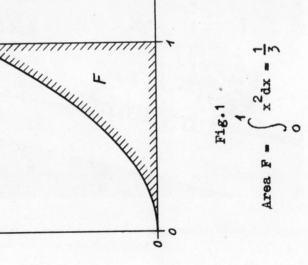

Fig.1

Area $F = \int\limits_{0}^{1} x^2\,dx = \frac{1}{3}$

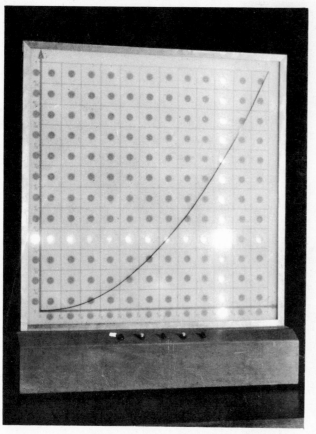

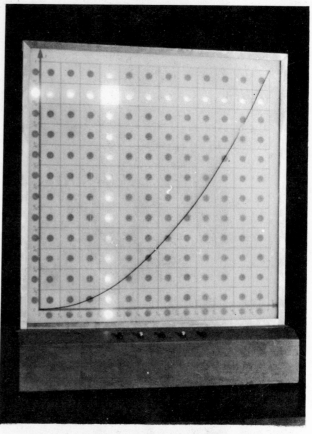

Fig. 3. Model for the Monte Carlo method Random
point x, y below the curve y = x².

Fig. 4. Model for the Monte Carlo method Ramdom
point x, y above the curve y = x².

Fig. 5.   Internal View of the model.
Right: 12 step telephone selector for the switching on the x-lamps.
Left: Electrical accessories.

second box (the y-box) are marked only by 0100, 0200, 0300, ..., 9700, 9800, 9900 corresponding to a partition of the y-interval from 0 to 1 into 100 subintervals.

The student with the x-box takes out a counter by chance, cries out for the audience and for her comrade the x-square read off, e.g. 1684, puts back the counter into the box, shakes the box well. The student with the y-box takes out a counter by chance, compares quickly the y-number read off, e g. 1300 or 4800, with the heard square, cries out just as it happens "below" or "above" (namely with regard to the curve y = x^2), puts back the counter, shakes the box well. I record runningly on the blackboard the number B of "below" and A of "above," e.g.

$$A = 101 \quad \text{and} \quad B = 49.$$

For the general surprise and pleasure, the Monte Carlo quotient

$$\frac{B}{A + B} = \frac{49}{150} \approx 0.327$$

is an approximate value for $\int_0^1 x^2 dx = \frac{1}{3}$. Some words about

the accuracy better than $\sqrt{\dfrac{1}{4(A + B)}} = \sqrt{\dfrac{1}{600}} \approx 0.04$ finish

the experiment in which the random choice of the pairs x, y of coordinates is realized by the two girl students with the help of the counters in the boxes.

In order to show the basic idea of the Monte Carlo method, the workshop of the institute built a model (Fig. 3, 4). Here, the x-interval 0 ... 1 is divided up into 12 subintervals, equally the y-interval 0 ... 1. The centers of the subintervals are marked by electrical lamps, just so the centers of the lattice formed in the x, y-plane by parallels to the axes through the partition points on the axes. A 12 step telephone selector (Fig. 5) switches on serially the x-lamps and another selector serially the y-lamps. Light flashes run along the x-axis and along the y-axis and may be stopped by pushing buttons by chance. So a random x and a random y are fixed. Another push button illuminates all lamps in the column and in the row of the chosen x- and y-points, most brightly the lamp at the crossing point. On the blackboard is recorded whether this random point is below (Fig. 3) or above (Fig. 4) a curve drawn on the front plexiglass plate of the model, e.g. $y = x^2$. Repeating the random process one gets rapidly the numbers A and B, e.g.

$$A = 105 \quad \text{and} \quad B = 45$$

giving

$$\frac{B}{A + B} = \frac{45}{150} = 0.3.$$

I hope that by the reported way the Monte Carlo idea will come into the scientific thinking already of the young students and therefore of the mathematicians, scientists and engineers of the future.

PART II.

BIBLIOGRAPHY

PART I: MONTE CARLO PROPER

Albert, G. E.

A GENERAL APPROACH TO THE MONTE CARLO ESTIMATION OF THE
SOLUTIONS OF CERTAIN FREDHOLM INTEGRAL EQUATIONS.
Working Paper, Oak Ridge National Laboratory.
   A thorough discussion and continuation of the work of
Cutkosky, Goertzel, Kahn and Doob on Monte Carlo estimation
of the solutions $\phi(x)$ of integral equations of the type

$$\phi(x) = g(x) + \lambda \int_R K(x,y)\phi(y)\,dy$$

and of estimating functionals

$$I = \int_R \phi(x) \cdot \psi(x)\,dx$$

of the solutions ϕ by means of a random walk. Part I reviews
previous work and the author approaches the problem of designing Monte Carlo processes for the estimation of $\phi(x)$ or a
functional of ϕ via the general theory of stochastic processes
involving an integral valued parameter. The general theory
for the design of estimation processes is given. Part II
continues the general theory and the use of representative
sampling for chain lengths is introduced. Part III continues
discussion of the use of representative (stratified) sampling
to improve the statistical efficiency of the experiment.

A GENERAL THEORY OF STOCHASTIC ESTIMATES OF THE NEUMANN SERIES
FOR THE SOLUTIONS OF CERTAIN FREDHOLM INTEGRAL EQUATIONS AND
RELATED SERIES. Oak Ridge National Laboratory, ORNL-1508,
Oak Ridge, Tennessee, August 28, 1953.
   Fundamentally, the aim of this report is to present:
(1) the application of rigorous stochastic process theory to
the generation of a unified theory of estimation processes
for the solution of

$$\phi(x) = g(x) + \lambda \int_R K(x,y)\phi(y)\,dy$$

at a single point $x = x_0$, (2) the application of elaborate
sampling schemes based upon simple distribution functions in
an attempt to realize an over-all computing efficiency by
appropriate balance between statistical efficiency and machine
efficiency, and (3) the estimation of the entire function
$\phi(x)$ by a weighted interpolation of many single-point estimates
of ϕ. Related estimation problems are mentioned only briefly.
(Author's Introduction)

Bellman, R.

A NOTE ON THE MONTE CARLO METHOD AND THE POTENTIAL EQUATION.
RAND RM-234, September 1, 1949.

This note is, in reality, a suggestion to the effect that it might well be fruitful to further investigate the possibility of forming a solution of one class of equations using solutions of another class. As stated, "....the important point here is that the Monte Carlo method may be used to obtain numerical solutions of the heat equation, and an indirect means is furnished for obtaining numerical solutions of the potential equation via the heat equation." An example of a solution of the potential equation obtained by combining two solutions of the heat equation is included.

Bernardini, G., Booth, E.T., and Lindenbaum, S.J.

THE INTERACTIONS OF HIGH ENERGY NUCLEONS WITH NUCLEI II.
Phys. Rev. 88: 1017-26, December 1, 1952.

Part I of this paper presented an analysis of the experimentally observed interactions of 300- to 400-Mev protons and neutrons with the nuclei of G-5 emulsion. General evidence for the nucleonic-cascade mechanism of interaction was deduced from these results. Goldberger [Phys. Rev. 74: 1268, 1948] had previously calculated the interaction of high-energy nucleons (~ 90 Mev) with heavy nuclei on the basis of an internal nucleonic cascade generated in a Fermi nucleon gas. However, the experimental test of these calculations by Hadley and York [Phys. Rev. 80: 345, 1950] was indecisive. Calculations basically similar to the Goldberger type were performed for these interactions, employing the Monte Carlo method to treat the rather complicated cascades involved. The theoretical and experimental results are compared in detail and found to be essentially in agreement within error limits. (Author)

Cameron, J. M.

MONTE CARLO EXPERIMENTS ON SEAC. Nat'l Bur. of Stds., SEL
Working Paper SEL-52-5, October 27, 1951.

Pseudo-random numbers γ_n, $(0 < \gamma_n < 1)$, defined by the following relations:

$$\gamma_n = 2^{42} P_n$$

$$P_{n+1} = 5^{17} \cdot P_n \text{ modulo } 2^{42}, \quad P_0 = 1$$

(i.e., P_{n+1} is the remainder left on dividing $5^{17} P_n$ by 2^{42}) were generated on SEAC. The paper contains a proof of the period of P_n, which is 2^{40}, the results of various tests of randomness applied to the numbers, and a description of several uses of the numbers in connection with statistical analysis, and gamma ray diffusion problems.

Carlson, B.

THE MONTE CARLO METHOD APPLIED TO A PROBLEM IN GAMMA-RAY DIFFUSION. Los Alamos Scientific Laboratory, AECU-2857, Contract (W-7405-eng-36), 1953.

Analytical techniques and procedures for solving a typical problem in applied mathematics, by Monte Carlo calculations performed on the Los Alamos 701 calculator, are presented. Basic geometrical and statistical concepts are illustrated in the case of scattering and absorption of gamma rays by the electrons of W. Scatter-processes described by the Klein-Nishina formula and absorption by a $e^{-7/2}$ law were used. (K.S.)

Cochran, W. G.

USE OF IBM EQUIPMENT IN AN INVESTIGATION OF THE 'TRUNCATED NORMAL' PROBLEM. Proceedings of the Research Forum, IBM Corp., N. Y., August 1946.

A sample of N normally distributed observations y_i is truncated from above at a known point t. The actual values of the y_i are known for all observations greater than t.

From these data the mean μ of the untruncated population may be estimated by maximum likelihood or by using the regression of the ordered observations y_i on auxiliary quantities x_i, where x_i is the mean value of the ith from the bottom in a normal sample of size N. By drawing 520 samples of size 20 from a table of random deviates, and truncating each sample at the same point, the maximum likelihood and the regression estimates of μ and σ were computed for each sample. In this way a comparison was made of the efficiencies of the two methods of estimation. (Author's Abstract)

Cüer, P. and Combe, J.

SUR LA RÉALIZATION D'UNE TECHNIQUE DE MONTE-CARLO POUR ÉTUDIER LE PASSAGE DES NUCLÉONS DE GRANDE ÉNERGIE À TRAVERS LES NOYAUX. Extrait des Comptes rendus des seances de l'Académie des Sciences, t. 238, p. 1799-1801, seance du 3 mai 1954.

On a mis au point une machine de Monte-Carlo complétée par une représentation mécanique spatiale du noyau pour étudier

séparément et rigoureusement la traversée des protons de 3/4o
NeV dans les noyaux légers et lourds de l'emulsion sensible.
Quelques paramètres comme le libre parcours moyen dans la
matière nucléaire et la distribution des moments dans les
noyaux sont encore mal définis expérimentalement. (Author's
Abstract)

A Monte Carlo machine supplemented with a spatial mechanical representation of a nucleus was used to study separately
and vigorously the passage of 340-Mev protons in light and
heavy nuclei of a sensitive emulsion. Some parameters such
as the mean free path in the nuclear material and the moment
distribution of nuclei are still badly defined experimentally.
(Nuclear Physics, Compt. rend. 238: 1799-1801, 1954, tr-auth)

Curtiss, J. H.

SAMPLING METHODS APPLIED TO DIFFERENTIAL AND DIFFERENCE EQUA-
TIONS. Proceedings Seminar on Scientific Computation, IBM
Corp., N. Y., November 1949.
    This paper consists of an exposition of the theory of
the Monte Carlo method as applied to elliptic boundary value
problems. New results on probable errors and on truncation
errors are included. Methods of sampling based on a priori
knowlege of the solution are discussed which, in favorable
cases, yield drastic reductions in the number of samples
required to achieve a given accuracy. (Author's Abstract)

The author presents a part of the theory dealing with
the use of probability methods for numerical solutions of
certain differential equations. A brief historical survey of
corresponding differential equations is followed by a discussion of the Monte Carlo method where the point of view is
reversed: the attempt being made to obtain solutions of given
differential or integro-differential equations by suitable
statistical experiments, or to study certain physical problems directly by probabilistic models without recourse to the
equations describing them.

The paper summarizes some of the recent work in this
direction. The diffusion equation is discussed; attention
centers mainly on Dirichlet's problem. Random walks leading
to the differential equation are generalized in various ways
and their properties studied. The degree of approximation
of solutions of the differential equation is estimated. The
dispersion of the statistical estimates together with the
economy of various sampling procedures is discussed. It is
followed by description and comparison of bookkeeping experiments performed on computing machines. (S. Ulam, Math. Rev.
13: 286, 1952.)

Curtiss, J. H. (Continued)

A UNIFIED APPROACH TO THE MONTE CARLO METHOD. Address presented at the Association for Computing Machinery meeting, May 3, 1952.

This paper summarizes the results of a study which the author has made of chain functions of the type

$$z_N = \psi(S_N) \left. \prod_1^N z(S_{k-1}, S_k) \right|, \quad \Sigma = (S_0) + \sum_1^N z_k, \text{ where}$$

S_0, S_1, ..., is a simple Markov chain. The author indicates that this study "provides a convenient unified background for most of the applications of the Monte Carlo method which have so far been made,..."

MONTE CARLO METHODS FOR THE ITERATION OF LINEAR OPERATORS. Nat'l Bur. of Stds., Rep. No. 2365, March 19, 1953.

A purely formal description of the type of problem dealt with is as follows. Let $c = c(x)$ and $u_0 = u_0(x)$ be real-valued functions defined on a coordinate space R, which may be multidimensional. Let $L = L(f)$ be a linear transformation defined on the space of all real-valued function f whose arguments belong to R. Required to calculate the sequence of functions u_1, u_2, ..., defined by the recursion formula

$$u_{N+1} = L(u_N) + c, \qquad N = 0, 1, 2, ...$$

The purpose of the paper is to present some theory which may be of interest for itself alone, which unifies and clarifies certain of the Monte Carlo devices which have been proposed, and which lays the groundwork for further numerical experimentation aimed at investigating the limits of usefulness of the method for non-stochastic problems.

Cutkosky, R. E.

A MONTE CARLO METHOD FOR SOLVING A CLASS OF INTEGRAL EQUATIONS. J. Res. of the Nat'l Bur. of Stds., 47: 113-115, 1951.

Certain types of matrices can be inverted by a Monte Carlo method that was devised by J. von Neumann and S. M. Ulam, and that appears in a paper written by G. E. Forsythe and R. A. Leibler. It is shown that this method, when suitably generalized, can be used to approximate the Neumann series solution of an integral equation. This procedure is then shown to

be similar to those used to solve certain problems dealing
with scattering of particles, which can be formulated in
terms of a nonhomogeneous integral equation, and which have
been described by Herman Kahn.[+] (Author's Abstract)

A random walk equivalent to the Neumann series solution
of an integral equation is described, and a diffusion analogy
and the problem of importance sampling are discussed briefly.

[+]Kahn, H. "Stochastic Attenuation Analysis."

L'auteur donne un procédé basé sur les probabilités pour
trouver des valeurs approchies de $\psi(x_k)$, x_k donné, $\psi(x)$
etant solution de l'equation integrale

$$\psi(x) = f(x) + \lambda \int_a^b K(x,y)\,\psi(y)dy.$$

Un procédé basé sur le même principe avait déjà été donné pour
des matrices par Forsythe et Leibler [Math. Tables and Other
Aids to Computation 4: 127-129, 1950; ces Rev. 12: 361].

The author gives a process, based on probabilities, by
which may be found the approximate values $\psi(x_k)$, given x_k,
where $\psi(x)$ is a solution of the integral equation

$$\psi(x) = f(x) + \lambda \int_a^b K(x,y)\,\psi(y)dy.$$

A process, based on the same principle, has already been given
by Forsythe and Leibler [Math. Tables and Other Aids to Computation 4: 127-129, 1950; these reviews 12: 361], for inversion
of matrices. (J. Kuntzmann, Math. Rev. 13: 590-591, 1952; translated by N. L. Rasmussen)

DeMarcus, W. C. and Nelson, L.

METHODS OF PROBABILITIES IN CHAINS APPLIED TO PARTICLE TRANS-
MISSION THROUGH MATTER. The Monte Carlo Method, AMS 12: 9-
11, 1951, Nat'l Bur. of Stds.
     The author prepares a solution for the problem in which a
steady distribution of sources is producing particles inside
and on the surfaces of a large bulk of matter, and the steady
state fate of these particles is derived.

The existence is assumed of a linear operator which, when
applied to the frequency distribution of particles produced in
unit time gives the frequency distribution of these particles

immediately after each has made one collision. If the result of successive applications of this operator tends to a limit, then the steady state fate of the particles may be obtained.

In the case of a slab limited by two parallel infinite planes, it is shown that the limiting power of the operator may be expressed in terms of sets of independent equations, the matrix of which may be evaluated by the Gaus-Seidel method. Hence, a Monte Carlo method of evaluating the matrix could be applied.

Donsker, M. D. and Kac, M.

THE MONTE CARLO METHOD AND ITS APPLICATIONS. Proceedings Computation Seminar, IBM Corp., N. Y., December 1949.
This paper is essentially the same as "A Sampling Method for Determining the Lowest Eigenvalue and the Principal Eigenfunction of Schroedinger's Equation." See review under this title; authors: Donsker, M. D. and Kac, M.

A SAMPLING METHOD FOR DETERMINING THE LOWEST EIGENVALUE AND THE PRINCIPAL EIGENFUNCTION OF SCHROEDINGER'S EQUATION. J. Res., Nat'l Bur. of Stds. 44:551-557, 1950.
The eigenvalues λ_j and the corresponding eigenfunctions of the one-dimensional Schroedinger equation

$$\frac{1}{2} \frac{d^2 \psi}{dx^2} - V(x) \psi(x) = -\lambda \psi , \qquad \lambda > 0,$$

are found by a method utilizing various probability techniques and sampling methods. These methods have become known as the Monte Carlo method. X_1, X_2, X_3, ... are independent identically distributed random variables, each having mean 0 and standard deviation 1.
Let

$$S_k = \sum_{n=1}^{k} X_n .$$

Then $\sigma(\alpha, t)$ is the limiting distribution function of the random variable $n^{-1} \sum_{k<nt} \cdot \frac{S_k}{\sqrt{n}}$. It is shown that the lowest eigenvalue is:

$$\lambda_1 = \lim_{t \to \infty} - \frac{1}{t} \log \int_0^{\infty} e^{-\alpha} d_\alpha \, \sigma(\alpha, t)$$

290

A more practical approximation is:

$$\lambda_1 \quad \frac{1}{t_2 - t_1} \log \frac{\int_0^\infty e^{-\alpha} d_\alpha \ \sigma(\alpha, t_1)}{\int_0^\infty e^{-\alpha} d_\alpha \ \sigma(\alpha, t_2)}$$

The Monte Carlo process consists in the calculation of $\sigma(\alpha, t_1)$, and $\sigma(\alpha, t_2)$ by a sampling process. The authors consider two examples: $V(x) = x^2$ and $V(x) = |x|$. For these n is selected to be 400, $t_1 = 5$, $t_2 = 3.75$; 100 samples were used. For λ_1, the agreement with the exact value is rather good. The second eigenvalue is also calculated. Here the agreement is poor. (S. C. van Veen, Math. Rev. 13: 590, 1952)

Edmundson, H. P.

MONTE CARLO MATRIX INVERSION AND RECURRENT EVENTS. MTAC 7, 41: 18-21, 1953.
Let $p_{ik} \geq 0 (i, k=1, \ldots m)$, and $\Sigma_{k=1}^m p_{ik} \quad 0$. Denote (q^{ik}) the inverse of the matrix $(q_{ik}) = (\delta_{ik} - p_{ik})$. Two different random variables based on a certain random walk with transition probabilities p_{ik} have been defined [see Forsythe and Leibler, same journal 4: 127-129, 1950; these Rev. 12: 361; Wasow, MTAC 6: 78-81, 1952] such that the expectation of these random variables is q^{ik}. The author proves that $q^{ik} - \delta_{ik} = r_{ik} q^{ik}$, r_{ik} is the probability that a walk starting from the point i will eventually visit the point k. This relation enables him to improve a result of Wasow [loc. cit.] comparing the variances of the two random variables. (W. Wasow, Math. Rev. 14, 10, November 1953)

Everett, C. J., Cashwell, E. D. and Rechard, O.W.

A MONTE CARLO DETERMINATION OF THE ESCAPE FRACTION FOR A SCATTERING SPHERICAL SHELL WITH CENTRAL POINT SOURCE. Los Alamos Scientific Laboratory (LA-1583), August 24, 1953.
Two types of Monte Carlo procedures were developed for the computation of the fraction of monoenergetic neutrons,

emanating from a central point source, which escape from the
surface of a hollow spherical shell after any number (≥ 0)
of elastic collisions. The shell is composed of heavy nuclei
with given elastic and inelastic cross sections and a given
differential cross-section curve for elastic scattering angle.
Both methods yield the distribution of escaped neutrons with
respect to the number of elastic collisions suffered. A computation of each type was made on the MANIAC for a particular
shell, and an estimate of the escape fraction (0.70871) was
obtained, based on a total sample of 215,000 source neutrons.
The result is in good agreement with that (0.707) obtained by
a modified transport theory. A comparison of the statistical
and transport methods in the case of a thicker shell should
be of greater interest, and a problem of this kind is being
done.   (Authors)

Everett, C. J. and Ulam, S.

MULTIPLICATIVE SYSTEMS I.   Proc. Nat'l Acad. Sci. U.S.A. 34:
403-405, 1948.
      What the authors call a multiplicative system is usually
referred to as a stationary branching process. The authors
consider the case where particles are of different kinds.
Each particle has well-defined probabilities of transmuting
into specified groups of particles of the various types, and
the particles are mutually independent in the statistical
sense. Usually one considers only certain random variables
(like population size) associated with the process. The
authors show how the boundary process itself can be described
in terms of graphs and they discuss the appropriate measure
set up in a sample space. (W. Feller, Math. Rev. 10: 132, 1949)

Fano, U.

MULTIPLE-SCATTERED GAMMA RAYS.   Paper presented at the Nat'l
Bur. of Stds. Institute for Numerical Analysis Symposium on
Monte Carlo, Los Angeles, June 29, 1949.
      A very informal and rather negative report on the role
of Monte Carlo in our gamma-ray penetration study. (Author's
Abstract)

Fermi, E. and Richtmyer, R. D.

NOTE ON CENSUS-TAKING IN MONTE CARLO CALCULATIONS. Los Alamos
Scientific Laboratory (AECD-3164; LADC-946), July 11, 1948;
Decl. May 22, 1951.
      An analysis is given of the proposal that in some Monte
Carlo problems census taking should be made on the basis of
distance traveled rather than time elapsed. The analysis given
is restricted to critical systems, and it is shown how to in-
terpret the resulting neutron distribution in this case. (Auth)

Forsythe, G. E. and Leibler, R. A.

MATRIX INVERSION BY A MONTE CARLO METHOD. MTAC IV, 31: 127-129, 1950.

The authors in this paper give an exposition of a method for inverting matrices devised by von Neumann and Ulam based on stochastic techniques. Under suitable hypotheses the authors are able to exhibit the desired game and establish its relevant properties. In general, the method is for each i, j to play a solitaire game whose expected payment is the (i, j)-th element of the inverse matrix. This expectation value is approximated by playing successively and calculating the average payment. (H. H. Goldstine, Math. Rev. 12: 361, 1951)

Fortet, R.

ON THE ESTIMATION OF AN EIGENVALUE BY AN ADDITIVE FUNCTIONAL OF A STOCHASTIC PROCESS, WITH SPECIAL REFERENCE TO THE KAC-DONSKER METHOD. J. Res. Nat'l Bur. Stds. 48: 68-75, 1952.

A sampling (Monte Carlo) method is described for the computation of the Fredholm determinant, and hence of the eigenvalues of certain Fredholm integral equations with positive definite kernel Γ (t, γ). The method is based on a theorem by Kac and Siegert [J. Appl. Phys. 18: 383-397, 1947; these Rev. 8: 522] which connects the Fredholm determinant of the integral equation with a Laplacian (i.e. Gaussian) process X(t) whose covariance is Γ (t, γ). Such a process X(t) is, in general, not easy to find. In the special case that Γ (t, γ) depends on t- γ only an appropriate X(t) can be constructed by means of a Poisson process. The second part of the paper contains a discussion of the various errors inherent in the method of Donsker and Kac [cf. same J. 44: 551-557, 1950; these Rev. 13: 590] for the determination of the lowest eigenvalue of Schroedinger's equation. [Reviewer's note: In an unpublished paper by M. Cohen and M. Kac it is shown that some of the bounds for the errors given by Fortet are wasteful by as much as a factor 5000.] (W. Wasow, Math. Rev. 13: 992, 1952)

Germond, H. H.

SUMMARY OF ROUND TABLE DISCUSSION AT THE NBSINA MONTE CARLO SYMPOSIUM, LOS ANGELES, JUNE 1949. The Monte Carlo Method, Nat'l Bur. of Stds. AMS 12: 39-42, 1951.

A synopsis of the comments of various participants in the Round Table discussion at the Monte Carlo Symposium at UCLA. Most of the comments mentioned were of a general nature.

Goertzel, G.

QUOTA SAMPLING AND IMPORTANCE FUNCTIONS IN STOCHASTIC SOLUTION OF PARTICLE PROBLEMS. Working Paper, ORNL Shielding Work Session, NDA, June 21, 1949.

In section 1 a general stochastic particle problem is defined. Section 3 defines a quota sampling method available for simplifying the solution of such a problem. In section 4 an importance function, $Q(\alpha)$ is defined such that if it were known and could be used in the quota sampling, the solution of the stochastic problem is greatly reduced in difficulty. Thus any function $q(\alpha)$, used in quota sampling should be selected to represent $Q(\alpha)$ as closely as one's knowledge permits.

In section 5 it is shown how to set up a pair of problems, such that the solution of each is the importance function for solving the other. Thus $Q(\alpha)$ may be estimated stochastically. (Author's Abstract)

Goertzel, G. and Householder, A. S.

DETERMINATION OF PARTICLE DISTRIBUTION BY COMBINED STOCHASTIC AND DETERMINISTIC PROCESSES. Nat'l Appl. Math. Lab Memo., October 27, 1948.

An abstract by Ulam and von Neumann [Bul. Amer. Math. Soc. 53: 1120, 1947] discusses the solution of a group of physical problems by means of a series of statistical experiments performed on a computing machine. The present paper shows in detail the processes to be used to perform such statistical experiments in order to solve a definite type of problem, e.g., the stopping of an electron in passage through matter.

Goertzel, G. and Kahn, H.

MONTE CARLO METHODS FOR SHIELD COMPUTATION. AECD-2807, Feb. 22, 1950; Decl. Mar. 17, 1950.

There is at the present time no reliable method available to compute the attenuation of a shield. In this report the application of the Monte Carlo method to this problem is discussed. First the basic method is described; then modifications are proposed in order to reduce this random sampling procedure to manageable proportions so that a penetration calculation can be carried out.

Hammer, P. C.

CALCULATION OF SHIELDING PROPERTIES OF WATER FOR HIGH ENERGY
NEUTRONS. Monte Carlo Method, Nat'l Bur. of Stds. AMS 12:
June 11, 1951.
    The problem of determining the shielding effectiveness
of a 100-cm thick wall of water to 14 Mev. neutrons normally
incident upon it was formulated by Dr. Maria G. Mayer and
the calculations carried out by the IBM group at Los Alamos.
The calculation of the locations and energies given by Dr.
Mayer is simple in that the algebraic formulas are well
adapted to calculation and the number of digits carried was
small. Use was made of the random number deck compiled by
RAND Corporation, and a natural logarithm deck. A detailed
card layout is given.

    In addition to the approximate solutions obtained, it
was found that problems of appreciably greater complexity
than the one here discussed can be done on standard IBM
equipment without much difficulty.

Hammersley, J. M. and Morton, K. W.

POOR MAN'S MONTE CARLO. J. Roy. Stat. Soc. Ser. B 16: 23-
38, 1954; discussion 61-75, 1954.
    Monte Carlo methods often are and always should be part
of the normal stock-in-trade of the ordinary practising statistician. This paper is an introduction to such methods,
with an emphasis on those that require little or no calculating machinery. Three worked numerical examples, arranged in
order of increasing difficulty, illustrate some of the more
important general precepts. The last of these examples
touches on some problems of self-avoiding walks, i.e., stochastic processes without multiple points. (Author's Summary).

    This paper and the subsequent discussion relate chiefly
to the art of applying Monte Carlo, and no brief summary can
do justice to either. The basic thesis can be inferred from
the title, that one does not necessarily need high speed
machines to use Monte Carlo effectively.

    The authors first point out that only the name and not
the method is new (the discussion brings out that King Solomon
was an early practitioner) and then discuss three problems:
the critical size of a nuclear reactor, the test of a quantum hypothesis, and self-avoiding walks. The last problem
is treated at greatest length. The section headings are

Introduction; The problem of excluded volume in high polymers; Reducing the Monte Carlo work by sampling technique; Reducing the Monte Carlo work by choice of recording technique; Inversely restricted sampling; Monte Carlo computing technique; Reporting Monte Carlo data; Estimation technique in Monte Carlo work; Artificial abatement of the randomness; Other sources of information. (A. S. Householder, Math. Rev. 16, 3: 287-88, 1955)

Hayward, E. and Hubbell, J. H.

THE ALBEDO OF VARIOUS MATERIALS FOR 1 MEV PHOTONS. Nat'l Bur. of Stds. Rep. No. 2768, NBS Proj. No. 0408-10-3110, 1953.

 The Monte Carlo method has been used to determine the albedo of 1 Mev photons reflected from semi-infinite slabs of water, aluminum, copper, tin and lead at various angles of incidence. The case histories of 67 photons were followed. For normal incidence the number varies from 33% for water to 0.5% for lead and the energy albedo from 5% for water to 0.1% for lead. (Author's Abstract)

Householder, A. S.

NEUTRON AGE CALCULATIONS IN WATER, GRAPHITE, AND TISSUE. Monte Carlo Method, Nat'l Bur. of Stds. AMS 12: 6-8, June 1951.

 Brief description of the method with summary of results (incomplete at the time of presentation). The method was straightforward and the problem represents one of the most elementary practical applications of Monte Carlo. (Author's Abstract)

THE MONTE CARLO METHOD. Chapter 8 from Principles of Numerical Analysis, McGraw-Hill, 1953.

 In many computations the occurrence of the maximum possible error may be extremely improbable and it may suffice to be able to say with probability p that the error in the result will not exceed δ. Thus, though the computation is strictly deterministic, statistical methods are used to appraise the results which are treated as an estimate rather than a true approximation. It is therefore reasonable to consider the feasibility of using non-deterministic methods for the computations themselves. This would mean obtaining an estimate of the desired quantity by means of some random sampling process, rather than obtaining an approximation by rigorous computation. This is the Monte Carlo method. The remainder of the chapter contains an example of Monte Carlo methods applied to a problem in numerical integration, and a bibliography.

Johnson, P. C. and Uffelman, F. C.

A PUNCHED CARD APPLICATION OF THE MONTE CARLO METHOD. Proceedings Computation Seminar, IBM Corp., N. Y., December 1949.

The authors state: "Assuming a monochromatic point source of neutrons of given energy, within an infinite medium of known constituents, hypothetical case histories for a number of these neutrons will be built up as they undergo a series of random collisions with the constituents of the selected medium. These collisions result in either an absorption or an elastic scattering of the neutrons, and the main work of this problem is to follow the selected neutrons through successive collisions until they either are absorbed or fall below a certain energy level."

Detailed procedures and card lay-outs are included. However, it must be remembered, as the authors point out, that the procedures outlined in this paper are for standard Type 602 or 604 IBM calculating punches along with the usual associated equipment. Thus, these detailed procedures might well have to be completely revised if other type computing equipment were to be used.

Kac, M.

ON SOME CONNECTIONS BETWEEN PROBABILITY THEORY AND DIFFERENTIAL AND INTEGRAL EQUATIONS. Proceedings of the 2nd Berkeley Symposium on Mathematical Statistics and Probability: 189-215, 1950; Univ. of California Press, Berkeley and Los Angeles, 1951.

Various links between probability theory and differential and integral equations are well-known. The aim of the present expository lecture was not to give a systematic survey but to illustrate, on a variety of examples, some new cross-connections and to illustrate new methods which are due largely to the author. First the connection of probability limit theorems with the distribution of certain functionals connected with Markovian processes is described (cf. Kac, Trans. Amer. Math. Soc. 65: 1-13, 1949; these Rev. 10: 383 for the case of the Wiener-Bachelier process). One is led to certain integral equations, which in particular cases reduce to differential equations. As applications the author considers the arc-sine law, problems connected with the Kolmogorov-Smirnov distribution (Proc. Nat. Acad. Sci. U.S.A. 35: 252-257, 1949; these Rev. 10: 614), and various representation problems. Of particular interest is the application to the ruin problem of processes which are related to symmetric stable distributions in the same way as the ordinary diffusion is related to the normal distribution. The general formulation of the problem is new (for the Cauchy process cf. Kac and Pollard, Canadian J. Math. 2: 375-384, 1950; these Rev. 12: 114).

So far differential and integral equations were applied to probability. Conversely, the author shows that probability can be used successfully (both heuristically and rigorously) to arrive at results about differential equations. In particular connections with the distribution of eigenvalues, the Weyl-Carleman theory, and potential theory are described. The arguments and methods cannot be reproduced in a few lines. (Reviewed by W. Feller)

Kahn, H.

PARTICLE HISTORIES FOR PLANE SLABS; RESEARCH MEMORANDUM. RAND Corp. RM-248 (RAND), Dec. 24, 1948.
A preliminary account of work on the application of sampling techniques to the problem of determining the transmission of radiation through shields is presented. It is believed that an efficient compromise has been reached between the calculation of a large number of easily calculated life histories of a particle and the calculation of a smaller number of more complicated histories. A method (the exponential transformation) for eliminating many of the difficulties of working with high attenuation is given, with details of quota sampling, combination of random sampling with numerical integration, extension to complicated problems, and generalization of the geometry.

MODIFICATION OF THE MONTE CARLO METHOD. Proceedings Seminar on Scientific Computation: 20-27, IBM, N. Y., November 1949.
The statistical sampling (Monte Carlo) procedures for the numerical solution of mathematical problems are based on an interpretation of the quantity to be calculated as the expected value of some random variable. The random variable and its probability distribution are not uniquely determined by the mathematical problem. The author discusses, for the problem of evaluating multidimensional integrals and for the solution of Fredholm integral equations, methods of choosing the random process so as to make the standard error as small as is practically possible. This amounts to finding a method of sampling that scans most carefully the regions that contribute most to the error. Hence the name "importance sampling" for this procedure. It is stated, without proof, that finding the theoretically best method of importance

sampling for an integral equation is equivalent to solving
the adjoint problem. For the actual computation the decision
has, however, to be made on the basis of physical intuition
and preliminary approximations, for which some suggestions
are given. (Reviewed by W. R. Wasow)

RANDOM SAMPLING (MONTE CARLO) TECHNIQUES IN NEUTRON ATTENU-
ATION PROBLEMS. Nucleonics 6, 5: 27-33, 1950; 6: 60-65.
        A discussion of the application of random sampling
techniques to the problem of neutron and gamma ray attenuation
in thick shields.

STOCHASTIC (MONTE CARLO) ATTENUATION ANALYSIS. RAND paper
P-88, RAND Corp., Santa Monica California, July 14, 1949.
        The paper gives a short, informal summary of the appli-
cation of random sampling methods to neutron attenuation
problems. It is primarily intended for engineers and physicists "having but a slight knowledge of statistics." In
addition to the straight probability analogue method of
estimating particle attenuation, various devices by which the
number of "case histories" needed to obtain statistically
reliable estimates are discussed informally. These devices
include: (1) Integration of multiple integrals by random
sampling. (2) The replacement of the physical situation with
a mathematical "analogue" whose solution has a known relation
to the original problem, but with a much larger expected
value of the parameter having a known relation to the parameter whose estimate is desired. (3) The application of
"quota sampling" or stratified sampling, concentrating the
study to those particles most likely to penetrate the shield.
(6) The utilization of the complete life histories of each
particle studied. (The paper is to be published in Nucleonics)

Kahn, H. and Harris, T. E.

ESTIMATION OF PARTICLE TRANSMISSION BY RANDOM SAMPLING.
Monte Carlo Method, Nat'l Bur. of Stds. AMS 12, June 11, 1951.
        The problem with which this paper is concerned is the
estimation of the probability that a particle is transmitted
through a shield when this probability is of the order of 10^{-6}
to 10^{-10}, and further, it is desired that this estimate be
accomplished by sampling a thousand "life histories." Three
techniques techniques are outlined by which this may be accomplished. These techniques may be referenced as (1) the splitting technique mentioned by von Neumann, (2) "importance"

299

sampling, and (3) a combination of analytical or numerical techniques with random sampling. However, before discussing the applications of these techniques to the calculation of shields, the authors indicate how these techniques could be applied to the numerical evaluation of a double integral. The physical problem is then outlined and the application of each of the above-mentioned techniques to this physical problem is discussed and certain equivalence relations are pointed out.

Kahn, H. and Marshall, A. W.

METHODS OF REDUCING SAMPLE SIZE IN MONTE CARLO COMPUTATIONS. Res. Soc. of Amer. I: 263-271, 1953.

Much of the currently available literature which concerns itself with Monte Carlo methods of computation is devoted to problems:

(a) of the transformation of non-probabilistic problems into what are, in one sense, their probabilistic analogs; e.g., solution of differential equations by Monte Carlo methods applied to suitable random-walk problems;

(b) of reducing the labor involved in obtaining sample observations by the use of special mechanical devices, cards, etc.;

(c) of sampling from specific probability distribution functions by means of some systematic use of samples drawn from the uniform distribution function.

Apart from a few papers, very little attention has been paid to the problem of reducing the sample size required to obtain answers (estimates) with a fixed level of accuracy (variance).

In this paper, the authors wish to formulate the general problem of Monte Carlo computations within the framework of mathematical statistics and to indicate briefly its relations to the theory of estimation and the design of experiments. In addition, several specific techniques for the reduction of sample sizes will be sketched out. For two of these, techniques referred to as importance sampling and correlation methods, illustrative examples will be worked out in some detail, both with regard to the problems of applying the techniques and the probable gains (reduction in the variance of the estimate obtained) and losses (increased cost of the individual observations). (Authors' Abstract)

Keilson, J.

THE NATURE OF THE MONTE CARLO METHOD. Cruft Laboratory Tech. Rep. 137, ONR Cont. N5ORI-76, Harvard Univ., Cambridge, 1951.
A survey is given of ideas underlying the various numerical approaches to the solution of differential and integral equations based on probability ideas and known as Monte Carlo methods.

King, G. W.

STOCHASTIC METHODS IN QUANTUM MECHANICS. Proceedings IBM Seminar on Scientific Computation, IBM Corp., N. Y., November 1949.
The author discusses the application of certain random-number techniques (Monte Carlo methods) in obtaining approximations to some of the many problems in chemistry where results to a few significant figures would be of great value. A rather detailed discussion of the difference equation of the Schroedinger equation as a diffusion equation is included. It is also stated that "the stochastic method could be used in the momentum representation of Schroedinger's equation. Here, integrations have been carried out, and again the use of random numbers seems to be the only practical method in many dimensions. Further, we have the prospect of using phase space itself. ...This possible use of phase space is mentioned to show that the stochastic method can use every bit of information about the system that is available, and that is a new mathematical method that can, if need be, by-pass differential and integral equations and go right to the heart of the physics of the problem." The connection between the Monte Carlo method and certain other iterative procedures is shown.

Examples of the applications of these techniques include the "Harmonic Oscillator" and the "Particle in a Box." Indications of the precision obtained in carrying out these examples is included. It is further pointed out that the random walk method can be used to obtain excited states by imposing nodes on the distribution.

FURTHER REMARKS ON STOCHASTIC METHODS IN QUANTUM MECHANICS. Proceedings Computation Seminar, IBM Corp., N. Y.: 92-94, December, 1949.
This paper supplements the paper above. It is shown that the random walk method of obtaining estimates gives a distribution of results exactly defined by the iterative method of solving difference equations. The point is made that the Monte Carlo method of finding the characteristic

vectors of a matrix is a "DUZ" method, i.e., it works equally well with a 2 x 2 or a 10,000 by 10,000 matrix. The advantage, for large matrices, is that instead of computing all terms in all elements of the nth power of a matrix, only a sample of, say, 1000 need be taken to obtain results to two or three significant figures.

REMARKS ON FINDING ROOTS OF, AND INVERTING, A MATRIX. Proceedings Industrial Computation Seminar, IBM Corp., N. Y., September 1950.

"The Essential Feature of the Monte Carlo method of inverting a matrix, or of finding its roots, is the well-known iterative procedure of raising the matrix to a high power. The reason the method does this can be easily seen as follows: Choose a row and a column at random and write down the matrix element, $a_{i\lambda}$. Then choose another element from the λ th row lying in column μ, say $a_{\lambda\mu}$. Again choose an element from the μth row, say $a_{\mu\nu}$. This is done N times. The choices are multiplied together,

$$a_{i\lambda} \cdot a_{\lambda\mu} \cdot a_{\mu\nu} \cdots a_{kj}.$$

We recognize this as a term in the ijth element of the Nth power of the matrix. If we took all possible choices of paths from row to column, starting at the ith row and ending at the jth column, and added the products, we would have precisely the value of the ijth element of the Nth power. The random procedure described above merely picks some terms from some elements at random. By having the probability of picking any element, say $a_{\mu\nu}$ proportional to its magnitude, the Monte Carlo method picks out the terms in proportion to their magnitude, and hence gets the principal term of the principal elements of the Nth power of the matrix."

BIASED RANDOM WALKS IN CLASSICAL, STATISTICAL AND QUANTUM MECHANICS. Off. of Nav. Res. Tech. Rep. 5, July 20, 1951.

It is known that if random walks in one dimension are biased so that one direction is favored over another, the distribution is determined by a Fokker-Planck equation with a linear term in $\partial / \partial x$. We have shown that if the biassing probability is chosen $1 \pm \Delta x/x$ for the two directions, the radial diffusion or Schroedinger's equation results. Other biases can give the more complicated differential equations of quantum mechanics.

If the bias is made to depend not on the location in space but on the previous history of the path (a Markoff process), no linear terms appear. The controlling equation is the diffusion equation with a modified diffusion coefficient. For example, in one dimension, if the probability of a particle continuing in the same direction is α (the probability of reversing its direction being $1-\alpha$), the diffusion coefficient is $\alpha/1-\alpha$ times that for the isotropic case. The method of proof can be readily extended to higher dimensions. It depends on classifying the particles on the direction they enter a lattice point. There is a difference equation for each class, and the algebraic condition for the simultaneous solution of these equations is simply that each flow obeys the diffusion equation.

An interesting example of use in the study of the random configurations of polymer chains is a bias forbidding the "particles" to re-enter a point they have just left (in three dimensions on a tetrahedral lattice). The distribution for such biased walks is again Gaussian, the diffusion coefficient being twice the isotropic value. The method can be extended to show that in the polymer case, steric effects and even excluded volume leave the distribution Gaussian, with a modified effective bond length.

The method has been used to improve the efficiency of the stochastic method of solving Schroedinger's equation by biassing the walks into regions where the potential function is important. (Author's Abstract)

STOCHASTIC METHODS IN STATISTICAL MECHANICS. The Monte Carlo Method, Nat'l Bur. of Stds. AMS 12: 12-18, 1951.
Calculations by modern computing machinery are essentially parallel. This feature is united to statistical mechanics, since this requires the numerical description of an ensemble of points in phase space, each describing one of all possible configurations of the thermodynamic system.

A polymer (as a system) is described by its coordinates as it lies in a tetrahedral lattice. Some energy effects can be introduced by simple counting, e.g., restricted rotation by the actual number of cis and trans linkages; the number of nearest approaches of the polymer to itself, etc.

This simple model still has too many complexions to be enumerated or even adequately sampled with automatic computing machinery. The system can be described in a phase space of fewer dimensions by the introduction of a Markoff process, which takes into account the fact that the complexions of a very large chain are determined by the interactions of atoms near each other, with the interactions asymptotically reducing to zero in a finite (and relatively small) number of atoms of separation.

The Markoff process is therefore of greater importance in the theory of high polymers, because it formulates the generally accepted concept of a statistical unit so that the properties of very long chains can be calculated, with known (small) fluctuation, from the properties of the statistical unit. It thus permits application of statistical mechanics to a wide variety of chains, by demanding only an exhaustive study of the complexions of the statistical unit, rather than of the whole system.

Thus the theoretical way is cleared for a chemical rather than a physical study of high polymers. Then the value of punched-card methods again comes to the fore; it is perfectly possible with automatic computing machines to make exhaustive studies of elaborate chain segments of 15-30 (backbone) atoms, and introduce a variety of chemical properties into the model. (Author's Summary)

MONTE CARLO METHOD FOR SOLVING DIFFUSION PROBLEMS. Industrial and Engineering Chemistry 43: 2475, 1951.
    After a general discussion of Monte Carlo methods applied to problems in engineering and physics, the author considers a diffusion problem in one dimension in finding the distribution of a dye which is being supplied to the center of a capillary tube and diffuses in time in both directions along the tube. The process is usually described by a differential equation for the dye concentration u:

$$\frac{\partial u}{\partial t} = D \frac{\partial^2 u}{\partial x^2}$$

for which explicit solutions in closed form are available. In the Monte Carlo method random digits supplied to an automatic computer determine a series of random walks. One thousand trials was usually found adequate, with a biasing procedure used to improve efficiency where only the tails of the final distribution are of interest. Generalization to three dimensions and the effect of boundary conditions and other factors are discussed.

THE MONTE CARLO METHOD AS A NATURAL MODE OF EXPRESSION OF A WORKING MODEL OF OPERATIONS. Presented to Operations Research Society of America, Nov. 17, 18, 1952.
    The method of random walks in solving problems has been known for many decades, but its recent activation arose in

304

operations research during the war because it is capable of handling a multiplicity and variety of stochastic dependences at an adequate level of accuracy. The method allows the setting up of a working model on which experimental operations can be tried out, not in terms of averages but as typical examples. In this way, not only expectations but deviations from the mean can be obtained where solutions cannot be found by ordinary statistical procedures.

The method has become even more attractive because its simplicity and tediousness are characteristics which appeal to computing machines. Moreover, a stochastic approach is hardly subject at all to ever-present machine errors.

Even when the operational problem has been reduced to conventional mathematical formulation, the Monte Carlo method can be effectively used, especially in three or more dimensions, because it is as easy to walk in several dimensions as in one, in a computer. Examples will be given of integration, solution of several types of differential and matrix equations. These mathematical uses can be understood by showing that the use of all random walks is equivalent to relaxation or difference-equation methods.

The Monte Carlo method can enter in fields where analytical methods have not yet been fully developed. One is the presence of a Markoff process, characteristic of many investigations in operations research.

The main deficiency is that accuracy is often not good enough even for operations research. Techniques of biassing random walks to improve sampling efficiency will be described. (Author's Abstract)

Little, Arthur D., Inc.

MONTE CARLO AT WORK. Ind. Bull. of Arthur D. Little, Inc. No. 270: 3-4, November 1950.
    A mathematical technique is helping research workers predict the outcome of situations where large numbers of individual particles are influenced in their behaviour partly by chance and partly by known or assumed principles. Called the Monte Carlo Method, the technique sets up a system of assumed methods or sequences of operations which serves as a model of the real situation. One application of the Monte Carlo method has been in studies of shielding against radioactivity in work on atomic energy. Neutrons from an atomic pile penetrate into concrete or water shields, and some get completely through.

Using the Monte Carlo method, an investigator may follow the progress of a simulated neutron through the shield, and use the information on its ultimate fate in designing shields to keep escape of neutrons and other radiation to a safe level.

McCracken, D. D.

THE MONTE CARLO METHOD. Scientific American 192, 5: 90, May 1955.

Monte Carlo methods are described and illustrated by the Buffon needle problem, by a simplified neutron diffusion problem and by an example from operations research.

Mann, H. B.

A THEORY OF ESTIMATION OF PARAMETERS FOR THE FUNDAMENTAL RANDOM PROCESS AND THE ORNSTEIN UHLENBECK PROCESS. WADC Tech. Rep. No. 53-39, Wright Air Development Center, Wright-Patterson Air Force Base, Ohio, March 1953.

A theory of estimation for the parameters of a Fundamental Random Process and of an Ornstein Uhlenbeck process is presented for the case that the mean value function is linear in the unknown parameters. Estimates are proposed for the unknown parameters, and their variances and covariances are derived. In the case of the Fundamental Random Process, the proposed estimates for the parameters of the mean value function are shown to be the best linear estimates. In the case of the Ornstein Uhlenbeck process, they are shown to be unbiased. If the mean value function is a polynomial or trigonometric polynomial, they are, moreover, asymptotically best linear estimates. The cases considered include the estimate of a periodic mean value function with known period. (Author's Abstract)

Mantel, N.

AN EXTENSION OF THE BUFFON NEEDLE PROBLEM. Ann. Math. Stat. 24: 674-677, 1953.

An empirical determination of the value of π by using variations of the Buffon needle problem. This first variation is to use a Cartesian Grid system instead of just parallel lines with calculations based on mean number of intersections. The second variation is to use the Cartesian Grid system but obtain estimates of π from the variation in the number of intersections from fall to fall. A comparison of the methods is made indicating that this last method produces much better estimates.

Mayer, M.

REPORT ON A MONTE CARLO CALCULATION PERFORMED WITH THE ENIAC. Monte Carlo Method, Nat'l Bur. of Stds. AMS 12: 19-20, 1951.

A short informal report on a neutron diffusion calculation performed on the ENIAC. The medium in question contained eight "Zones" of different materials, with different mean free paths and different relative probabilities of the possible events occurring at collision. The method of calculation was the "usual" one of random variation of the positional, velocity, and energy coordinates of particles. A "distance census" was taken, i.e., the census of a population of neutrons stated at a time t=0 was taken after each neutron had travelled a certain prescribed distance, giving an estimate of the flux of neutrons in phase space.

Merrill, L. C.

NOTE ON MONTE CARLO METHOD. Fairchild Engine and Airplane Corp. Rep. No. NEPA-1013, May 10, 1949.

A fourth method of easing the difficulties encountered in applying a Monte Carlo calculation to a highly attenuating shield is presented which does not appear in NEPA-860-STR-10 (Dec. 30, 1948). This method possesses the property that all the neutrons sent into the shield emerge or go back to the source, while the statistics can still be made good. A calculation at each collision is an added necessity.

Metropolis, N. and Ulam, S.

THE MONTE CARLO METHOD. J. Amer. Stat. Assoc. 44: 335-341, 1949.

The authors present the motivation and general description of a method which deals with certain problems by identifying their solutions with those of corresponding probability problems. The latter solutions are to be found approximately by sampling. (J. L. Doob, Math. Rev. 11: 138, 1950)

A computational method is presented and discussed, the mathematical theory of which is indicated by the following: The process is a combination of stochastic and deterministic flows. It consists of repeated applications of matrices, as in Markov chains, and completely specified transformations, e.g., the transformation phase space as given by the Hamilton differential equations. One feature is that it allows the acquisition by operators on functions obeying a differential equation without the point-by-point knowledge of the functions which are solutions of the equation. Thus the values of the first few moments of a distribution, or the first few coefficients in the expansion of a solution into a Fourier series, may be determined without the necessity of first obtaining the function itself. (Author)

Meyer, H., Lytle, E., Gephart, L. and Rasmussen, N.

INVERSION OF MATRICES BY MONTE CARLO METHODS. WADC Tech. Rep. 54-56, Air Research and Development Command, Wright-Patterson Air Force Base, Ohio, 1954.

It is intended here to describe the methods of inverting certain matrices by use of Monte Carlo techniques. Following the introductory remarks, there is a description of the methods used. This is in turn followed by an adaptation of these methods to the use of the IBM 403 Tabulator. Some detailed examples are included. (Authors' Abstract)

Muller, M.

SOME MONTE CARLO METHODS FOR THE DIRICHLET PROBLEM. Thesis, University of California at Los Angeles, 1954.

The research has involved two conceptually different approaches for the Dirichlet problem with comments for other boundary value problems and other numerical methods.

1. Continuous Methods. Monte Carlo techniques are introduced using stochastic models which are Markov processes. This material includes the N-dimensional Spherical, General Spherical, and General Dirichlet Domain processes. These processes are proved to converge with probability 1 and thus yield direct statistical estimates of the solution to the N-dimensional Dirichlet problem. The results are obtained without requiring any further restrictions on the boundary or the function defined on the boundary in addition to those required for the existence and uniqueness of the solution to the Dirichlet problem. A detailed study is made for the N-dimensional Spherical process. This includes a study of the order of the average number of steps required for convergence. Asymptotic confidence intervals are obtained. When computing effort is measured in terms of the order of the average number of steps required for convergence, the often-made conjecture that the computing effort of a Monte Carlo procedure should be a linear function of the dimensionality of the problem is shown to be true for the cases considered. Comments are included regarding the application of these processes on digital computers. Truncation methods are suggested.

2. Discrete Methods. Following the more classical Monte Carlo approaches, statistical estimates for discrete approximations to the Dirichlet problem are investigated. This leads

to a study of random walks on closed neighbor simplex networks. Criteria for optimum operator approximations and admissible networks for finite difference techniques are formulated. The approach looks promising for the higher dimensional problems which will depend for their solutions on the use of high speed electronic computing equipment. These results may also find application in Relaxation methods. For the two dimensional Dirichlet problem this approach adds further justification for the networks already in use. It is shown that it is not always possible to obtain better finite difference operators by increasing the number of neighboring points. (Author's Abstract)

Murray, F. J.

SOME APPLICATIONS OF THE MONTE CARLO METHOD. Presented to Operations Research Society November 17, 18, 1952.
Certain phenomena of solid-state physics, such as the order-disorder problem and the phenomenon of the Curie point, will be considered as illustrations of possible applications of the Monte Carlo method. Its use will be compared with other procedures of computation. (Author's Abstract)

Nygaard, K.

ON THE SOLUTION OF INTEGRAL EQUATIONS BY MONTE CARLO METHODS. Norwegian Defence Res. Estab., Rep. No. F-R 94: 9, 1952.
The equations are of the form

$$H(x) = f(x) + K \int_a^b H(\xi)K(\xi,x)d\xi,$$

where K, f, and k are positive, $\int_a^b f(x)dx=1$, $\int_a^b K(\xi,x)dx \leqq 1$,

$k \leqq 1$. Divide the interval (a,b) into 10^p subintervals (x_n, x_{n+1}) with a "representative abscissa" ξ_n on each satis-

fying $\int_{x_n}^{\xi_n} f(x)dx = \int_{\xi_n}^{k_{n+1}} f(x)dx = 10^{-p}/2$. Select $x_0 = \xi_n$ by

a p-digit "Random number." For x_1, make subdivisions based on $K(x_0,x)$, select x_1 as a representative abscissa, or else terminate the process if the q-digit random number $R_2 \geq$

$$10^q \int_a^b K(x_0,x)dx.$$ Terminate the process if an r-digit random number $R_3 > k.10^r$; otherwise subdivide by $K(x_1,x)$... If from N sequences, on any interval (x',x'') there are C points having successors, then C/N is an estimate of $\int_{x'}^{x''} H(x)dx$. The same sequences can be used for the equation on a subinterval (a',b') of (a,b). Extension is made to the complex case. (A.S. Householder, Math. Rev. 13: 1952)

Opler, A.

MATRIX INVERSION ON IBM ACCOUNTING MACHINE. Proceedings of Industrial Computation Seminar: 94, IBM Corp., N. Y., September 1950.
    This is a brief description of material covered fully in MTAC V, 35: 115-120, 1951 under the title "Monte Carlo Matrix Calculations with Punched Card Machines."

MONTE CARLO MATRIX CALCULATION WITH PUNCHED CARD MACHINES. MTAC V, 35: 115-120, 1951.
    The matrix inversion scheme of Forsythe and Leibler has been adapted for use with a punched card tabulator. A deck of punched cards is so prepared that Markov chains starting in the ith row and ending in the jth column are formed. Randomly occurring stop cards terminate the random walks after 1,2,3... steps to form the terms required in the series expansion of $(I-A)^{-1}$. The wiring of the tabulator provides for 150 draws in each of n games each minute. If chains are terminated after exactly r steps (instead of by use of stop cards) matrices may be raised directly to the rth power. (Author's Abstract)

    The von Neumann-Ulam Monte Carlo procedure for matrix inversion described by Leibler and the reviewer (same J. 4: 127-129, 1950; these Rev. 12: 361), is adapted to an IBM 405 tabulator for matrices of orders up to 10, depending on the number of available selectors. The procedure is here limited to the inversion of I-A, where $\sum\limits_{j=1}^{n} |a_{ij}| < 1$ for each i. A

deck is prepared for the matrix A, with a relative frequency of j punches in the ith card columns equal to $|a_{ij}|$, and with certain other punches. After one pass of the deck the tabulator prints total draws, total games, and net scores, which are readily convertible into one row of the approximate inverse matrix. The author says that the working procedure is far simpler than for any previously reported inversion procedure, and that the number of operations grows like n^2. (For elimination procedures the number grows like n^3.) Three examples are given for n = 7. Wiring directions are given. The author says the IBM 101 statistical machine can handle n up to 30. If $\sum\limits_{j=1}^{n} a_{ij} = 1$, a modified procedure calculates a matrix power A^r. (G. E. Forsythe, Math. Rev. 13: 284, 1952)

APPLICATION OF COMPUTING MACHINES TO ION EXCHANGE COLUMN CALCULATIONS. Ind. and Eng. Chem. 45: 2621-2633, 1953.

A punched card operated computing machine was used to investigate the application of computing machines to prediction of ion exchange column performance. Linear and non-linear nonequilibrium performance was calculated by a finite difference method.

Results show that these machines can evaluate the solutions to equations based in the equilibrium stage approach and on the kinetic-diffusion treatment. Relative accuracies of various computing techniques are compared. (Author's Abstract)

Page E. S.

THE MONTE CARLO SOLUTION OF SOME INTEGRAL EQUATIONS. Proc. Cambridge Philos. Soc. 50: 414-425, 1954.

Let $M(Z) = \alpha(Z) + \int\limits_{0}^{h} K(Z,y)M(y)dy$ be an integral

equation for M(Z), where $\alpha(Z)$ and K(Z,y) are continuous functions such that the Neumann series converges and that unity is not an eigenvalue. Generalizing a result of Cutkosky [J. Res. Nat'l Bur. of Stds. 47: 113-115, 1951; these Rev. 13: 590], the author defines several random variables, based on

311

suitable Markov processes, such that M(Z) is their expected value. The relative advantages of these random variables for a numerical solution of such integral equations by statistical sampling are discussed by studying and comparing their variances. Some theorems are proved concerning the best choice of the transition probability function that underlies the Markov process. Experiments on the EDSAC indicate that the methods described may compete with more conventional numerical techniques if the following three conditions are satisfied: (i) an accuracy of 10% is satisfactory; (ii) the values of the solution at only a few points are required; (iii) the interval (0,h) is fairly large. (W. Wasow, Math. Rev. 16, 3: 291, 1955.)

Rosenbluth, M.

PROOF OF VALIDITY ON MONTE CARLO METHOD FOR CANONICAL AVERAGING. Los Alamos Sci. Lab. (Cont. W-7405-Eng-36) AECU-2773, 1953.

In a previous article |J. Chem. Phys. 21: 1087, 1953| a prescription was given for moving from point to point in the configuration space of a system in such a way that averaging over many moves is equivalent to a canonical average over configuration space. The prescription is suitable for electronic machine calculations and provides the basis for calculations described elsewhere. The purpose of this paper is to present a more rigorous proof of the method. (Author)

Seebeck, C. L.

THE MONTE CARLO METHOD. Manuscript, University of Alabama, 1953.

A discussion of Monte Carlo methods used in summation of series, matrix inversion, differential equation integration and integral equations. There are examples of each and a bibliography.

Shoor, B. A., Nelson, L., DeMarcus, W. and Echols, R. L.

A MONTE CARLO TECHNIQUE FOR ESTIMATING PARTICLE ATTENUATION IN BULK MATTER. Monte Carlo Method, Nat'l Br. of Stds., AMS 12: 24-26, June 11, 1951.

The work described in this paper was accomplished at Northrop and was carried on through the sponsorship and cooperation of NEAP. A procedure is described for computing the attenuation characteristics of bulk materials for high energy particles. The approach has been strictly of the Monte Carlo type, with the emphasis on accuracy, versatility, and speed.

The Monte Carlo method is described as the representation of a physical or mathematical system by a sampling operation satisfying the same probability laws. The authors state that this description is particularly apt, for it is a concise statement of the fundamental concept of this method. At the time this work was being accomplished, the computing facility which was being used was considered to be unique. A rather detailed statement of the problem, along with a fairly complete indication of the steps involved in the Monte Carlo process is included in this write up. The order and manner in which these steps are accomplished appear to be, at least in part, a function of the computing facility. The authors state in conclusion that "We find on the average that an attenuation study is adequately represented by a thousand particles with an average particle handling in the machine of six seconds per process. We can on the average, run approximately 400 particle life histories per 8-hour working day and accumulate the required statistical data."

Siegert, A.

ON THE ACCURACY OF A PROCEDURE OCCURRING IN THE MONTE CARLO METHOD. Los Alamos Sci. Lab., AECD-3159; LADC-948, Jan. 7, 1948.

Assuming that after an actual run the numbers of original cards (representing source neutrons) belonging to a class $k(k = 0 \ldots K)$ are observed to be

$n_k \left[\sum_0^K n_k = n \right]$ --the classification being made according to

the number of descendants of given specification--calculation has been made of the joint probability density for the probabilities ϕ_k that an original card will be of class k.

From this joint probability density, the distributions of

$$
n \sum_0^K \frac{(\phi_k - n_k/n)^2}{n_k/n} \quad \text{and} \quad \sum_0^K \alpha_k \phi_k
$$

(α_k arbitrary) have been computed. The former indicates how well the actual probabilities ϕ_k are approximated by the numbers n_k/n; the latter can be used to obtain the probable error in the total number of descendants of given specifications. (Author)

Spinrad, B., Goertzel, G., and Snyder, W.

AN ALIGNMENT CHART FOR MONTE CARLO SOLUTION OF THE TRANSPORT PROBLEM. Monte Carlo Method, Nat'l Bur. of Stds., AMS 12: 4-5, 1951.

The paper contains a discussion of sample procedures for applying the Monte Carlo method in solving integral equations of the Fredholm type,

$$Q(x) = f(x) + \lambda \int_a^b K(x,t)Q(t)dt$$

where λ, f, and K are non-negative.

The two-dimensional procedure is a nomographical one of performing random walks between two scales. It is one of the few Monte Carlo hand methods on record. Deviations on the order of 10 percent are reported.

Thomas, L. H.

A COMPARISON OF STOCHASTIC AND DIRECT METHODS FOR THE SOLUTION OF SOME SPECIAL PROBLEMS. Presented before the Oper. Res. Soc. of America, 17 November 1952.

The amount of computing work required to reach a given precision by stochastic and by various direct methods is estimated for certain special problems. These comprise the evaluation of the definite integrals of functions of various types over multi-dimensional domains; the solution of the diffusion equation over various domains; and the solution of the wave equation. The conclusion is reached that while stochastic methods may be useful for rough surveys, precise results will usually require much less work by direct methods. (Author's Abstract)

Tocher, K. D.

THE APPLICATION OF AUTOMATIC COMPUTERS TO SAMPLING EXPERIMENTS. J. Roy. Stat. Soc. XVI, B: 39-60, 1954; discussion, 61-75.

This paper describes some of the problems that arise when automatic computers are used for conducting sampling experiments. The generation of random elements is discussed in detail and some methods of producing random variable with common distribution are described. The use of sampling methods to evaluate multivariate integrals is discussed.

Finally, a program is devised to conduct a special form of a restricted random walk. (Author's Summary)

The paper reviewed above (paper by Hammersley and Morton) discusses Monte Carlo without, and the present paper with, high speed machinery. Nearly half of the paper is devoted to the development of a program for machine computation of the self-avoiding walk problem (thus proving, according to Hammersley and Morton, how difficult it is for machines to do "organizational," as distinct from arithmetic, work). The rest of the paper, and most of the discussion, relate to random and pseudo-random numbers, and to the question, when should Monte Carlo be used. The author gives an excellent discussion of the multiple-integral problem, comparing the adequacy of the Monte Carlo estimate with the numerical evaluation.

Probably the most useful portion of this paper is that which relates to random numbers. Topic headings include: Production of random sequences from non-random sequences; Production of uniformly distributed random variables; Sequences produced by recurrent relations; The "middle-of-the-square" process; The multiple method; Auto-regressive schemes; Suggested procedure for forming random digits on an automatic computer; Construction of samples from the common distributions on a computer.

The paradox of deterministically computing a "random" sequence naturally comes in for some discussion. This might have been more profitable if the author had thought to make an important distinction: there are random processes, and there are sequences produced by random (or more or less random) processes, but there is no such thing as a random sequence (or set). For making certain assertions about the outcome of a Monte Carlo computation it is sufficient that the process producing certain data be random, but, as Hammersley and Morton point out in the discussion, this is not always necessary.

This is a minor criticism. On the whole, papers and discussion are well worth careful perusal by prospective practitioners. (A. S. Householder, Math. Rev. 16, 3: 288, 1955)

Todd, J.

EXPERIMENTS ON THE INVERSION OF A 16 x 16 MATRIX. NBS Appl. Math. Ser. 29: 113-115, 1953.
    Results of experiments, involving 1000 and 10,000 walks per row, in inverting a matrix by the process described by G. E. Forsythe and R. A. Leibler are given. The process is found to be very inefficient compared with conventional methods. (Author's Abstract)

MATRIX INVERSION BY A MONTE CARLO METHOD.   NBS Working Paper
50-2, February 1950.
  An exposition of a paper by Forsythe and Leibler, MTAC
4: 127-129, 1950.   A 2 x 2 matrix is inverted by a Monte
Carlo method using an ICC table of random digits and carrying
out a series of random walks.   The simple special case is
analyzed, with a proof of the result, and the method then extended to more general cases.   The method described will work
when   max |characteristic roots of A| < 1 where A = (a_{ij}) =
I-B and B is the n x n matrix we wish to invert.

SOLUTION OF DIFFERENTIAL EQUATIONS BY SAMPLING METHODS, PART
I.   EXPERIMENTS ON A TWO-DIMENSIONAL CASE USING SEAC.   NBS
Working Paper CL 50-3, April 1, 1951.
  The problem considered was the solution of

$$\frac{\partial^2 v}{\partial x^2} + \frac{\partial^2 v}{\partial y^2} = 0 \qquad \text{for } 0 < x < 1 \\ 0 < y < 1$$

where

$$\left. \begin{array}{l} V(x,1) = \sin \pi x \\ V(x,0) = 0 \end{array} \right] \; 0 \leq x \leq 1$$

$$\left. \begin{array}{l} V(0,y) = 0 \\ V(1,y) = 0 \end{array} \right] \; 0 \leq y \leq 1$$

The exact solution is $\dfrac{\sin \pi x \sinh \pi y}{\sinh \pi}$.

  This differential equation was replaced by the corresponding difference equation, using intervals in x and y of
1/16.   The random numbers were generated on SEAC by a single
operation, low-order multiplication.

  The paper summarizes the results graphically.   Both
simple sampling and importance sampling methods were used.
In this case the importance sampling method did not seem
worthwhile.

EXPERIMENTS IN THE SOLUTION OF DIFFERENTIAL EQUATIONS BY
MONTE CARLO METHODS.   J. Wash. Acad. Sci. 44, 12: 377-381, 1954.
  The problem was the solution of $\dfrac{\partial^2 v}{\partial x^2} + \dfrac{\partial^2 v}{\partial y^2} = 0$, for

$0 < x < 1$, $0 < y < 1$ with boundary conditions $V(x,1) = \sin \pi x$, $V(x,0) = 0, 0 < x < 1$ and $V(0,y) = 0$, $V(1,y) = 0$, $0 < y < 1$ by Monte Carlo methods. The points $(1/2, 1/2)$ $(3/4, 3/4)$, $(3/4, 1/4)$ and $(7/8, 1/2)$ were evaluated with SEAC using this method. He concludes that Monte Carlo is not the economical method for this case. Considerable details as to procedure and the results are given.

Ulam, S.

RANDOM PROCESSES AND TRANSFORMATIONS. Proceedings of the International Congress of Mathematicians: 264-75, 1950.
    This is a general point of view and specific problems connected with the relation between descriptions of physical phenomena by random processes and the theory of probabilities on the one hand and the deterministic descriptions by methods of classical analysis in mathematical physics on the other. Procedures of random processes are formulated which will permit heuristic and also quantitative evaluations of the solution of differential or integral-differential equations.

ON THE MONTE CARLO METHOD. Proceedings of a Second Symposium on Large-Scale Digital Calculating Machinery: 207-212, 1949; Harvard University Press, Cambridge, 1951.
    This is a general description of the Monte Carlo method, which is the use of sampling procedures to estimate such quantities as complicated probabilities, definite integrals over the unit cube in n dimensions, and solutions of partial differential equations of diffusion type. The author stresses the need for "importance sampling" in all these applications. He illustrates the possibility of expressing solutions of other types of partial differential equations in terms of properties of solutions of equations of diffusion type, so that more equations may respond to a Monte Carlo approach. It is pointed out that a formal system of mathematics can be described geometrically, and that a theorem then asserts that a certain set is vacuous. It is suggested that a difficult theorem might be approached heuristically by the attempt to construct points of the set by certain random choices in n dimensions (Monte Carlo). Failure would lend credibility to the theorem. (Reviewed by G. E. Forsythe)

Votaw, D. F., Jr. and Rafferty, J. A.

HIGH SPEED SAMPLING. MTAC V, 33: 1-8, 1951.
    The authors point out the desirability of introducing the high speed operations of electronic digital computing

devices into "synthetic" sampling in statistics. Three avenues of approach are outlined: (1) the construction of a high speed sampling machine (HSSM) such that from any given distribution function, F(x), a large number of random samples of a given size could be drawn, (2) to use the HSSM to draw a large number of (random) samples from a standard distribution function and by means of a high speed computing unit transform each into a (random) sample from any pre-assigned distribution function, (3) use the HSSM and (by means of special high speed acceptance-rejection procedures regarding randomly selected values from a standard distribu-tion function) effectively draw random samples directly from a preassigned distribution function. It is indicated that either the second or third of these possibilities would appear to be easier to achieve than the first.

Five reasonably well-known methods for the selection of random numbers are outlined. Thereafter acceptance-rejection methods of obtaining (seven) empirical random sampling dis-tributions are outlined.

Wasow, W.

RANDOM WALKS AND THE EIGENVALUES OF ELLIPTIC DIFFERENCE EQUATIONS. J. Res. Nat'l Bur. of Stds. 46: 65-73, 1951.
The aim of this paper is to describe and investigate a random walk procedure that can be used to approximate the solutions of elliptic partial differential equations con-taining the unknown function itself and not only its deriva-tives. The method also leads to a scheme for the numerical determination of the lowest eigenvalue of such differential equations.

As a computational technique, our method is somewhat similar to the one used by Donsker and Kac for the calcula-tion of the lowest eigenvalue of Schroedinger's equation, but the underlying theory is more elementary than the the-orem on Wiener integrals of (4) used in Donsker and Kac (3).

Like all computational methods based on random sampling, those described in the present paper require the use of a high-speed calculating machine. Numerical tests are in progress.

The random walks considered lead to difference equations. By virtue of known results (1), (6) the solutions thus ob-tained are, for small step length, approximations to the corresponding solutions of the limiting differential equations.

Let the symbol Δ denote the finite difference analogue of the Laplace operator, i.e.,

$$\Delta y(x,y) = \quad 1/h^2\Big[u(x + h,y) + u(x-h,y) +$$
$$u(x,\ y+h) + u(x,\ y-h) - 4u(x,y)\Big]$$

Then we shall be concerned with the difference equation

$$\Delta u + g(x,y)u = 0$$

where $g(x,y)$ is to be sufficiently regular to guarantee convergence of the solutions considered to those of the corresponding differential equation.

Everything that follows can be easily extended to more than two dimensions. Extensions to other elliptic differential equations are also possible.

In sequel, the word "point," without further specification, is mean to refer to the points of a square lattice with mesh length h. (Author's Introduction).

A NOTE ON THE INVERSION OF MATRICES BY RADOM WALKS. MTAC VI 38: 78-81, 1952.
A discussion of the paper by Forsythe and Leibler (MTAC IV: 127-129, 1950) in the light of previous work by the author (see NBS J. Res. 46: 65-73, 1951) and J. H. Curtiss (see Proc. IBM Seminar on Sci. Comp., Nov. 1949). The underlying theory and the similarities and differences in the various approaches to this problem are discussed.

Wilson, R. R.

THE RANGE AND STRAGGLING OF HIGH ENERGY ELECTRONS. The Phys. Rev. 84, 1: 100-103, October, 1951.
Simple expressions are derived for the range and straggling of individual electrons. Large energy losses due to bremsstrahlung make the average range smaller than would be calculated from the average energy loss. Effects of multiple scattering are included. The results are in good agreement with numerical calculations by the Monte Carlo method. (Author's Abstract)

SHOWERS PRODUCED BY LOW ENERGY ELECTRONS AND PHOTONS. The Monte Carlo Method, NBS, AMS: 12: 1-3, 1951.
The problem of computing the photon showers produced by electrons and photons impinging on a shield is treated. High energy showers lend themselves to accurate calculation because the probabilities for radiation and pair production are independent of energy, and ionization is not important in the

development of the form of the shower. Just the opposite is true of low energies, and because of their inherently statistical nature, showers lend themselves to easy treatment by the Monte Carlo method.

The procedure explained is a simple, graphical and mechanical one, the electrons and photons studied were followed through successive intervals of the medium, the fate of them being decided from one of a family of curves drawn on a rotating drum, the movement of which is random. Accuracy of about ten percent is to be expected with this procedure.

MONTE CARLO STUDY OF SHOWER PRODUCTION. The Phys. Rev. 86, 3: 261-269, May 1952.
Electron-and photon-initiated showers in lead have been calculated in a simple Monte Carlo manner for energies from 20 to 500 Mev. The results, exhibited in a series of transition curves, show considerable differences from the results of conventional cascade theory in that the number of electrons at the maximum are fewer and the shower is more penetrating.

The effects of multiple Coulomb scattering of the electrons have been included and depend markedly on the measurement considered. Thus, ionization currents are only slightly changed (the transition curves are foreshortened by about one-half radiation length)', while the number of electrons counted behind lead plates in a cloud chamber can be reduced by as much as 50 percent by effects of multiple scattering. This result is nearly independent of the incident energy.

The final curves obtained are compared with the ionization measurement of Blocker, Kenney, and Panofsky and the cloud-chamber measurements of A. M. Shapiro. The agreement is satisfactory.

A simple quasi-analytic cascade theory is developed in which known low energy solutions are used to obtain successively higher eneegy solutions. (Author's Abstract)

Woodbury, W. W.

MONTE CARLO CALCULATIONS. Proc. Sem. on Sci. Comp., IBM Corp., N. Y., November 1949.
This paper covers the application of a unique calculator: the prototype of the Card-Programmed Calculator constructed from an IBM type 603 multiplier and type 405 printer, to problems in neutron diffusion. Emphasis is on the calculator.

The author included the following comment, with the above abstract of his contribution to the Monte Carlo method, "A considerable part of the literature labelled 'Monte Carlo' is of the above genre; that is, it covers the numerical simulation of a physical experiment wherein some of the physical parameters are probabilities. It might be well to indicate this in the bibliography in connection with all such papers." (Author's Abstract)

Yowell, E. C.

A MONTE CARLO METHOD OF SOLVING LAPLACE'S EQUATION. Proc. Comp. Sem: 87-91, IBM Corp., N. Y., December 1949.
    The solution of Laplace's Equation in two dimensions by random walk methods is discussed informally, and the analysis chart for such a computation on the IBM type 604 Electronic Punch is given. The paper is followed by an interesting discussion of the feasibility of performing random walks "backwards" to reduce the labor involved if only the solution at a single point is desired.

ADDENDA, PART I.

Gephart, L. S.

A STUDY OF THE EFFECT OF NONNORMALITY ON SAMPLING DISTRIBUTIONS OF THE RANGE. Aeronautical Research Laboratory, Wright Air Development Center, WADC Tech. Rep. 55-128, March 1955.
    This paper contains the results of a study of the effects of nonnormality of the population on sampling distributions of the range. Thirteen distributions were prepared in a form suitable for sampling. The distributions utilized were the normal, four Pearsonian Type III, and eight specified by Edgeworth series. Effects of nonnormality on the range were estimated from sampling distributions composed of ranges of 2,000 samples. Sample sizes of 3, 5, 7, and 10 were investigated for each of the above-mentioned thirteen populations. Summary type results are given. It is planned that a related study on the average range will be undertaken and will utilize some of the data of this paper.

Hoffman, J., Metropolis, N. and Gardiner, V.

STUDY OF TUMOR CELL POPULATIONS BY MONTE CARLO METHODS.
Science 122, 3167: 465-466, September 1955.
    The digital computer MANIAC is given a probability
distribution for the intermitotic times and, by the Monte
Carlo method, grows the hypothetical population, or "tumor,"
beginning with one cell. As this cell grows, the machine
plays the game of chance determining when division occurs,
the rules of the game being given by the probability distribution.

    The Monte Carlo method affords a means of bridging the
gap between cell sizes and time parameters in a cell's life.

    An unexpected finding in the computations was that the
average mitotic index in freely growing cell populations is
not always simply related to the time parameters of the
life-cycle.

Metropolis, N., Rosenbluth, A., Rosenbluth, M., Teller, A. and
Teller, E.

EQUATION OF STATE CALCULATIONS BY FAST COMPUTING MACHINES.
J. of Chem. Phys., June 1953.
    A general method, suitable for fast computing machines,
for investigating such properties as equations of state for
substances consisting of interacting individual molecules
is described. The method consists of a modified Monte Carlo
integration over configuration space. Results for the two-
dimensional rigid-sphere system have been obtained on the
Los Alamos MANIAC and are presented here. These results are
compared to the free volume equation of state and to a four-
term virial coefficient expansion.

Rosenbluth, M. and Rosenbluth, A.

FURTHER RESULTS ON MONTE CARLO EQUATIONS OF STATE. J. of
Chem. Phys., May 1954.
    The equation of state of three-dimensional hard spheres
has been obtained by the Monte Carlo method. Some qualitative results for a system of two-dimensional molecules with
Lennard-Jones interaction are also given, as well as a
general discussion of the usefulness and limitations of the
Monte Carlo method.

PART II.

THE GENERATION AND TESTING OF RANDOM DIGITS
AND KNOWN SOURCES OF RANDOM DIGIT TABLES.

Azorin, F. and Wold, H.

PRODUCT SUMS AND MODULUS SUMS OF H. WOLD'S NORMAL DEVIATES. Trabajos Estadistica 1: 5-28, 1950 (English and Spanish).

Recently Wold [Random Normal Deviates, Cambridge, 1948; these Rev. 10: 553] published a table containing 25,000 random normal deviates. These occupy 50 pages, with 10 columns of 50 numbers each on a page. If x_{ij} and x_{jk} are the numbers on line k of columns i and j, respectively, on the same page, the present table gives the values of

$$W_{ij} = \sum_{k=1}^{50} x_{ik} x_{jk} \quad ; \quad V_i = \sum_{k=1}^{50} |x_{ik}| .$$

Tests as to whether the W_{ij} and the V_i follow their expected theoretical distributions are presented. The product sums are intended to facilitate artificial sampling experiments relating to the distribution of correlation coefficients. The modulus sums, which were a by-product, appear to have less immediate utility. (W. G. Cochran, Math. Rev. 13: 478, 1952)

Blanch, G. and Yowell, E. C.

A GUIDE TO TABLES ON PUNCHED CARDS. MTAC 5: 185-212, 1951.
This paper contains a list of tables on punched cards, including several tables of random numbers.

Brown, B.

SOME TESTS OF THE RANDOMNESS OF A MILLION DIGITS. The RAND Corp., Paper No. P-44, Santa Monica, California, October 19, 1948.
The randomness of a table of a million digits produced at Project Rand by a random digit generator was examined by applying four tests. The four tests were: (1) Frequency test, (2) Poker test, (3) Serial test and (4) Run test. The complete table of a million digits was subjected to the

first two tests. The last two tests were applied to a sample
of 50,000 digits from the table. All computations were
accomplished by means of I.B.M. equipment.

There was no evidence of any unusual divergence from the
theoretical expectations in any of the tests. It would be
difficult to construct a series of digits which would succeed
in evading all four of these tests. The examination of the
million digits did not reveal any bias. There was nothing
to indicate that the digits were not being produced with
equal probabilities. (Author's Summary)

Brown, G. W.

HISTORY OF RAND'S RANDOM DIGITS. The Monte Carlo Method,
Nat'l Bur. of Stds., AMS 12, 1951.
A description of the development of Rand's "Derived Random Number Table of One Million Digits." An "electronic
roulette wheel" was used to generate the digits. "A random
frequency pulse source was gated by a constant frequency
pulse, about once a second, providing on the average about
100,000 pulses in one second. Pulse standardization circuits
passed the pulses to a five place binary counter, so that in
principle the machine is like a roulette wheel with 32 positions making on the average about 3,000 revolutions each
turn. A binary-to-decimal conversion was used, throwing away
12 out of the 32 positions, and the resulting random digit
was fed to an IBM punch, yielding punched card tables of random digits." Various run tests were made including the
standard tests used by Kendall and Smith. The original table
had a small but perceptible odd-even bias which was removed
by adding (modulo 10) the digits in each card, digit by digit,
to the corresponding digits of the previous card.

Calcutta Statistical Laboratory

RANDOM SAMPLING NUMBERS, CALCUTTA STATISTICAL TABLES (1).
Statistical Laboratory, Calcutta, 1941.

Dodd, E. L.

A TRANSFORMATION OF TIPPETT RANDOM SAMPLING NUMBERS INTO
NUMBERS NORMALLY DISTRIBUTED. Bol. Mat. 15: 73-77, 1942.
Tippett's random sampling numbers are 4-digit numbers
which may be considered as independent observations (without
replacement) from the population of all 4-digit numbers,

where each 4-digit number has the probability 10^{-4}. The author describes a method of transforming these numbers into numbers which may be considered as independent observations from a normal population with zero mean and unit variance. The transformation is carried out as follows. Each Tippett number is considered with a decimal point prefixed and a 5 affixed. For any such Tippett number y the corresponding transformed number x is the solution of the equation $y = f(x)$, where

$$F(x) = (2\pi)^{-1/2} \int_{-\infty}^{x} e^{-t^2/2} dt$$

The transformed values of the first 800 Tippett numbers are given in a table. (Reviewed by A. Wald, Math. Rev. 5: 43, 1944)

CERTAIN TESTS FOR RANDOMNESS APPLIED TO DATA GROUPED INTO SMALL SETS. Econometrica 10: 249-257, 1942.

The author has devised four simple tests of randomness of digits applicable, for example, in the case of a decimal system to Tippett's table of random numbers: (1) an order test based on pairs of integers in which a given pair of integers ab is classed as "up" (for a decimal system) of integers $a < b$ or $a = b = 5,6,7,8,9$ and down otherwise, under the hypothesis of randomness $P(\text{up}) = P(\text{down}) = 1/2$. (2) An order test based on triples of integers such that, for a decimal system of integers, a, b, c is designated as "up" if $a \leq b \leq c$ ($a < c$) or $a = b = c \geq 5$, "down" if $a > b < c$ under the hypothesis of randomness $P(\text{up}) = P(\text{down}) = .215$, $P(\text{max}) = P(\text{min}) = .285$. (3) A range test based on the range of a set of k integers, in which the range r is defined as the difference between the least and greatest integers in the set. Under the hypothesis of randomness in a decimal system, Dodd gives probabilities of the various values of $r(0,1,2 \ldots 9)$ for $k = 2,3,4,5,6$. (4) A replication test in which the probability is given that a set of k integers will contain s doubles, t triples, n quadruples, v quintuples and w sextuples. Numerical values of probabilities are given for the hypothesis of randomness of numbers in a decimal system and for $k = 5$. (Reviewed by S. S. Wilks, Math. Rev. 4, 4: 108, 1943)

Forsythe, G. E.

GENERATION AND TESTING OF RANDOM DIGITS AT THE NATIONAL
BUREAU OF STANDARDS, LOS ANGELES. The Monte Carlo Method,
Nat'l Bur. of Stds. AMS 12, 1951.
   Three methods of generating digits on the IBM Elec-
tronic Calculating Punch Type 604:

   A. From the middle of the square of a four-digit
number a_n, a four digit number$_{n+1}$ was extracted, and the
process repeated. For example if $a_1 = 1234$, then $a_1^2 =$
01522756 whence $a_2 = 5227$, etc.

   B. From the middle of the product of two four-digit numbers a_n and a_{n+1} a four-digit number a_{n+2} was extracted, etc.

   C. From the product of a five-digit number a_n' and an
eight-digit number a_{n+1} an eight-digit number a_{n+2} was extracted, and from a_{n+1} a certain five-digit number a_{n+1}' was
$(n=1,2,3,...)$. As actually run, $a_1' = 34567$ and $a_2 = 98765432$.
Then $a_2' = 76543$, $a_1'a_2 = 3414024687944$, $a_3 = 40246879$, etc.

Methods A and B were not expected to produce uniformly distributed digits and apparently did not. Method C was more
promising. However, after various tests the author states,
"Method C is not recommended for the generation of random
digits, because the distribution of pairs of digits appears
to be variable and not uniform."

Gage, R.

CONTENTS OF TIPPETT'S "RANDOM SAMPLING NUMBERS." J. Amer.
Stat. Assoc. 38: 223-227, 1943.

Good, I. J.

THE SERIAL TEST FOR SAMPLING NUMBERS AND OTHER TESTS FOR
RANDOMNESS. Proc. Cambridge Phil. Soc. 49, 2: 276-284, 1953.
   In the serial test for sampling numbers an expression
$\overline{\psi^2}$ is used. It is in the form of a sum of squares and has
previously been supposed to have asymptotically a χ^2
(γ-variate) distribution. By evaluating $E(\overline{\psi^2})$ it is shown

326

that this supposition cannot be correct, since $E(\overline{\psi^2})$ is not equal to the number of degrees of freedom. The evaluation is based on some results which can be used for testing a wide class of properties of random sequences. The definition of $\overline{\psi^2}$ is generalized to deal with subsequences of length ν (instead of length 2) and the generalized $\overline{\psi^2}$, or $\overline{\psi^2_\nu}$, is then decomposed into a linear form of simple variates defined in terms of discrete Fourier transforms. When the number, t, of digits in the sample space is prime these simple variates are shown to have asymptotically independent χ^2 distributions with one degree of freedom each. The coefficients of the linear form are not 1 but they become 1 when the first and second differences with respect to ν are taken.

Thus $V\overline{\psi^2_\nu}$ and $V^2\overline{\psi^2_\nu}$ have asymptotically χ^2 distributions. The work is closely related to that of Bartlett and Vajda. (Author's Abstract) (Also reviewed by S. W. Nash, Math. Rev. 15, 8: 727, 1954.)

Greenwood, R. E.

COUPON COLLECTOR'S TEST FOR RANDOM DIGITS. MTAC 9, 49: 1-5, 1955.
The coupon collector's test for random digits is defined, probabilities are listed and the test applied to the sequences of digits in approximations to π and e. The distribution of the lengths of sequences required to give a set of K different digits, $K \leq 10$, compared with the theoretically computed distributions is called the coupon collector's test.

Gruenberger, F.

TESTS OF RANDOM DIGITS. MTAC 4, 32: 244-45, 1950.
The four tests for local randomness proposed by Kendall and Smith were routenized for IBM computation. The results for the poker test are given for part of Kendall and Smith's table of random digits. (Author's Abstract)

Gruenberger, F. and Mark, A. M.

THE d^2 TEST OF RANDOM DIGITS. MTAC 5, 34: 109-10, 1951.
This is a test for randomness of numbers which are to be used in Monte Carlo work. The random numbers are taken as

coordinates of points in a unit square; the distribution of the distances between pairs of points is compared with the theoretical. The article shows the d^2 analysis on the Wisconsin table of random digits. The d^2 test is probably more stringent than those of Kendall and Smith. (Author's Abstract)

Hamaker, H. C.

A SIMPLE TECHNIQUE FOR PRODUCING RANDOM SAMPLING NUMBERS. Nederl. Akad, Wetensch., Proc. 52: 145-150, 1949.
    Random sampling numbers were produced by spinning a ten-sided prism. The usual tests of randomness were applied. A fuller description is given in the paper reviewed below.

RANDOM SAMPLING NUMBERS. Statistica, Rijswijk 2: 97-106, 1948 (Dutch-English Summary)
    Detailed report on the experiments described in the paper reviewed above. (Reviewed by W. Feller, Math. Rev. 11: 260, 1950)

Hammer, P. C.

THE MID-SQUARE METHOD OF GENERATING DIGITS. The Monte Carlo Method, Nat'l Bur. of Stds. AMS 12, 1951.
    A ten-digit number is squared and the middle ten digits of the result retained to give "random digits" and to continue the process. This is a repeating sequence with a period of less than 10^{10}. One may rationalize the method somewhat as follows. Suppose the numbers x one obtains are uniformly distributed from 0 to 1 (assuming the decimal form). Then the distribution $y = x^2$ has a density function $(1/2)y^{-1/2}$.

    Considering the process of selection one can see that a rather slight bias to small numbers occurs. Tests applied consisted of Chi-square tests for distribution of digits and in serial correlations between each digit and all its neighbors and between each digit and all digits in each of 10 positions of the first five succeeding 10-digit numbers. The tests indicated nothing seriously amiss and the sequence was used.

Horton, H. B.

A METHOD FOR OBTAINING RANDOM NUMBERS. Ann. Math. Stat. 19: 81-85, 1948.
    Consider n roulette wheels each divided into two arcs

and arranged in series so that the kth wheel determines which arc on the (k+1)th wheel will be called 0 and which 1. The final outcome of an n-tuple trial is 0 or 1 and the author shows that the corresponding probabilities tend to 1/2 as n , irrespective of the possible bias of the individual wheels. An unbiased passage from the dyadic to the decimal system is described. (Reviewed by W. Feller, Math. Rev. 9: 450, 1948)

Horton, H. B. and Smith, R. T., III

A DIRECT METHOD FOR PRODUCING RANDOM DIGITS IN ANY NUMBER SYSTEM. Ann. Math. Stat. 20: 82-90, 1949.
    Suppose that the random digits 0,1 ..., n-1 are produced by means of independent trials so that the outcome $k(0 \leq k \leq n-1)$ at the sth trial has probability $p_{k,s}$. Add the digits obtained in s trials and reduce the sum modulo n. Let $\pi_{k,s}$ be the probability that the result is k. Using the technique of non-stationary Markov chains, the authors show that $\pi_{r,s} \rightarrow 1/n$ as $s \rightarrow \infty$. A similar result is derived for the case of random numbers with fixed but unequal probabilities. The preparation and tests of a set of random digits are discussed in detail. (Reviewed by W. Feller, Math. Rev. 10: 550, 1949)

Juncosa, M. L.

RANDOM NUMBER GENERATION ON THE BRL HIGH-SPEED COMPUTING MACHINES. Ballistic Res. Lab. Rep. No. 855, Aberdeen Proving Ground, Maryland, May 1953.
    Procedures requiring very few orders and storage for generation of pseudo-random numbers on the ORDVAC, EDVAC, and ENIAC are described. The results of some statistical tests performed on some numbers produced by the method on ORDVAC are given. A mathematical appendix contains the number-theoretic background and theorems used in the description of the method. (Author's Abstract)

Kendall, M. G.

A THEORY OF RANDOMNESS. Biometrika 32: 1-15, 1941.
    In this paper the author presents some comments on a theory of randomness bearing some resemblance to von Mise's theory of Kollectivs. The principal departure from von Mise's theory lies in an attempt to supplant the idea of the

irregular Kollectiv by considering infinite "proper suites" and aggregates of "selectors" to be applied to them. By a suite the author means an infinite sequence of "characteristics," each of which may be one of r symbols, say A_1, A_2, ..., A_r. By a proper suite K is meant one in which the proportion of A_i's in the first n elements of the suite tends to a limit as $n \to \infty$ for i=1,2,...,r. By a selector S is meant an infinite sequence of increasing positive integers. If those numbers in K are chosen whose ordinals are the numbers appearing in S, a derived suite SK is obtained. If the limiting frequency of A_i in SK is the same as for A_i in K, then K is said to be random for A_i with respect to S. Selector domains, statistical independence, convolution and local randomness are defined and briefly discussed. Several simple properties of derived suites are given, but the author does not go beyond his definitions to any significant extent. A considerable number of results, which are not referred to by the author, have been published by Copeland and Wald, dealing with the problem of the measure of selectors (represented, for example, as binary numbers) which preserve the limiting frequencies in the original suite, and related problems. Most of the paper is devoted to a general non-mathematical discussion of the notion of randomness in practical statistics from the point of view of the theory outlined at the beginning of the paper. (Reviewed by S. S. Wilks, Math. Rev. 3: 1, 1942)

Kendall, M. G. and Smith, B. B.

RANDOMNESS AND RANDOM SAMPLING NUMBERS. J. Roy. Stat. Soc. 101: 147-166, 1938)
    A general discussion of randomness and random sampling with particular reference to sets of "locally random digits." Four tests for local randomness are given. A "Randomizing Machine" is described and a set of 5,000 digits obtained by using the machine is given. The four tests of local randomness are applied to this set and to the first and last thousands of L. H. C. Tippett's Random Sampling Numbers with results of the tests tabulated and compared.

RANDOM SAMPLING NUMBERS. Tracts for Computers No. XXIV, Cambridge Univ. Press, 1951.
    A table of 100,000 random digits in blocks of 1000. The introduction contains a short discussion of random sampling numbers, and a description of the four tests used on the present table.

Lehmer, D. H.

MATHEMATICAL METHODS IN LARGE-SCALE COMPUTING UNITS. Proc. of a 2nd Symp. on Large-Scale Digital Calculating Machinery, pp. 141-146, 1949; Harvard Univ. Press, 1951.

The aim of this paper is to discuss in a general way certain features of the mathematics that are characteristic of the large-scale digital computing machines. Special attention is given to the problem of generating random numbers. The author's proposal for generating a sequence of "random" 8-decimal numbers u_n is to start with some number $u_o \neq 0$, multiply it by 23, and subtract the two-digit overflow on the left from the two right hand digits to obtain a new number u_1. By repeating this process he generates a sequence u_n which he shows has a repetition period of 5,882,352. An IBM 602A was used to generate 5000 numbers of such a sequence. Four standard tests (unspecified) were applied to check the "randomness" and the sequence passed all four. The author observes, however, that all of the members of the sequence he chose were divisible by 17. (Reviewed by R. Hamming).

Metropolis, N. Reitwiesner, G. and von Neumann, J.

STATISTICAL TREATMENT OF FIRST 2000 DECIMAL DIGITS OF e AND π CALCULATED ON THE ENIAC. MTAC 4: 109-111, 1950.

A statistical survey of the first 2000 decimal digits of e and π has failed to disclose any significant deviations from randomness for π, but it has indicated quite serious ones for e.

Meyer, H. A., Gephart, L. S. and Rasmussen, N. L.

ON THE GENERATION AND TESTING OF RANDOM DIGITS. WADC Tech. Rep. 54-55, Air Res. and Dev. Command, Wright-Patterson Air Force Base, Ohio, 1954.

After a brief outline of the historical facts connected with the generation of generally available sets of random digits, the concepts of randomness and local randomness are defined and discussed. The four standard tests for local randomness proposed by Kendall and Smith are described, and a modification of one of these, the gap test, is proposed. A test for the local randomness of sets of random digits to be used in certain Monte Carlo calculations is also described.

Two fundamentally different methods of generating sets of random digits are distinguished and discussed, namely (1) methods, mechanical or otherwise, of selecting digits randomly from a uniform population of digits, and (2) arithmetical schemes for the production of sets of "pseudo-random" digits.

L. H. C. Tippett's set of random sampling numbers are tested for local randomness by the six different tests discussed; it is found that the series should be used with caution, especially in small sampling surveys. (Authors' Abstract)

Moore, P. G.

A SEQUENTIAL TEST FOR RANDOMNESS. Biometrika 40: 111-115, 1953.
The problem frequently arises of deciding whether a sequence of observations, each observation falling into one of two alternative categories or types, occurs in a random order. David (1947) has considered the "group" test in some detail. The hypothesis H_0, that we are considering here states that there is randomness within the sequence against an alternative H_1, that there is dependence of the kind found in a simple Markov chain. David's test is based on the number of groups of a common type which the observations form when placed in order in the sequence.

In this paper we deal with another form of this procedure which leads to a sequential test. This has obvious advantages in that the amount of data which must be collected in order to obtain a decision is not fixed beforehand. It may be that the first few values will suffice to make a decision one way or the other and only in cases which lie in between will a long sequence of observations be necessary. This form of procedure may well mean a large saving of time, money and materials. (Author's Introduction)

Nair, K. N.

ON TIPPETT'S RANDOM SAMPLING NUMBERS. Sankhya 4: 65-72, 1938.

von Neumann, J.

VARIOUS TECHNIQUES USED IN CONNECTION WITH RANDOM DIGITS. The Monte Carlo Method, Nat'l Bur. of Stds. AMS 12, 1951.
A general discussion of the use of random numbers in high speed computation with particular regard to "(How can

one produce a sequence of random decimal digits--a sequence
where each digit appears with probability one-tenth and where
consecutive ones are independent of each other in all combinations? (B) How can one produce random real numbers according to an assigned probability distribution law?" The
critical effect of rounding off errors and the need for statistical tests are emphasized. Several methods of obtaining
numbers to satisfy non-uniform probability distributions are
discussed.

Peatman, J. G. and Shafer, K.

A TABLE OF RANDOM NUMBERS FROM SELECTIVE SERVICE NUMBERS.
J. Psychology 14: 295-305, 1947.
        A short table of random numbers (1600 in all) from
selective service drawings, together with tests of randomness
and examples of their use is presented.

RAND Corporation

DERIVED RANDOM NUMBER TABLE OF ONE MILLION DIGITS. Punched
Card Table No. 0017, RAND Corp., Santa Monica, California.
        Digits of 0(1)9 drawn at random, with equal probability,
50 random digits per card; 20,000 cards.

ONE HUNDRED THOUSAND DEVIATES FROM N(0,1). Punched Card
Table No. 0019, RAND Corp., Santa Monica, California.
        Random Gaussian deviates, x from N(0,1).
        Range: $-4.417 \leq x \leq 4.417$; x to 3D; x^2 to 6D.

5D GAUSSIAN ERROR FUNCTION TABLE. Punched Card Table No.
0005, Set .001, RAND Corp., Santa Monica, California.

$$E'(x) = \frac{1}{\sqrt{2\pi}} e^{-x^2/2}, \qquad E(x) = \int_0^x \frac{1}{2\pi} e^{-t^2/2} dt$$

Range: $0 \leq x \leq 4.751$, intervals of .005, prepared for linear
interpolation. The cards contain lower x, upper x, A', B',
A and B.

A MILLION RANDOM DIGITS WITH 100,000 NORMAL DEVIATES. The
Free Press, Glencoe, Illinois, 1955.
        The text preceding the tables discusses the method by

which the tables were produced, the tests made to free the tables from bias, and procedures for using the tables without the introduction of bias by the user.

The tables were prepared by the RAND Corporation in connection with its research for the United States Air Force. The "author" of the tables was an electronic equivalent of a 32-place roulette wheel. (Also reviewed by M. Muller, Math. Rev. 16, 7: 749-750, 1955)

Snedecor, G. W.

EVERYDAY STATISTICS. Brown and Company, pp. 9-11, 1950. Table of 10,000 random digits in groups of five.

Steinhaus, H.

TABLE OF SHUFFLED FOUR-DIGIT NUMBERS. Rozprawy Mat. 6: 1-46, 1954. (Polish, Russian and English)
This is a table of the 10,000 four-digit numbers 0000-9999 arranged in a supposedly random way. Since the table contains each number once and only once it can be used for sampling problems in which samples, once drawn, are not replaced. Thus it could be used for a schedule for the retirement of bonds. By reading the digits vertically by fours, instead of horizontally, one obtains an ordinary random number table in which numbers may be missing or may occur more than once. No tests have been made of the actual randomness obtained. The table was produced by hand by a series of randomizing transformations applied to a table of 100 rows and columns. (Reviewed by D. H. Lehmer, Math. Rev. 15, 7: 636, 1954)

Teichroew, D.

DISTRIBUTION SAMPLING WITH HIGH SPEED COMPUTERS. Dissertation North Carolina State College, 1953.
The development of high speed computing machines in recent years has greatly increased the scope of numerical methods of solving mathematical problems. One of the numerical problems of interest to statisticians is the tabulation of distribution functions. High speed computing machines can be used to tabulate distribution functions either by numerical integration or by sampling. If the problem can be reduced to one of integration in one, two or three dimensions, it is usually practical and economically feasible to use numerical integration. If integration in more than three dimensions is

required, in general, sampling appears to be the most practical method. This thesis is concerned with the techniques required to use high speed computers as efficiently as possible for distribution sampling.

The techniques discussed are for (a) increasing the accuracy of distribution sampling, (b) calculating variates having a uniform distribution, and (c) transforming these to variates having an arbitrary distribution. Several methods are given for improving the accuracy in sampling; these methods can be developed parallel to similar methods used in survey sampling. The computation of uniform variates can be accomplished fairly readily by the "residue class" method and the transformation to other distributions can be done most efficiently by the use of the polynomial approximation method. To illustrate the last two techniques some results are obtained by using these methods to estimate the power of some nonparametric tests. (Author's Abstract)

Tippett, L. H. C.

RANDOM SAMPLING NUMBERS. Tracts for Computers No. XV, Cambridge Univ. Press, 1950.
A table of 41,600 random digits arranged in quartets with a Foreword by K. Pearson.

Vickery, C. W.

ON DRAWING A RANDOM SAMPLE FROM A SET OF PUNCHED CARDS. J. Roy. Stat. Soc. Suppl. 6: 62-66, 1939.
The problem of drawing a random sample from a set of punched cards frequently presents itself to the practical statistician. This paper suggests a machine technique for drawing a random sample from punched cards with the aid of random sampling cards. It also describes a random sampling machine by means of which a random sample may be drawn automatically from a set of punched cards without the use of sampling numbers.

Walsh, J. E.

CONCERNING COMPOUND RANDOMIZATION IN THE BINARY SYSTEM. Ann. Math. Stat. 20: 580-589, 1949.
Let us consider a set of approximately random binary digits obtained by some experimental process. This paper outlines a method of compounding the digits of this set to obtain a smaller set of binary digits which are much more nearly random. The method presented has the property that the number of

digits in the compounded set is a reasonably large fraction
(say of magnitude 1/3 to 1/4) of the original number of
digits. If a set of very nearly random decimal digits is
required, this can be obtained by first finding a set of very
nearly random binary digits and then converting these digits
to decimal digits.

The concept of "maximum bias" is introduced to measure
the degree of randomness of a set of digits. A small maximum
bias shows that the set is very nearly random. The question
of when a table of approximately random digits can be considered suitable for use as a random digit table is investigated. It is found that a table will be satisfactory for the
usual types of situations to which a random digit table is
applied if the reciprocal of the number of digits in the
table is noticeably greater than the maximum bias of the
table. (Author's Abstract)

Horton's method of adding independent binary digits
modulo 2 to reduce their bias [same Ann. 19: 81-85, 1948;
these Rev. 9: 450], is modified by permitting the same digit
to be used more than once. This introduces dependence into
the resulting digits, but the author shows an example in
which his method wastes fewer digits than does Horton's while
achieving the same control of the maximum absolute difference
from 1/2 of the conditional probability that a digit is 0.
(Reviewed by J. L. Hodges, Jr., Math. Rev. 11: 260, 1950)

AN EXPERIMENTAL METHOD FOR OBTAINING RANDOM DIGITS AND PER-
MUTATIONS. U.S. Nav. Ord. Test Stat., China Lake, California.
Abstracted: Ann. Math. Stat., p. 647, 1952.
This paper presents an easily applied method for obtaining random binary digits and random permutations. The procedure consists in flipping ordinary minted coins and combining the results of the flips in an appropriate manner. Digits
and permutations obtained according to the method of this
paper can be considered sufficiently random for any practical
application. It appears likely that these digits and permutations are much more nearly random than most of those now
available in printed tables. Moreover, any possibility of
bias from misuse of tables is avoided. The method presented
is particularly suitable for use with respect to experimental
designs. Only a few random permutations are ordinarily required for a given experimental design. (Author's Abstract)

Wold, H.

RANDOM NORMAL DEVIATES. 25,000 Items Compiled from Tract No.
XXV (M. G. Kendall and B. B. Smith's Tables of Random Sampling
Numbers). Cambridge Univ. Press, 1948.
The normal deviates are given to two decimal places.

Four different tests of randomness and normality were applied
to all blocks of 500, 5,000 and 25,000 numbers. These tests
are a sum test, square sum test, range test, and sign run
test, for each of which the rejection level was P = 2%. One
set of 5,000 failed to pass the range test, three sets of 500
failed to pass the sign run test, and one set of 500 failed
to pass the square sum test. Finally, the agreement of the
distribution of P values in each of these tests with the rectangular distribution was tested by the Chi-square method
and by a method of Kolmogoroff. (Reviewed by H. Chernoff,
Math. Rev. 10: 553, 1949)

Young, L. C.

ON RANDOMNESS IN ORDERED SEQUENCES. Ann. Math. Stat. 12:
293-300, 1941.

Given a finite ordered sequence $x_1, x_2, \ldots, x_n$ of n measurement, the author chooses the statistic

$$C = 1 - \sum_1^{n-1} (x_i - x_{i+1})^2 \left[2 \sum_1^n (x_i - \bar{x})^2 \right]^{-1}$$

as the basis of a test of randomness, where $\bar{x}$ is the average.
Significance levels of the absolute value of C are given for
samples from 8 to 25. The field of application of the C test
is briefly discussed and an illustration from the field of
quality control is given. (Reviewed by W. A. Shewhart, Math.
Rev. 3: 174, 1942)

Yule, G.

A TEST OF TIPPETT'S RANDOM SAMPLING NUMBERS. J. Roy. Stat.
Soc. 101: 167-172, 1938.

The author tests the leading digit of the four-figure
numbers in Tippett's tables, adding them in sequences of five
and comparing the distribution of the sums with expectation.
He states the results "appear to confirm the impression of
'patchiness,' especially in the earlier part of the Tables.."

Zia-ud-Din, M., and Moin-ud-Din Siddiqi, M.

RANDOM SAMPLING NUMBERS. Proc. 2nd Pakistan Stat. Conference,
Univ. of Dacca: 91-98, 1952; Lahore, 1953.

A table of 8000 random sampling numbers was constructed
using two decks of playing cards with kings, queens, jacks
removed. After shuffling, one card was drawn and its number
noted, 10 serving as 0. (Reviewed by S. W. Nash, Math. Rev.
15, 3: 239, 1954)

PART III.

ARTICLES AND BOOKS, MOSTLY WITHOUT ABSTRACTS, IN WHICH SAMPLING IS PRIMARILY RELIED UPON FOR A SOLUTION OR VERIFICATION.

Baker, G. A.

THE SIGNIFICANCE OF THE PRODUCT-MOMENT COEFFICIENT OF CORRELATION WITH SPECIAL REFERENCE TO THE CHARACTER OF THE MARGINAL DISTRIBUTIONS. J. Amer. Stat. Assoc. 25: 387-396, 1930.

RANDOM SAMPLING FROM NON-HOMOGENEOUS POPULATIONS. Metron. 8: 1-21, 1930.

THE RELATION BETWEEN THE MEANS AND VARIANCES, MEANS SQUARED AND VARIANCES IN SAMPLES FROM COMBINATIONS OF NORMAL POPULATIONS. Ann. Math. Stat. 2: 333-354, 1931.

DISTRIBUTION OF THE MEANS DIVIDED BY THE STANDARD DEVIATIONS OF SAMPLES FROM NON-HOMOGENEOUS POPULATIONS. Ann. Math. Stat. 3: 1-9, 1932.

TEST OF HOMOGENEITY FOR NORMAL POPULATIONS. Ann. Math. Stat. 12: 233-236, 1941.

DISTRIBUTION OF THE RATIO OF SAMPLE RANGE TO SAMPLE STANDARD DEVIATION FOR NORMAL AND COMBINATIONS OF NORMAL DISTRIBUTIONS. Ann. Math. Stat. 17: 366-369, 1946.

PROPERTIES OF SOME TESTS IN SEQUENTIAL ANALYSIS. Biom. 37: 334-346, 1950. (Reviewed by J. Wolfowitz, Math. Rev. 12, 4: 346, 1951)

Berkson, J.

A NOTE ON THE CHI-SQUARE TEST, THE POISSON AND THE BINOMIAL. J. Amer. Stat. Assoc. 35: 362-67, 1940. (Reviewed by J. Neyman, Math. Rev. 1, 11: 347, 1940)

Bispham, J. W.

AN EXPERIMENTAL DETERMINATION OF THE DISTRIBUTION OF THE PARTIAL CORRELATION COEFFICIENT IN SAMPLES OF THIRTY. Metron. 2: 684-696, 1923.

338

Brownlee, J.

    SOME EXPERIMENTS TO TEST THE THEORY OF GOODNESS OF FIT.
    J. Roy. Stat. Soc. 87: 76-82, 1924.

Carlson, J. L.

    A STUDY OF THE DISTRIBUTION OF MEANS ESTIMATED FROM SMALL
    SAMPLES BY THE METHOD OF MAXIMUM LIKELIHOOD FOR PEARSON'S
    TYPE II CURVE. Ann. Math. Stat. 3: 86-107, 1932.

Cheriyan, K. C.

    DISTRIBUTIONS OF CERTAIN FREQUENCY CONSTANTS IN SAMPLES FROM
    NON-NORMAL POPULATIONS. Sankhya 7: 159-166, 1945.
    (Reviewed by R. L. Anderson, Math. Rev. 7, 6: 317, 1946)

Chesire, L., Oldis, E. and Pearson, E. S.

    FURTHER EXPERIMENTS ON THE SAMPLING DISTRIBUTION OF THE CORRE-
    LATION COEFFICIENT. J. Amer. Stat. Assoc. 27: 121-128, 1932.

Church, A. E. R.

    ON THE MEANS AND SQUARED STANDARD DEVIATIONS OF SMALL SAMPLES
    FROM ANY POPULATION. Biom. 18: 321-394, 1926.

Clark, A. L.

    AN EXPERIMENTAL INVESTIGATION OF PROBABILITY. Canadian J. of
    Res. 9: 402-414, 1933.

    EXPERIMENTAL PROBABILITY. Canadian J. of Res. 11: 658-664, ·
    1934.

    PROBABILITY EXPERIMENTALLY INVESTIGATED. Canadian J. of Res.
    15: 149-153, 1937.

Cochrane, D. and Orcutt, G. H.

    APPLICATION OF LEAST SQUARES REGRESSION TO RELATIONSHIPS CON-
    TAINING AUTO-CORRELATED ERROR TERMS. J. Amer. Stat. Assoc.
    44: 32-61, 1949.

Craig, C. C.

AN APPLICATION OF THIELE'S SEMI-INVARIANTS TO THE SAMPLING
PROBLEM. Metron. 7: 3-74, 1928.

Das, A. C.

ON THE ESTIMATION OF PARAMETERS IN A RECURSIVE SYSTEM.
Sankhya 11: 273-280, 1951.

DeLury, D. B.

ON THE PLANNING OF EXPERIMENTS FOR THE ESTIMATION OF FISH
POPULATIONS. J. Fish. Res. Brd, Canada 8: 281-307, 1951.

Dixon, W. J.

ANALYSIS OF EXTREME VALUES. Ann. Math. Stat. 21: 488-506,
1950.

PROCESSING DATA FOR OUTLIERS. Biometrics 9: 74-89, 1953.
(Reviewed by Ingram Olkin, MTAC 8, 47: 154, 1954)

Dunlap, H. F.

AN EMPIRICAL DETERMINATION OF THE DISTRIBUTION OF MEANS,
STANDARD DEVIATIONS AND CORRELATION COEFFICIENTS DRAWN FROM
RECTANGULAR POPULATIONS. Ann. Math. Stat. 2: 66-81, 1931.

Eden, T. and Yates, F.

ON THE VALIDITY OF FISHER'S z TEST WHEN APPLIED TO AN ACTUAL
EXAMPLE OF NON-NORMAL DATA. J. Agric. Sci. 23: 6, 1933.

Foster, F. G. and Stuart, A.

DISTRIBUTION-FREE TESTS IN TIME-SERIES BASED ON THE BREAKING
OF RECORDS. J. Roy. Stat. Soc. Ser. B. 16: 1-13; discussion
13-22, 1954. (Reviewed by S. W. Nash, Math. Rev. 16, 4: 385,
1955)

Greenwood, M. and White, J. D. C.

A BIOMETRIC STUDY OF THE PHAGOCYTOSIS WITH SPECIAL REFERENCE
TO THE "OPSONIC INDEX." Second Memoir: On the distribution
of the means of samples. Biom. 7: 505-530, 1909.

Hall, P.

THE DISTRIBUTION OF MEANS FOR SAMPLES OF SIZE N DRAWN FROM
A POPULATION IN WHICH THE VARIABLE TAKES VALUES BETWEEN 0
AND 1, AND ALL SUCH VALUES BEING EQUALLY PROBABLE.
Biom. 19: 240-244, 1927.

Hamaker, H. C.

RANDOM FREQUENCIES, AN EXPEDIENT FOR THE CONSTRUCTION OF ARTI-
FICIAL SAMPLES OF LARGE SIZE. Statistica, Rijswijk 2: 129-
137, 1948.

RANDOM SAMPLING FREQUENCIES; AN IMPLEMENT FOR RAPIDLY CON-
STRUCTING LARGE-SIZE ARTIFICIAL SAMPLES. Nederl. Akad.
Wetensch Proc. 52: 432-439, 1949. (Both Reviewed by W. Feller,
Math. Rev. 11, 3: 191, 1950)

Hansmann, G. H.

ON CERTAIN NON-NORMAL SYMMETRIC FREQUENCY DISTRIBUTIONS.
Biom. 26: 129-195, 1934.

Hartar, H. L.

ON THE DISTRIBUTION OF WALD'S CLASSIFICATION STATISTIC. Ann.
Math. Stat. 22: 58-67, 1951. (Reviewed by G. E. Noether,
Math. Rev. 12, 8: 620-621, 1951)

Hey, G. B.

A NEW METHOD OF EXPERIMENTAL SAMPLING ILLUSTRATED ON CERTAIN
NON-NORMAL POPULATIONS. Biom. 30: 68-80, 1938.

Holzinger, K. and Church, A. E. R.

ON THE MEANS OF SAMPLES FROM A U-SHAPED POPULATION. Biom.
20A: 361-388, 1928.

Kendall, D. G. and Rankin, R. A.

ON THE NUMBER OF POINTS OF A GIVEN LATTICE IN A RANDOM HYPER-
SPHERE. Quart. J. Math., Oxford Ser. (2) 4: 178-189, 1953.
(Reviewed by R. Bellman, Math. Rev. 15, 3: 237, 1954)

Kendall, M. G. Sheila, F. H. and Smith, B. B.

THE DISTRIBUTION OF SPEARMAN'S COEFFICIENT OF RANK CORRELA-
TION IN A UNIVERSE IN WHICH ALL RANKINGS OCCUR AN EQUAL NUMBER
OF TIMES. Biom. 30: 251-273, 1938.

Kermack, W. O. and McKendrick, A. B.

TESTS FOR RANDOMNESS IN A SERIES OF OBSERVATIONS. Proc. Roy.
Soc. Edin. 57: 228-240, 1937.

Kerrich, J. E.

AN EXPERIMENTAL INTRODUCTION TO THE THEORY OF PROBABILITY.
J. Jorgensen and Company, Copenhagen, 1946.
(Reviewed by W. Feller, Math. Rev. 7, 9: 456, 1946)

Kondo, T.

ON THE STANDARD ERROR OF THE MEAN SQUARE CONTINGENCY.
Biom. 21: 376-428, 1929.

Kullback, S.

NOTE ON A MATCHING PROBLEM. Ann. Math. Stat. 10: 77-80, 1939.

Kullback, S. and Frankel, A.

A SIMPLE SAMPLING EXPERIMENT ON CONFIDENCE INTERVALS. Ann.
Math. Stat. 11: 209-213, 1940. (Reviewed by S. S. Wilkes,
Math. Rev. 1, 11: 347, 1940)

MacKay, A. T.

THE DISTRIBUTION OF THE ESTIMATED COEFFICIENT OF VARIATION.
J. Roy. Stat. Soc. 94: 564-567, 1931.

Mahalanobis, P. C.

TABLES OF RANDOM SAMPLES FROM A NORMAL POPULATION. Sankhya
1: 289-328, 1934.

Massey, F. J.

THE KOLMOGOROV-SMIRNOV TEST FOR GOODNESS OF FIT. J. Amer. Stat. Assoc. 46: 68-78, 1951.

Matthai, A. and Kannan, M. B.

THE APPLICABILITY OF LARGE SAMPLE TESTS FOR MOVING AVERAGE AND AUTOREGRESSIVE SCHEMES TO SERIES OF SHORT LENGTH--AN EXPERIMENTAL STUDY, PART I. MOVING AVERAGES. Sankhya 11: 218-238, 1951.

Nair, A. N. K.

DISTRIBUTION OF "STUDENT'S" "t" AND THE CORRELATION COEFFI-CIENT IN SAMPLES FROM NON-NORMAL POPULATIONS. Sankhya 5: 383-400, 1941. (Reviewed by A. Wald, Math. Rev. 4, 6: 164, 1943)

Newman, D.

THE DISTRIBUTION OF RANGE IN SAMPLES FROM A NORMAL POPULATION, EXPRESSED IN TERMS OF AN INDEPENDENT ESTIMATE OF STANDARD DEV-IATION. Biom. 31: 20-30, 1939. (Reviewed by A. A. Bennett, Math. Rev. 1, 4: 153; 1940)

Neyman, J. and Pearson, E. S.

ON THE USE AND INTERPRETATION OF CERTAIN TEST CRITERIA FOR PURPOSES OF STATISTICAL INFERENCE. Biom. 20: 175-240, 1928; and Biom. 20A: 263-294, 1928.

FURTHER NOTES ON THE CHI-SQUARE DISTRIBUTION. Biom. 22: 298-305, 1930-31.

Pearson, E. S.

BAYES THEOREM, EXAMINED IN THE LIGHT OF EXPERIMENTAL SAMPLING. Biom. 17: 388-442, 1925.

Pearson, E. S. and Adyanthaya, N.

THE DISTRIBUTION OF FREQUENCY CONSTANTS IN SMALL SAMPLES FROM SYMMETRICAL POPULATIONS. Biom. 20A: 356-360, 1928.

343

Pearson, E. S. assisted by Adyanthaya, N. K. and others

THE DISTRIBUTION OF FREQUENCY CONSTANTS IN SMALL SAMPLES FROM NON-NORMAL SYMMETRICAL AND SKEW POPULATIONS. Biom. 21: 259-286, 1929.

Pearson, E. S.

NOTE ON DR. CRAIG'S PAPER SAMPLING WHEN THE PARENT POPULATION IS OF PEARSON'S TYPE III, Biom. 21: 287-293, 1929 . Biom 21: 294-302, 1929.

SOME NOTES ON SAMPLING TESTS WITH TWO VARIABLES. Biom. 21: 337-360, 1929.

THE ANALYSIS OF VARIANCE IN CASES OF NON-NORMAL VARIATION. Biom. 23: 114-133, 1931.

THE TEST OF SIGNIFICANCE FOR THE CORRELATION COEFFICIENT. J. Amer. Stat. Assoc. 26: 128-134, 1931.

THE TEST OF SIGNIFICANCE FOR THE CORRELATION COEFFICIENT-- SOME FURTHER RESULTS. J. Amer. Stat. Assoc. 27: 424-426, 1932.

A COMPARISON OF β_2 AND MR. GEARY'S ω_n CRITERIA. Biom 27: 333-352, 1935.

SOME ASPECTS OF THE PROBLEM OF RANDOMIZATION. Biom. 29: 53-64, 1937.

Pearson, E. S. and Welch, B. L.

NOTES ON SOME STATISTICAL PROBLEMS RAISED IN MR. BAYES PAPER. J. Roy. Stat. Soc. Suppl. 4: 94, 1937.

Pearson, K.

FURTHER REMARKS ON THE z-TEST. Biom. 23: 408-415, 1931.

EXPERIMENTAL DISCUSSION OF THE (χ^2, P) TEST FOR GOODNESS OF FIT. Biom. 24: 351-381, 1932.

ON A NEW METHOD OF DETERMINING "GOODNESS OF FIT." Biom. 26: 425-442, 1934.

ON THE CONSTANTS OF INDEX-DISTRIBUTIONS AS DEDUCED FROM THE LIKE CONSTANTS FOR THE COMPONENTS OF THE RATIO, WITH SPECIAL REFERENCE TO THE OPSONIC INDEX. Biom. 7: 531-541, 1909.

Pepper, J.

THE SAMPLING DISTRIBUTION OF THE THIRD MOMENT COEFFICIENT--
AN EXPERIMENT. Biom. 24: 55-64, 1932.

Price, G. R.

SCIENCE AND THE SUPERNATURAL. Science 122, 3165: 359-367, 1955.
    This is one of a multitude of possible references concern-
ing experiments dealing with psychic phenomena (with references
and notes).

Quenouille, M. H.

APPROXIMATE TESTS OF CORRELATION IN TIME SERIES. J. Roy. Stat.
Soc. Ser. B 11: 68-84, 1949. (Rev. by P. Whittle, Math. Rev.
11, 4: 262, 1950)

Rao, C. R.

THE APPLICABILITY OF LARGE SAMPLE TESTS FOR MOVING AVERAGE AND
AUTOREGRESSIVE SCHEMES TO SERIES OF SHORT LENGTHS--AN EXPERI-
MENTAL STUDY: PART III. The discriminant function approach
in the classification of time series. Sankhya 11: 257-272, 1951.

Rietz, H. L.

ON THE DISTRIBUTION OF THE "STUDENT" RATIO FOR SMALL SAMPLES
FROM CERTAIN NON-NORMAL POPULATIONS. Ann. Math. Stat. 10:
265-274, 1939. (Rev. by J. Neyman, Math. Rev. 1, 1: 23, 1940)

Robinson, S.

AN EXPERIMENT REGARDING THE CHI-SQUARE TEST. Ann. Math. Stat.
4: 285-287, 1933.

Rosander, A. C.

THE USE OF INVERSIONS AS A TEST OF RANDOM ORDER. J. Amer. Stat.
Assoc. 37: 352-358, 1942.

Roux, J. M. Le

A STUDY OF THE DISTRIBUTION OF THE VARIANCE IN SMALL SAMPLES.
Biom. 23: 134-190, 1931.

Rushton, S.

    ON A SEQUENTIAL t-TEST. Biom. 37: 326-333, 1950.

Sastry, A. S. R.

    BIAS IN ESTIMATION OF SERIAL CORRELATION COEFFICIENTS.
Sankhya 11: 281-296, 1951. (Rev. by P. Whittle, Math. Rev.
14, 1: 66, 1953)

    SOME MOMENTS OF MOMENT STATISTICS AND THEIR USE IN TESTS OF
SIGNIFICANCE IN AUTOCORRELATED SERIES. Sankhya 11: 297-308,
1951. (Rev. by D. G. Chapman, Math. Rev. 14, 1: 66, 1953)

Sheppard, W. F.

    THE FIT OF A FORMULA FOR DISCREPANT OBSERVATIONS. Phil.
Trans. Roy. Soc. 228A: 115-150, 1928.

Shewhart, W. A. and Winters, F. W.

    SMALL SAMPLES--NEW EXPERIMENTAL RESULTS. J. Amer. Stat.
Assoc. 23: 144-153, 1928.

"Sophister"

    DISCUSSION OF SMALL SAMPLES DRAWN FROM AN INFINITE SKEW
POPULATION. Biom. 20A: 389-423, 1928.

"Student"

    THE PROBABLE ERROR OF THE MEAN. Biom. 6: 1-25, 1908.

    PROBABLE ERROR OF A CORRELATION COEFFICIENT. Biom. 6: 302-
310, 1908.

    AN EXPERIMENTAL DETERMINATION OF THE PROBABLE ERROR OF DR.
SPEARMAN'S CORRELATION COEFFICIENTS. Biom. 13: 263-282, 1921.

Sukhatme, P. V.

    ON THE DISTRIBUTION OF CHI-SQUARE IN SAMPLES OF THE POISSON
SERIES. J. Roy. Stat. Soc. Suppl. 5: 75-79, 1938.

Sun, C. P.

ON THE EXAMINATION OF FINAL DIGITS BY EXPERIMENTS IN
ARTIFICIAL SAMPLING. Biom. 20A: 64-68, 1928.

Tang, Y.

CERTAIN STATISTICAL PROBLEMS ARISING IN PLANT BREEDING.
Biom. 30: 29-56, 1938.

Thompson, C. M.

AN INVESTIGATION INTO THE ADEQUACY OF DR. WILK'S CURVES.
Biom. 29: 127-132, 1937.

Tippett, L. H. C.

ON THE EXTREME INDIVIDUALS AND THE RANGE OF SAMPLES TAKEN
FROM A NORMAL POPULATION. Biom 17: 364-387, 1925.

Uhler, H. S.

APPROXIMATIONS EXCEEDING 1300 DECIMALS FOR $\sqrt{3}$, $1/\sqrt{3}$ AND
SIN $\pi\sqrt{3}$ AND DISTRIBUTION OF DIGITS IN THEM. Proc. Nat.
Acad. Sciences 37: 443-447, 1951.

MANY-FIGURE APPROXIMATIONS TO $\sqrt{2}$, AND DISTRIBUTION OF DIGITS
IN $\sqrt{2}$ and $1/\sqrt{2}$. Proc. Nat. Acad. Sciences 37: 63-67, 1951.

Weldon, W. F. R.

INHERITANCE IN ANIMALS AND PLANTS. Lectures on the Method
of Science. Clarendon Press, Oxford, 1906.

Working, H.

A RANDOM-DIFFERENCE SERIES FOR USE IN THE ANALYSIS OF TIME
SERIES. J. Amer. Stat. Assoc. 29: 11-24, 1934.

Yule, G. U.

ON THE APPLICATION OF THE CHI-SQUARE METHOD TO ASSOCIATION AND
CONTINGENCY TABLES WITH EXPERIMENTAL ILLUSTRATION. J. Roy.
Stat. Soc. 35: 95-104, 1922.

PART IV.

A SELECTION OF ARTICLES AND BOOKS ON OR MAKING USE OF
STOCHASTIC PROCESSES, INCLUDING EXTRACTS FROM A
BIBLIOGRAPHY SUPPLIED BY D. G. KENDALL,
MOSTLY WITHOUT ABSTRACTS.
Included are references presumed closely enough
associated with the theory and application of
the Monte Carlo method to warrant inclusion.

Arley, N.

ON THE THEORY OF STOCHASTIC PROCESSES AND THEIR APPLICATION TO
THE THEORY OF COSMIC RADIATION. New York (Wiley) 1948; first
printing 1943. (Rev. by W. Feller, Math. Rev. 7, 5: 209, 1946)

ON THE BIRTH-AND-DEATH PROCESS. Skand. Akt. Tidsskrift: 21-26,
1949.

Arley, N. and Borchsenius, V.

ON THE THEORY OF INFINITE SYSTEMS OF DIFFERENTIAL EQUATIONS,
AND THEIR APPLICATION TO THE THEORY OF STOCHASTIC PROCESSES
AND THE PERTURBATION THEORY OF QUANTUM MECHANICS. Act Math.,
76: 261-322, 1945.

Arley, N. and Buch, K. A.

INTRODUCTION TO THE THEORY OF PROBABILITY AND STATISTICS. New
York (Wiley) 1950. (Rev. by J. Wolfowitz, Math. Rev. 11, 3:
187-188, 1950)

Armitage, P.

THE STATISTICAL THEORY OF BACTERIAL POPULATIONS SUBJECT TO
MUTATION. J. Roy. Stat. Soc. (B) 14: 1-33, 1952.

Bailey, N. T. G.

A SIMPLE STOCHASTIC EPIDEMIC. Biom. 37: 193-202, 1950.

ON ESTIMATING THE SIZE OF MOBILE POPULATIONS FROM RECAPTURE
DATA. Biom. 38: 293-306, 1951.

Bartlett, M. S.

SOME EVOLUTIONARY STOCHASTIC PROCESSES. J. Roy Stat. Soc. (B) 11: 211-229, 1949.
This paper gives a general survey of additive (random walk) processes and multiplicative processes. Applications of random walk processes with absorbing barriers are first discussed; a general differential equation for the characteristic function of a Markoff process is then noted, and used to study some multiplicative processes arising in the theory of population growth, cascade showers and epidemics. (Author's Abstract) (Also rev. by J. L. Doob, Math. Rev. 11: 672, 1950)

THE DUAL RECURRENCE RELATION FOR MULTIPLICATIVE PROCESSES. Proc. Cambridge Soc. 47: 821-825, 1951.

THE FREQUENCY GOODNESS OF FIT TEST FOR PROBABILITY CHAINS. Proc. Cambridge Phil. Soc. 47: 86, 1951.
A goodness of fit statistical test for an observed sequence from a finite regular Markoff chain is derived. (As a special case this applies to the testing of random sequences). (Author's Abstract)

RECURRENCE AND FIRST PASSAGE TIMES. Proc. Cambridge Phil. Soc. 49: 266-275, 1953.
A systematic discussion of formulae for the distribution of recurrence and first passage times of states of a stochastic process, including those for Markoff processes with a continuous time parameter and for times conditional on certain intermediate conditions being fulfilled. (Author's Abstract) (Also rev. by T. E. Harris, Math. Rev. 14, 9: 887, 1953)

STOCHASTIC PROCESSES OR THE STATISTICS OF CHANGE. Appl. Stat. 2: 44, 1953.
A non-technical survey of stochastic processes, as they arise in physics and communication engineering, industry, economics, biology and medicine. The Monte Carlo method is referred to, and used to study the properties of a stochastic model for successive measles outbreaks in a boarding school. (Author's Abstract)

AN INTRODUCTION TO STOCHASTIC PROCESSES WITH SPECIAL REFERENCE TO METHODS AND APPLICATIONS. London (Cambridge) 1955.

Bartlett, M. S. and Kendall, D. G.

ON THE USE OF THE CHARACTERISTIC FUNCTIONAL IN THE ANALYSIS OF SOME STOCHASTIC PROCESSES OCCURRING IN PHYSICS AND BIOLOGY. Proc. Cambridge Phil. Soc. 47: 65-76, 1951.

Bartlett, M. S. and Rajalakshman, D. V.

GOODNESS OF FIT TESTS FOR SIMULTANEOUS AUTOREGRESSIVE SERIES.
J. Roy. Stat. Soc. (B) 15: 108-115, 1953.
    Statistical tests are developed for the goodness of fit
of autoregressive models to correlations obtained from simultaneous stationary time-series. These are checked by reference to artificial series constructed from random numbers
(in one case it is demonstrated that the set of 'random numbers" used in the construction of the series was not random).
(Author's Abstract) (Also rev. by D. G. Chapman, Math. Rev.
15, 4: 333, 1954)

Bellman, R. and Harris, T.

ON THE THEORY OF AGE-DEPENDENT STOCHASTIC BRANCHING PROCESSES.
Proc. Nat. Acad. Sci. U.S.A. 34: 601-604, 1948.
(Rev. by J. L. Doob, Math. Rev. 1: 311, 1949)

ON AGE-DEPENDENT BINARY BRANCHING PROCESSES. Ann. Math. (2)
55: 280-295, 1952.
(Rev. by J. L. Doob, Math. Rev. 13, 1952)

Bellman, R.

ON A NEW ITERATIVE ALGORITHM FOR FINDING THE SOLUTIONS OF
GAMES AND LINEAR PROGRAMMING PROBLEMS. The RAND Corp., P-473,
Santa Monica, California, June 1953.
    Since every linear programming problem of conventional
type can be transformed into a symmetric game, this technique
may be applied to the solution of linear programming problems.
A variant of the differential equation approach is presented
which converges more rapidly than the original and in its
limit obtains a process with an exponential rate of convergence. The differential equation is replaced by a difference
equation.

    The method has been tried on a number of examples and in
all cases it seems to yield the value of the game very rapidly.
It seems admirably suited to determining the value of the maximum or minimum rather than the variables which yield the
critical value. (Author's Introduction)

Bernardelli, H.

POPULATION WAVES. J. Burma Res. Soc. 31: 1-18, 1941.

Bhabha, H. J.

ON THE STOCHASTIC THEORY OF CONTINUOUS PARAMETRIC SYSTEMS AND
ITS APPLICATION TO ELECTRON CASCADES. Proc. Roy. Soc. London
(A) 202: 301-322, 1950.

Bhabha, H. J. and Ramakrishnan, A.

THE MEAN SQUARE DEVIATION OF THE NUMBER OF ELECTRONS AND
QUANTA IN THE CASCADE THEORY. Proc. Indian Acad. Sci. 32:
141-153, 1950.

Bochner, S.

STOCHASTIC PROCESSES. Ann. of Math. 48: 1014-1061, 1947.

Borel, E.

SUR L'EMPLOI DU THÉORÈME DE BERNOUILLI POUR FACILITER LE CAL-
CUL D'UNE INFINITÉ DE COEFFICIENTS. APPLICATIONS AU PROBLÈME
DE L'ATTENTE À UN GUICHET. C. R. Acad. Sci. 214: 452-6, 1942.

Chandrasekhar, S.

STOCHASTIC PROBLEMS IN PHYSICS AND ASTRONOMY. Rev. Mod. Phys.
15: 1-89, 1943.
(Rev. by J. L. Doob, Math. Rev. 4: 249, 1943)

Chitty, D. and Leslie, P. H.

THE ESTIMATION OF POPULATION PARAMETERS FROM DATA OBTAINED BY
MEANS OF THE CAPTURE-RECAPTURE METHOD. Biom. 38: 262-92, 1951.

Cochran, W. G.

THE PRESENT STATUS OF BIOMETRY. 2e Congrès Intern. de Biométrie
(Genève): 1-19, 1949.

Consael, R.

SUR UN GÉNÉRALIZATION DU PROCESSUS DE PÓLYA. Bull. Classe des
Sci. (Acad. Roy. de Belgique) (5) 34: 863-876, 1948.

Consael, R.

SUR QUELQUES PROCESSUS STOCHASTIQUES DISCONTINUS À DEUX VARI-
ABLES ALÉATOIRES.   Ibid., 35: 399-416; 743-755, 1949.

SUR QUELQUES POINTS DE LA THÉORIE DES PROCESSUS STOCHASTIQUES.
Ibid., 36: 870-879, 1950.

Coolidge, J.

AN INTRODUCTION TO MATHEMATICAL THEORY OF PROBABILITY.   Oxford,
1925.

Cramér, H.

RANDOM VARIABLES AND PROBABILITY DISTRIBUTIONS.   Cambridge,
1937.

MATHEMATICAL METHODS OF STATISTICS.   Princeton, 1946.
(Reviewed by M. Kac, Math. Rev. 8, 1: 39-40, 1947)

THE ELEMENTS OF PROBABILITY THEORY AND SOME OF ITS APPLICATIONS.
New York (Wiley) 1955.   (Reviewed by J. Wolfowitz, Math. Rev.16,
7: 722, 1955; K.L. Chung, Bull. Am. Math. Soc. 61: 449, 1955)

Curtiss, J. H.

SAMPLING METHODS AND STOCHASTIC PROCESSES IN NUMERICAL ANALYSIS.
N.B.S. Working Paper, 1951.
     This paper includes a mathematical treatment of uniform
distributions and transformations, sums of various independent
random variables, and an introduction to stochastic processes
including Markov chains.   He concludes with a chapter on chain
functions of several types and their recursion relations.

David, F. N.

PROBABILITY THEORY FOR STATISTICAL METHODS.   Cambridge, 1951.

THE DISTRIBUTION OF RANGE IN CERTAIN NON-NORMAL POPULATIONS.
Biom. 41: 463-468, 1954.
     By performing the indicated integration in the well-known
formulae for the cumulative distribution function and expected

value of the range of a population with density function f(x) for five parent populations, the author gives exact specialized expressions for these. Numerical comparisons with normal populations are made. The statement that an estimate of standard deviation which "is unlikely to be seriously biased therefore will provide satisfactory control limits for the mean" is hardly tenable. (Reviewed by H. Teicher, Math. Rev. 16, 6: 603, 1955)

Dean, A. C. R. and Hinshelwood, C. N.

THE APPLICABILITY OF THE STATISTICAL FLUCTUATION TEST. Proc. Roy. Soc. London (B) 139: 236-250, 1952.

Doob, J. L. and Ambrose, W.

ON TWO FORMULATIONS OF THE THEORY OF STOCHASTIC PROCESSES DEPENDING UPON A CONTINUOUS PARAMETER. Ann. Math. (2) 41: 737-745, 1940. (Reviewed by W. Feller, Math. Rev. 2: 108, 1941)

Doob, J. L.

WHAT IS A STOCHASTIC PROCESS? Amer. Math. Monthly 49: 648-653, 1942. [MF 7814] (Reviewed in Math. Rev. 4: 103, 1943)

STOCHASTIC PROCESSES. New York (Wiley) 1953. (Reviewed by D. G. Kendall, Math. Rev. 15, 5: 445-447, 1954)

Dvoretzky, A. and Erdos, P.

SOME PROBLEMS ON RANDOM WALK IN SPACE. Proc. of 2nd Symp. on Math. Stat. and Probability: 353-367, 1950; Univ. of Cal. Press, Berkeley and Los Angeles, 1951. (Reviewed by S. Kakutani, Math. Rev. 13: 852, 1952)

Feller, W.

DIE GRUNDLAGEN DER VOLTERRASCHEN THEORIE DES KAMPFES UMS DASEIN IN WAHRSCHEINLICHKEITSTHEORETISCHER BEHANDLUNG. Acta Biotheoretica 5: 11-40, 1939.

ON THE INTEGRAL EQUATION OF RENEWAL THEORY. Ann. Math. Stat. 12: 243-267, 1941.

ON A GENERAL CLASS OF 'CONTAGIOUS' DISTRIBUTIONS. Ann. Math. Stat. 14: 389-400, 1943.

Feller, W. (Cont'd)

ON THE THEORY OF STOCHASTIC PROCESSES, WITH PARTICULAR REFER-
ENCE TO APPLICATIONS. Proc. Berkeley Symp. on Math. Stat.
and Probability: 403-432, 1945, 1946; Univ. of Calif. Press,
Berkeley and Los Angeles, 1949. (Reviewed by J. L. Doob,
Math. Rev. 10: 385, 1949)

AN INTRODUCTION TO PROBABILITY THEORY AND ITS APPLICATION, I.
New York (Wiley) 1950. (Reviewed by R. Fortet, Math. Rev.
12, 6: 424, 1951)

DIFFUSION PROCESSES IN GENETICS. Proc. 2nd Berkeley Symp. on
Math. Stat. and Probability: 227-246, 1951; Univ. of Calif.
Press, Berkeley and Los Angeles, 1951.

Finney, D. J.

ERRORS OF ESTIMATION IN INVERSE SAMPLING. Nature (London) 160:
195, 1947.

ON A METHOD OF ESTIMATING FREQUENCIES. Biom. 36: 233-234, 1949.

PROBIT ANALYSIS. A Statistical Treatment of the Sigmoid Response Curve (2nd edition). London (Cambridge) 1952.
(Reviewed by R. L. Anderson, Math. Rev. 14, 1: 66-67, 1953)

Finney, D. J. and Martin, L.

A RE-EXAMINATION OF RAHN'S DATA ON THE NUMBER OF GENES IN
BACTERIA. Biometrics 7: 133-144, 1951.

Fisher, R. A.

ON THE DOMINANCE RATIO. Proc. Roy. Soc. Edin. 42: 321-341, 1922.

THE GENETICAL THEORY OF NATURAL SELECTION. Oxford, 1930.

Foster, F. G. and Good, I. J.

ON A GENERALIZATION OF PÓLYA'S RANDOM-WALK THEOREM. Quart. J.
of Math. Oxford Ser. (2) 4: 120-126, 1953. (Reviewed by K. L.
Chung, Math. Rev. 14, 11: 1101, 1953)

Fréchet, W. H.

RECHERCHES THÉORIQUES MODERNES SUR LE CALCUL DES PROBABILITÉS,
II. Paris, 1938.

Fry, T. C.

 PROBABILITY AND ITS ENGINEERING USES. New York (D. van
 Nostrand) 1929.

Furry, W. H.

 ON FLUCTUATION PHENOMENA IN THE PASSAGE OF HIGH ENERGY ELECTRONS
 THROUGH LEAD. Phys. Rev. 52: 569-581, 1937.

Galton, F. and Watson, H. W.

 ON THE PROBABILITY OF THE EXTINCTION OF FAMILIES. J. Anthrop.
 Inst. 4: 138-144, 1874.

Gihman, I. I.

 ON THE EMPIRICAL DISTRIBUTION FUNCTION IN THE CASE OF GROUPING
 OF THE DATA. Doklady. Akad. Nauk. SSSR (N.S.) 82: 837-840,
 1952. (Reviewed by G. E. Noether, Math. Rev. 13: 666, 1952)

Gnedenko, B. V.

 SOME RESULTS ON THE MAXIMUM DISCREPANCY BETWEEN TWO EMPIRICAL
 DISTRIBUTIONS. Doklady. Akad. Nauk. SSSR (N.S.) 82: 661-663,
 1952. (Reviewed by K. L. Chung, Math. Rev. 13: 760, 1952)

Gnedenko, B. V. and Kolmogorov, A. N.

 LIMIT DISTRIBUTIONS FOR SUMS OF INDEPENDENT RANDOM VARIABLES.
 Cambridge (Addison-Wesley) 1954. (Reviewed in Math. Rev. 16,
 1: 52, 1955)

Gnedenko, B. V. and Korolyuk, V. S.

 ON THE MAXIMUM DISCREPANCY BETWEEN TWO EMPIRICAL DISTRIBUTIONS.
 Doklady. Akad. Nauk. SSSR (N.S.) 80: 525-528, 1951.
 (Reviewed by W. Feller, Math. Rev. 13: 570-571, 1952)

Gnedenko, B. V. and Mihalevic, V. S.

 TWO THEOREMS ON THE BEHAVIOR OF EMPIRICAL DISTRIBUTION FUNCTIONS.
 Doklady. Akad. Nauk. SSSR (N.S.) 85: 25-27, 1952.
 (Reviewed by K. L. Chung, Math. Rev. 14: 60, 1953)

Gnedenko, B. V. and Mihalevic, V. S.   (Cont'd)

ON THE DISTRIBUTION OF THE NUMBER OF EXCESSES OF ONE EMPIRICAL
DISTRIBUTION FUNCTION OVER ANOTHER.   Doklady. Akad. Nauk. SSSR
(N.S.) 82: 841-843, 1952 (Russian).
(Reviewed by K. L. Chung, Math. Rev. 13: 760, 1952)

Gnedenko, B. V. and Rvaceva, E. L.

ON A PROBLEM OF COMPARISON OF TWO EMPIRICAL DISTRIBUTIONS.
Doklady. Akad. Nauk. SSSR (N.S.) 82: 513-516, 1952 (Russian).
(Reviewed by K. L. Chung, Math. Rev. 13: 760, 1952)

Goldstein, S.

ON DIFFUSION BY DISCONTINUOUS MOVEMENTS, AND ON THE TELEGRAPH
EQUATION.   Quart. J. Mech. Appl. Math. 4: 129-156, 1951.
(Reviewed by M. Kac, Math. Rev. 13: 960, 1952)

Good, I. J.

THE NUMBER OF INDIVIDUALS IN A CASCADE PROCESS.   Proc.
Cambridge Phil. Soc. 45: 360-363, 1949.

RANDOM MOTION ON A FINITE ABELIAN GROUP.   Proc. Cambridge
Phil. Soc. 47: 756-762, 1951.   (Reviewed by K. L. Chung, Math.
Rev. 13: 363, 1952)

Grenander, U.

STOCHASTIC PROCESSES AND STATISTICAL INFERENCE.   Ark. f. Mat.
1: 195-277, 1950.

Haldane, J. B. S.

A LABOUR-SAVING METHOD OF SAMPLING.   Nature (London): 155;
49-50, 1945.

ON A METHOD OF ESTIMATING FREQUENCIES.   Biom. 33: 222-225,
1945.

SOME STATISTICAL PROBLEMS ARISING IN GENETICS.   J. Roy. Stat.
Soc. (B) 11: 1-9, 1949.

Hammersley, J. M.

ELECTRONIC COMPUTORS AND THE ANALYSIS OF STOCHASTIC PROCESSES.
MTAC 4: 56-57, 1950.

CAPTURE-RECAPTURE ANALYSIS. Biom. 40: 265-278, 1953.
   This paper presents a new method for the analysis of
capture-recapture data. Previous methods have employed deterministic or partially stochastic models of the population
under study; the new method not only provides a fully stochastic model, but it also allows death-rates to depend upon both
current time and the health and age of the separate individuals. The numerical analysis associated with the method is,
however, heavy, and can only be recommended when one wants to
extract the maximum amount of information from data which have
required much effort or time to collect. The method is illustrated by an estimation of the death-rate of Alpine Swifts
(Apus melba) in the wild state. Some thirty years having been
spent in collecting these data, it does not seem disproportion-
ate to have spent several months in computing the results.
The larger part of the calculation was done on ordinary desk
calculators.

   Some unusual problems in maximum-likelihood are discussed.
(Author's Abstract)

MARKOVIAN WALKS ON CRYSTALS. Composito Mathematica 11: 171-
186, 1953.
   This work originated in a metallurgical problem on the
diffusion of electrons in a crystal structure. This problem
is a special case of some general theory on the asymptotic
distribution of the sum of a large number of vectors selected
from a fixed set of vectors by a Markovian process of finite
order. This extends the work of Romanovsky, who treated the
corresponding problem for scalars selected by a Markovian
process of order unity. (Author's Summary)

Harris, T. E.

BRANCHING PROCESSES. Ann. Math. Stat. 19: 474-494, 1948.
(Reviewed by J. L. Doob, Math. Rev. 10: 311, 1949)

SOME MATHEMATICAL MODELS FOR BRANCHING PROCESSES. Proc. 2nd
Berkeley Symp. on Math. Stat. and Probability: 305-328, 1951.

Hartley, H. O. and Fitch, E. R.

A CHART FOR THE INCOMPLETE BETA-FUNCTION AND THE CUMULATIVE
BINOMIAL DISTRIBUTION. Biom. 38: 423-426, 1951.

Jánossy, L.

NOTE ON THE FLUCTUATION PROBLEM OF CASCADES. Proc. Phys. Soc. (London) (A) 63: 241-9, 1950.

Juncosa, M. L. and Young, D. M.

A MATHEMATICAL FORMULATION FOR ORDVAC COMPUTATION OF THE PROBABILITY OF KILL OF AN AIRPLANE BY A MISSILE. BRL Rep. No. 867, Ballistic Res. Lab., Aberdeen Proving Ground, Maryland, 1953.

In Ballistic Research Laboratories Memorandum Report No. 530, "Lotto Method of Computing Kill Probability of Large Warheads," F. G. King describes a random sampling method for determining kill probabilities of a large warhead against an airplane. To obtain the results the method requires a physical model, hand drawing of random numbers, and the use of kill probability curves for the vulnerable components of the airplane.

In this report a mathematical model for the purpose of solving the problem on a high-speed digital computing machine is presented. This model is based on J. von Neumann's suggestion that the airplane be replaced by several ellipsoids resembling the fuselage, wings, and engines. The necessary formulas for computation are derived from the basic geometric model.

The kill probabilities are determined by three-dimensional integrals which are evaluated either by random sampling methods or by straightforward numerical quadratures. These methods are compared from the viewpoints of accuracy, speed, and machine storage requirements. Limited comparison of the results and some remarks about applicability of more general problems are also made.

The method of generation of the pseudo-random numbers used in the random sampling procedures is also described in the appendix. (Authors' Abstract)

Kac, M.

ON A PROBLEM CONCERNING PROBABILITY AND ITS CONNECTION WITH THE THEORY OF DIFFUSION. Bull. Amer. Math. Soc. 46: 534-537, 1940. (Reviewed by W. Feller, Math. Rev. 1: 344, 1940)

RANDOM WALK IN THE PRESENCE OF ABSORBING BARRIERS. Ann. Math. Stat. 16: 62-67, 1945. (Reviewed by D. Blackwell, Math. Rev. 6: 233, 1945)

RANDOM WALK AND THE THEORY OF BROWNIAN MOTION. Amer. Math. Monthly 54: 369-391, 1947. (Reviewed by M. Loeve, Math. Rev. 9: 46, 1948)

Karmel, P. H.

    THE RELATIONS BETWEEN MALE AND FEMALE REPRODUCTION RATES.
    Population Studies 1: 249-274, 1947.

    THE RELATIONS BETWEEN MALE AND FEMALE NUPTIALITY IN A STABLE
    POPULATION. Ibid. 1: 353-387, 1948.

    AN ANALYSIS OF THE SOURCES AND MAGNITUDE OF INCONSISTENCIES
    BETWEEN MALE AND FEMALE NET REPRODUCTION RATES IN ACTUAL
    POPULATIONS. Ibid. 2: 240-273, 1948.

Keilson, J.

    THE STATISTICAL NATURE OF INVERSE BROWNIAN MOTION IN VELOCITY
    SPACE. Tech. Rep. No. 127, Cruft Lab. Harvard Univ., (ONR
    Cont. N5ori-76), Cambridge, 1951.
        In this report the stochastic nature of the velocity
    fluctuations of a particle moving in a gas is examined. It
    is shown that Smoluchowski's equation governing the motion is
    equivalent to Boltzmann's equation which is regarded as basic
    to the description of all such stochastic processes. Ordinary
    Brownian motion is examined from this point of view and with
    the help of a number of simple assumptions on the scattering
    process a characteristic Fokker-Planck equation is obtained.
    Finally, inverse Brownian motion, that of a light particle in
    a heavy gas is considered. (Author's Abstract)

Kelly, C. D. and Rahn, O.

    THE GROWTH RATE OF INDIVIDUAL BACTERIAL CELLS. J. Bacteriology
    23: 147-153, 1932.

Kendall, D. G.

    A REVIEW OF SOME RECENT WORK ON DISCONTINUOUS MARKOFF PROCESSES
    WITH APPLICATIONS TO BIOLOGY, PHYSICS AND ACTUARIAL SCIENCE.
    J. Roy. Stat. Soc. 110: 130-137, 1947.

    ON THE GENERALIZED BIRTH-AND-DEATH PROCESS. Ann. Math. Stat.
    19: 1-15, 1948.

    ON SOME MODES OF POPULATION GROWTH LEADING TO R.A. FISHER'S
    LOGARITHMIC SERIES DISTRIBUTION. Biom. 35: 6-15, 1948.

    ON THE ROLE OF VARIABLE GENERATION TIME IN THE DEVELOPMENT OF
    A STOCHASTIC BIRTH PROCESS. Biom. 35: 316-30, 1948.

Kendall, D. G.   (Cont'd)

STOCHASTIC PROCESSES AND POPULATION GROWTH.   J. Roy. Stat. Soc.
(B) 11: 230-64; 266-267; 281-282, 1949.   (Reviewed by J. L.
Doob, Math. Rev. 11: 672, 1950)

AN ARTIFICIAL REALISATION OF A SIMPLE BIRTH-AND-DEATH PROCESS.
J. Roy. Stat. Soc. (B) 12: 116-119, 1950.

RANDOM FLUCTUATIONS IN THE AGE-DISTRIBUTION OF A POPULATION
WHOSE DEVELOPMENT IS CONTROLLED BY THE SIMPLE BIRTH-AND-DEATH
PROCESS.   J. Roy. Stat. Soc. (B) 12: 278-285, 1950.

SOME PROBLEMS IN THE THEORY OF QUEUES.   J. Roy. Stat. Soc. (B)
13: 184-185, 1951.

ON THE CHOICE OF A MATHEMATICAL MODEL TO REPRESENT NORMAL
BACTERIAL GROWTH.   J. Roy. Stat. Soc. (B) 13: 41-44, 1952.

Kendall, M. G.

THE ADVANCED THEORY OF STATISTICS.   Volume 1, 4th edn., London
1948; Volume 2 appeared in 1946 (2nd edn. 1947).
(Volume 1 reviewed by H. Scheffe, Math. Rev. 6, 1: 89-91, 1945)
(Volume 2 reviewed by J. Wolfowitz, Math. Rev. 8, 8: 473, 1947)

Kitagawa, Tosio

RANDOM INTEGRATIONS.   Bull. Math. Stat. 4: 15-21, 1950.
(Reviewed by R. H. Cameron and J. M. Shapiro, Math. Rev. 14, 5:
457, 1953.

THE t-DISTRIBUTIONS CONCERNING RANDOM INTEGRATIONS.   Mem. Fac.
Sci. Kyusyu Univ. A. 8: 31-41, 1953.   (Reviewed by H. P.
Mulholland, Math. Rev. 15, 10: 886, 1954)

Kolmogorov, A.

GRUNDBEGRIFFE DER WAHRSCHEINLICHKEITSRECHNUNG.   English translation, Berlin (Springer) 1933.

SULLA TEORIA DI VOLTERRA DELLA LOTTA PER L'ESISTENZA.   Giorn.
Ist. Ital. Attuari 7: 74-80, 1936.

CONFIDENCE LIMITS FOR AN UNKNOWN DISTRIBUTION FUNCTION.   Ann.
Math. Stat. 12: 461-463, 1941.

FOUNDATIONS OF THE THEORY OF PROBABILITY.   English translation,
New York (Chelsea) 1950.

Kolmogoroff, A., Petrovsky, I. and Piscounoff, N.

ETUDE DE L'EQUATION DE LA DIFFUSION AVEC CROISSANCE DE LA
QUANTITE DE MATIERE ET SON APPLICATION A UN PROBLEME BIO-
LOGIQUE. Bull. Univ. Etat. Moscow (A) (I) 6: 1-25, 1937.

Kolmogoroff, A. and Dmitriev, N. A.

BRANCHING STOCHASTIC PROCESSES. C. R. Acad. Sci. U.R.S.S.
(N.S.) 56: 5-8, 1947.

Kolmogoroff, A. and Savostyanov, B. A.

THE CLACULATION OF FINAL PROBABILITIES FOR BRANCHING RANDOM
PROCESSES. Ibid., 56: 783-786, 1947 (Russian).

Lauwerier, H. A.

A LINEAR RANDOM WALK WITH A PARTLY REFLECTING PARTLY ABSORBING
BARRIER. Appl. Sci. (B) 2: 294-300, 1952.
(Reviewed by W. Wasow, Math. Rev. 13: 852, 1952)

Lea, D. E. and Coulson, C. A.

THE DISTRIBUTION OF THE NUMBER OF MUTANTS IN BACTERIAL POPULA-
TIONS. J. Genetics 49: 264-285, 1949.

Le Cam

UN INSTRUMENT D'ÉTUDE DES FONCTIONS ALÉATOIRES: LA FONCTION-
ELLE CARACTÉRISTIQUE. Comptes Rendus 224: 710-711, 1947.

Lehman, R. S.

A PROBLEM ON RANDOM WALK. Proc. 2nd Berkeley Symp. on Math.
Stat. and Probability: 263-268, 1950; Univ. of Calif. Press,
Berkeley and Los Angeles, 1951.
(Reviewed by J. Riordan, Math. Rev. 13: 363, 1952)

Leslie, P. H.

ON THE USE OF MATRICES IN CERTAIN POPULATION MATHEMATICS.
Biom. 33: 183-212, 1945.

SOME FURTHER NOTES ON THE USE OF MATRICES IN POPULATION
MATHEMATICS. Ibid., 35: 213-245, 1948.

Lévy, P.

PROCESSUS STOCHASTIQUES ET MOUVEMENT BROWNIEN. Paris, 1948.

Lewis, E. G.

ON THE GENERATION AND GROWTH OF A POPULATION. Sankhya 6:
93-96, 1942.

Lotka, A. J.

THE EXTINCTION OF FAMILIES. J. Washington Acad. of Sci. 21:
377-80 and 453-9, 1931.

ANALYSE DÉMOGRAPHIQUE AVEC APPLICATION PARTICULIÈRE A L'ESPÈCE
HUMAINE. Act. Sci. Ind.: 780 (Paris) 1939.

POPULATION ANALYSIS AS A CHAPTER IN THE MATHEMATICAL THEORY OF
EVOLUTION. Essays on Growth and Form presented to D'Arcy
Wentworth Thompson 1945 (edited by W. E. Le Gros Clark and
P. B. Medawar), Oxford.

APPLICATION OF RECURRENT SERIES IN RENEWAL THEORY. Ann. Math.
Stat. 19: 190-206, 1948.

Lundberg, O.

ON RANDOM PROCESSES AND THEIR APPLICATION TO SICKNESS AND
ACCIDENT STATISTICS. Uppsala, 1940.
(Reviewed by W. Feller, Math. Rev. 2, 7: 230, 1941)

Luria, S. E. and Delbruck, M.

MUTATIONS OF BACTERIA FROM VIRUS SENSITIVITY TO VIRUS RESIST-
ANCE. Genetics 28: 491-511, 1943.

McCrea, W. H. and Whipple, F. J. W.

RANDOM PATHS IN TWO AND THREE DIMENSIONS. Proc. Roy. Soc.
Edin. 60: 281-298, 1940. (Reviewed by W. Feller, Math. Rev.
2: 107, 1941)

McKendrick, A. G.

STUDIES ON THEORY OF CONTINUOUS PROBABILITIES, WITH SPECIAL
REFERENCE TO ITS BEARING ON NATURAL PHENOMENA OF A PROGRESSIVE
NATURE. Proc. London Math. Soc. (2) 13: 401-416, 1914.

Malécot, G.

LES PROCESSUS STOCHASTIQUES DE LA GÉNÉTIQUE. Coll. Intern. du C.N.R.S. 13: 121-126, 1949.

LES MATHÉMATIQUES DE L'HÉRÉDITÉ. Paris, 1948.

QUELQUES SCHEMES PROBABILISTES SUR LA VARIABILITÉ DES POPULA-TIONS NATURELLES. Ann. de l"Univ. de Lyon (A) 13: 37-60, 1950.

Markov, A. A.

CALCULUS OF PROBABILITY. Moscow, 4th ed. (Russian), 1924.

Martin, L.

ÉVOLUTION DE LA BIOMÉTRIE. Bull. de l'Inst. Agronom. de Gembloux 17: 43-66, 1948-49.

Matthai, A.

ON SELECTING RANDOM NUMBERS FOR LARGE-SCALE SAMPLING. Sankhya 13: 257-260, 1954.
    In this paper certain methods and details in the matter of selecting random numbers, on a large scale, are given.

Mihalevic, V. S.

ON THE MUTUAL DISPOSITION OF TWO EMPIRICAL DISTRIBUTION FUNC-TIONS. Doklady. Akad. Nauk. SSSR (N.S.) 85: 485-488, 1952. (Reviewed by K. L. Chung, Math. Rev. 14: 297, 1953)

Mises, R. von

PROBABILITY, STATISTICS AND TRUTH. London, 1936. Original German editions 1928 and 1936, Vienna and Berlin. (Reviewed by B. O. Koopman, Math. Rev. 1, 2: 61, 1940)

Moran, P. A. P.

SOME REMARKS ON ANIMAL POPULATION DYNAMICS. Biometrics 6: 250-258, 1950.

ESTIMATION METHODS FOR EVOLUTIVE PROCESSES. J. Roy. Stat. Soc. (B): 141-146, 1951.

A MATHEMATICAL THEORY OF ANIMAL TRAPPING. Biom. 38: 307-311, 1951.

Morse, P. M. and Kimball, G. E.

METHODS OF OPERATIONS RESEARCH. New York (Wiley) 1951.
    This book shows how the techniques of a scientific method
used during World War II can be used by executives to help
make decisions in any field--industrial, governmental or mili-
tary. It is, however, primarily a book on the methods and
tools of the subject, and as such is aimed at the worker in
the field. There is a table of random digits, one of random
angles and one of random normal deviates to be used in computing probabilities by sampling. There are also tables of the
binomial, normal and Poisson distributions. (Also reviewed
by N. J. Fine, Math. Rev. 13: 364-365, 1952)

Mourier, E.

SUR L'ESPÉRANCE MATHÉMATIQUE D'UN ÉLÉMENT ALÉATOIRE DANS UN
ESPACE DE BANACH. C. R. Acad. Sci. 229: 1300-1301, 1949.

PROPRIÉTÉS DES CARACTÉRISTIQUES D'UN ÉLÉMENT ALÉATOIRE DANS
UN ESPACE DE BANACH. Ibid, 231: 447-476, 1948.

Moyal, J. E.

STOCHASTIC PROCESSES AND STATISTICAL PHYSICS. J. Roy. Stat.
Soc. Ser. B 11: 150-210, 1949. (Reviewed by J. L. Doob, Math.
Rev. 11: 672, 1950)

Newcombe, H. E.

DELAYED PHENOTYPIC EXPRESSIONS OF SPONTANEOUS MUTATIONS IN
ESCHERICHIA COLI. Genetics 33: 447-476, 1948.

Otter, R.

THE MULTIPLICATIVE PROCESS. Ann. Math. Stat. 20: 206-224,1949.

Park, T.

EXPERIMENTAL STUDIES OF INTERSPECIES COMPETITION, I. Ecol.
Monographs 18: 265-308, 1948.

Pólya, G.

SUR QUELQUES POINTS DE LA THÉORIE DES PROBABILITÉS. Ann. Inst.
H. Poincare 1: 117-161, 1930.

Prendeville, B. J.

    (No Title); reference: J. Roy. Stat. Soc. (B) 11: 273, 1949.

Rahn, O.

    A CHEMICAL EXPLANATION OF THE VARIABILITY OF THE GROWTH RATE.
J. Gen. Physiology 15: 257-277, 1932.

    CHEMISTRY OF CELL GROWTH, II. Cold Springs Harbour Symp. on
Quant. Biol. 2: 63-69, 1934.

Ramakrishnan, A.

    STOCHASTIC PROCESSES RELATING TO PARTICLES DISTRIBUTED IN A
CONTINUOUS INFINITY OF STATES. Proc. Cambridge Phil. Soc.
46: 595-602, 1950.

    SOME SIMPLE STOCHASTIC PROCESSES. J. Roy. Stat. Soc. (B) 13:
131-140, 1951.

Reich, E.

    A RANDOM WALK RELATED TO THE CAPACITANCE OF THE CIRCULAR PLATE
CONDENSER. Quart. of Appl. Math., October, 1953.
    It is shown that the solution of Love's equation for the
capacitance of the circular plate condenser can be expressed
in terms of the mean duration of a certain one-dimensional
random walk with absorbing barriers. The interpretation as a
random walk makes it possible to confirm the fact that the
actual capacitance of the condenser is always larger than the
value given by the standard approximation for small separations, and yields an upper bound as well. In addition to its
theoretical interest, the random walk appears to provide a
practical means for the calculation of the capacitance by a
Monte Carlo technique. (Author's Abstract)

Savostyanov, B. A.

    ON THE THEORY OF BRANCHING RANDOM PROCESSES. C. R. Acad. Sci.
U.R.S.S. 59: 1407-1410, 1948 (Russian).

Steffensen, J. F.

    OM SANDSYNLIGHEDEN FOR AT AFKOMMET UDDØR. Matem. Tidesskrift
B: 19-23, 1930.

Steffensen, J. F.   (Cont'd)

DEUX PROBLÈMES DU CALCUL DES PROBABILITÉS. Ann. Inst. H.
Poincare 3: 319-344, 1933.

Taub, A. H.

A SAMPLING METHOD FOR SOLVING THE EQUATIONS OF COMPRESSIBLE
FLOW IN A PERMEABLE MEDIUM. Proc. of Midwestern Conf. on
Fluid Dynamics: 121-127, 1950; J. W. Edwards, Ann Arbor,
Michigan, 1951.
     "In this paper we investigate a single particle under-
going a Markov process and treat the transition probabilities
of that process as the Maxwell-Boltzmann distribution function of a gas. We shall show that, if one then defines density, velocity, pressure, and heat flow as in kinetic theory,
these quantities satisfy the partial differential equations
describing the behavior of a fluid in a permeable medium.
The transition probabilities of a Markov process may be calculated by a sampling (Monte Carlo) method with the aid of
automatic computing machines. If this is done, then the
results quoted above enable one to determine the behavior of
fluids in a permeable medium without any reference to the
partial-differential equations themselves. The errors involved are errors due to the size of the sample taken and may
be readily estimated." (From the Author's Introduction)

Tchen, Chan-Mou

STOCHASTIC PROCESSES AND DISPERSION OF CONFIGURATIONS OF
LINKED EVENTS. J. Res. Nat'l Bur. of Stds. 46: 480-488, 1951.
(Reviewed by K. L. Chung, Math. Rev. 13: 141, 1952)

Teichroew, D.

EMPIRICAL SAMPLING DISTRIBUTIONS II. Nat'l Bur. of Stds. Rep.
No. 1621, Preprint, April 15, 1952.
     In this report a generalization of standard empirical
sampling methods has been considered. The generalization consists of sampling from one distribution while estimating the
sampling distribution of statistics in samples from another
distribution. Two estimators are considered, namely, the
"arithmetic mean" and a "ratio" estimator. The variance of
the "arithmetic mean" estimator can be expressed as a definite
integral while for the "ratio" only an asymptotic variance can
be obtained in general. In either case these expressions are
too complex to be of practical help in determining the distribution from which samples should be taken. An example is

given to show that it is (at least theoretically) possible to find a distribution which would lead to estimates with lower variance than can be obtained with standard methods. (Author's Summary)

DISTRIBUTION SAMPLING WITH HIGH SPEED COMPUTERS. Ph.D. Thesis, North Carolina State College, 1953.

Thompson, W. R. and Soper, H. E.

ON THE REPRODUCTION OF ORGANISMS WITH OVERLAPPING GENERATIONS. Bull. Entom. Res. 22: 147-172, 1931.

Tweedie, M. C. K.

INVERSE STATISTICAL VARIATES. Nature 155: 453, 1945 (London).

Uhlenbeck, G. E.

THEORY OF RANDOM PROCESSES. Rep. No. 454, Radiation Laboratory Univ. of California, October, 1943.
    A survey is given of the theory of random processes, which forms the basis for the investigation of all fluctuation phenomena. The main purpose is to show how to treat systematically and quantitatively problems occurring especially in the statistical analysis of noise. (Author's Abstract)

Uspensky, J. V.

INTRODUCTION TO MATHEMATICAL PROBABILITY. New York (McGraw-Hill) 1937.

Vickery, C. W.

EXPERIMENTAL DETERMINATION OF EIGENVALUES AND DYNAMIC INFLUENCE COEFFICIENTS FOR COMPLEX STRUCTURES SUCH AS AIRPLANES. Fairchild Aircraft Corp., Hagerstown, Maryland. Typewritten manuscript, February 8, 1954.
    This paper describes a simple experimental technique for determining eigenvalues and dynamic influence coefficients applicable to airplanes. A dynamic influence coefficient μ_{ij} is defined as the response of the system at station i to a unit impulse at station j. The dynamic influence coefficients so defined are complex functions. These dynamic influence coefficients completely characterize the vibrational properties of the system. (Author's Introduction)

Vol Terra, V.

LEÇONS SUR LA THÉORIE MATHÉMATIQUE DE LA LUTTE POUR LA VIE.
Paris, 1931.

Wald, A.

ASYMPTOTIC PROPERTIES OF THE MAXIMUM LIKELIHOOD ESTIMATE OF
AN UNKNOWN PARAMETER OF A DISCRETE STOCHASTIC PROCESS. Ann.
Math. Stat. 19: 40-46, 1948.

Wall, F. T.

MEAN DIMENSIONS OF RUBBER-LIKE POLYMER MOLECULES. J. of Chem.
Phys. 21, 11: 1914-1919, 1953.
     The mean square end-to-end separations of coiling type
polymer molecules have been calculated by two different approximate methods, taking into account the effect of excluded
volumes. One of the methods is the equivalent of a first-
order perturbation calculation using unrestricted random walk
as a starting approximation. The other method involves the
use of certain plausible functional terms valid for large
values of the chain lengths. The calculations have been carried out for three, two and one dimensions and the results
are analyzed to provide an insight into factors which might
determine convergence or divergence of the quotient $(r_n^2)_{Av}/n$
(the mean-square length divided by the number of links). It
appears that the quotient converges in three (or more) dimensions, but diverges for a lower number of dimensions.
(Author's Abstract)

Wall, F. T., Hiller, L. A., Jr. and Wheeler, D. J.

STATISTICAL COMPUTATION OF MEAN DIMENSIONS OF MACROMOLECULES I.
J. of Chem. Phys. 22, 6: 1036-1041, 1954.
     The configuration of flexible coiling type polymer mole-
cules has been investigated statistically with a high-speed
electronic digital computer by generation of large numbers of
"random walks." These walks were carried out subject to the
excluded volume effect in simple cubic and tetrahedral lattices.
It was found that the walk attrition obeys an exponential decay
law with a half-walk of 6.7 steps in the cubic lattice and 17.3
steps for the tetrahedral. Mean square end-to-end separations,
$(r_n^2)_{Av}$, were also obtained, and two distinct kinds of empirical
formulas have been fitted to the data. So far, the statistical
data are insufficient to establish unequivocally the nature of
the functional dependence of $(r_n^2)_{Av}$ for large values of n, the

number of steps. A study was also made on the probabilities
of ring closures for restricted random walks in the cubic
system. It was found that for rings greater than 6 steps,
the probability of formation varies inversely as the square
of the ring size. (Author's Abstract)

Wall, F. T., Hiller, L. A., and Atchinson, W. F.

STATISTICAL COMPUTATION OF MEAN DIMENSIONS OF MACROMOLECULES.
II. J. of Chem. Phys. 23, 5: 913-921, 1955
     Random walks subject to the excluded volume effect have
been generated by means of a high-speed electronic digital
computer for four different two-dimension lattices. A semi-
empirical theory has also been developed for interpreting the
statistical data. From the results obtained it is possible
to show for several two-dimensional lattices that the quotient
$(r_n^2)_{Av}/n$ diverges as $n \longrightarrow \infty$, where $(r_n^2)_{Av}$ is the mean square
length of permissible walks of n steps. This conclusion was
reached by using an appropriate difference equation in con-
junction with data on the mean square lengths of successful
walks and the mean square lengths of failures resulting from
ring closures. Integration of that difference equation indicates that if n is sufficiently large, $(r_n^2)_{Av}$ is proportional
to n^A, where A depends upon the lattice system. (Author's
Abstract)

Wasow, W.

ON THE MEAN DURATION OF RANDOM WALKS. J. Res. Nat'l Bur. of
Stds. 46: 462-471, 1951. (Res. Paper 2215).
(Reviewed by J. L. Doob, Math. Rev. 12: 726, 1951)

ON THE DURATION OF RANDOM WALKS. Ann. Math. Stat. 22: 199-
216, 1951. (Reviewed by M. Kac, Math. Rev. 14, 10: 994, 1953)

Wilks, S. S.

MATHEMATICAL STATISTICS. Princeton, 1944.
(Reviewed by J. Neyman, Math. Rev. 5: 41, 1944)

Wintner, Aurel

ASYMPTOTIC DISTRIBUTIONS AND INFINITE CONVOLUTIONS. Princeton,
1938.

Wold, H.

A LARGE-SAMPLE TEST FOR MOVING AVERAGES. J. Roy. Stat. Soc.
(B) 11: 297-305, 1949. (Reviewed by A. Blake, Math. Rev. 11:
674, 1950.

SUR LES PROCESSUS STATIONNAIRES PONCTUELS. Le Calcul des
Probabilites et ses Applications. Colloques Internationaux
du Centre National de la Recherche Scientifique, Paris, 1949.
(Reviewed by J. L. Doob, Math. Rev. 11: 258, 1950)

Woodward, P. M.

A STATISTICAL THEORY OF CASCADE MULTIPLICATION. Proc.
Cambridge Phil. Soc. 44: 404-412, 1947.

Yaglom, A. M.

CERTAIN LIMIT THEOREMS OF THE THEORY OF BRANCHING RANDOM
PROCESSES. C. R. Acad. Sci. U.R.S.S. 56: 795-798, 1947.

Yule, G. O.

A MATHEMATICAL THEORY OF EVOLUTION, ETC. Phil. Trans. Roy.
Soc. London (B) 213: 21-87, 1925.

Adyanthaya, N., 343, 344
Albert, G. E., xi, xii, xvii, 10, 11, 37, 284
Alei, 29
Allen, J. S., xi
Ambrose, W., 353
Anderson, R. L., 339, 354
Arley, N., 348
Armitage, P., 348
Arnold, H. J., xi, xvii, 12, 80
Astrachan, M., xii
Atchinson, W. F., 369
Azorin, F., 323

Bachelier, 297, 318
Bailey, N. T. G., 348
Baker, G. A., 338
Bartlett, M. S., 327, 349, 350
Bayes, 343, 344
Beach, L. A., xi, xii, xvii, 12, 13, 103
Bellman, R., xii, 285, 341, 350
Bennett, A., 343
Berger, M., xi, xii, xvii, 12, 13, 89
Berkson, J., 338
Bernardelli, H., 350
Bernardini, G., 285,
Bernouilli, 351
Bethe, 29
Bhabha, H. J., 351
Bispham, J. W., 338
Blackwell, D., 358
Blake, A., 370
Blanch, G., 323
Blocker, 320
Bochner, S., 351
Boltzmann, 359
Booth, E. T., 285
Borchsenius, V., 348
Borel, 45, 351
Brown, B., 323, 324

Brown, G. W., 324
Brown, R. K., xii
Brownlee, J., 339
Buch, K. A., 348
Bucher, B. D., xi, xvii, 12, 80
Burkett, F. J., xii
Butler, J. W., xii, xviii, 9, 10, 157, 184, 249

Callander, W. F., xii
Cameron, J. M., 15, 19, 26, 27, 285
Cameron, R. H., 360
Carleman, 298
Carlson, B., 286
Carlson, J. L., 339
Cashwell, E. D., xii, 291, 292
Cauchy, A. L., 298
Chandrasekhar, S., 351
Chapman, D. G., 346, 350
Cheriyan, K. C., 339
Chernoff, H., 337
Chesire, L., 339
Chitty, D., 351
Chung, K. L., 352, 354, 355, 356, 363, 366
Church, A. E. R., 339, 341
Clark, A. L., 339
Clark, W. E. LeG., 362
Cochran, W. G., 286, 323, 351
Cochrane, D., 339
Cohen, M., 293
Combe, J., 286, 287
Compton, 89
Consael, R., 352
Cook-Leurgans, 29
Coolidge, J.
Copeland, 330
Coulomb, 35, 36, 320
Coulson, C. A., 352, 361
Courant, R., 197, 232
Craig, C. C., 340, 344

NAME INDEX

Hadley, 285
Hald, A., 242, 247
Haldane, J. B. S., 356
Hall, P., 341
Hamaker, H. C., 328, 341
Hammer, P. C., 16, 295, 328
Hammersley, J. M., xii, 12, 74, 295, 296, 315, 357
Hammersmith, J. L., xii
Hamming, R., 331
Handy, B. F., Jr., 19
Hansmann, G. H., 341
Hanson, W. D., xii
Harris, T. E., 5, 6, 299, 300, 349, 350, 357
Harrison, J. O., Jr., xiii
Hartar, H. L., 341
Hartley, H. O., 238, 247, 357
Hayward, E., 98, 296
Hellyer, S., xiii
Hey, G. B., 341
Hilbert, 197, 232
Hiller, L. A., Jr., 368, 369
Hinshelwood, C. N., 353
Hodges, J. L., Jr., 336
Hoel, P. G., 247
de Hoffman, 29
Hoffman, J., 322
Holzinger, K., 341
Horowitz, M., xi, xiii
Horton, H. B., 328, 329, 336
Horton, T. R., xiii
Householder, A. S., v, ix, xi, xiii, xv, 27, 198, 199, 202, 230, 232, 294, 296, 310, 315
Hoy, W. W., xiii
Hubbard, C. P., 56
Hubbell, J. H., xiii, 98, 296
Hurd, C. C., xi, xii, xiii
Hyman, M. A., xiii

Jánossy, L., 358
Johnson, P. C., 297
Jones, 322
Jordan, T. L., Jr., xiii
Juncosa, M. L., 15, 19, 21, 28, 329, 358

Kac, M., vi, 4, 290, 201, 293, 297, 298, 318, 352, 356, 358, 369
Kahn, H., xii, xiii, xv, xviii, 1, 5, 10, 11, 12, 13, 37, 94, 107, 140, 146, 249, 257, 264, 284, 289, 294, 298, 299, 300
Kakutani, S., 353
Kannan, M. B., 343
Karmel, P. H., 359
Keilson, J., 301, 359
Kelly, B., xiii
Kelly, C. D., 359
Kendall, D. G., ix, 341, 349, 353, 359, 360,
Kendall, M. G., 324, 327, 328, 329, 330, 331, 336, 337, 342, 348, 360
Kenney, 47, 320
Kermack, W. O., 342
Kerrich, J. E., 342
Kersh, R., 18
Khintchine, 131
Kimball, G. E., 364
King, F. G., 358
King, G. W., 301, 302, 303, 304, 305
Kitagawa, Tosio, 360
Klein-Nishina, 92, 105, 286
Kolmogorov, A. N., 297, 337, 343, 355, 360, 361
Kondo, T., 342
Koopman, B. O., 363
Korolyuk, V. S., 355
Kruskal, M., 32
Kullback, S., 342
Kuntzmann, J., 289

Ladd, B., xiii
Laplace, P. S., 321
Lauwerier, H. A., 361
Lea, D. E., 361
LeCam, 361
Lehman, R. S., 361
Lehmer, D. H., 16, 17, 26, 27, 331, 334
Leibler, R. A., xiii, 288, 289, 291, 293, 310, 315, 316, 319
Leighton, W., xiii
Lekkerkerker, C. G., 19, 21, 27
Lennard-Jones, 322

373

SOURCE INDEX

JOURNALS

SOURCE INDEX

OTHER REFERENCES

382